C0-EES-746

Henry Van Engen

Maurice L. Hartung

Harold C. Trimble

Emil J. Berger

Ray W. Cleveland

Seeing through mathematics

Book 3, part 2

Scott, Foresman and Company
Chicago, Atlanta, Dallas
Palo Alto, Fair Lawn, N.J.

This is Part 2 of the ninth book of
The Basic Mathematics Program, published
by Scott, Foresman and Company.

The authors of this book are:
Henry Van Engen, Professor of Education and Mathematics, University of Wisconsin;
Maurice L. Hartung, Professor of Education, University of Chicago;
Harold C. Trimble, Professor of Education, Department of Education, Ohio State University;
Emil J. Berger, Coördinator of Mathematics, St. Paul Public Schools, St. Paul, Minnesota;
Ray W. Cleveland, Supervisor of Elementary and Secondary Mathematics, Rahway Public Schools, Rahway, New Jersey.

The following persons served as advisors to the authors:
Ralph Crouch, Head, Department of Mathematics, New Mexico State University;
Charles J. A. Halberg, Jr., Associate Professor of Mathematics, University of California, Riverside;
Paul J. Kelly, Professor of Mathematics, University of California, Santa Barbara;
Michael Millar, Assistant Professor, Department of Mathematics, State College of Iowa.

The following persons served as consultants in preparing this book:
A. B. Evenson, Assistant Superintendent, Secondary Education, Edmonton Public Schools, Edmonton, Alberta, Canada;
E. Glenadine Gibb, Professor of Mathematics, State College of Iowa;
Warren A. Parnell, Mathematics Instructor, Northeast Intermediate School, Midland, Michigan;
Wayne H. Peterson, Head of the Department of Mathematics, Marcus Whitman Junior High School, Seattle, Washington;
James E. Stochl, Assistant Professor of Education, University of Minnesota;
Ray Walch, Director of Mathematics, K-12, Public Schools, Westport, Connecticut.

This book was prepared by the editorial staff under the direction of George E. Russell, General Editor for Mathematics, and Clarence E. Olander, Associate Mathematics Editor. This book was designed by William Nicoll and illustrated by Paul Hazelrigg.

Contents of Book 3

The work in *Seeing Through Mathematics, Book 3*, is organized in nine units. Units 17 through 20 are contained in Part 1. Units 21 through 25 are contained in Part 2. The nine units are:

17 Vectors
Directed segments and ordered pairs as examples of vectors, force and velocity, addition, scalar multiplication, vector space

18 The real-number system
Integers and rational numbers as subsets of real numbers, properties and theorems, real numbers as example of an ordered field

19 Logic and the nature of proof
The logical connectives, patterns of inference, direct and indirect proof, the nature of a mathematical system

20 Algebraic expressions
Integral powers, linear and second-degree polynomials, rational expressions, square root, rational powers

21 Equivalent conditions in one variable
Simple and compound linear conditions, absolute value, conditions involving absolute value

22 Relations and functions
A relation as a subset of a Cartesian set, domain and range of a relation, functions

23 Linear and quadratic functions
The linear function and its graph, the quadratic function and its graph, solving quadratic conditions, conditions involving radicals

24 Systems of conditions
Graphic and algebraic analysis of systems of linear conditions, maxima and minima of functions, linear programming problems

25 Permutations, combinations, and probability
Notation and formulas for permutations and combinations, the binomial theorem, the binomial distribution

Contents of Book 3 part 2

The organization of the work included in each unit is shown in a panel on the first page of the unit.

As you approach the end of the *Seeing Through Mathematics* series, we would like to recall for you how your knowledge of mathematics has progressed from simple arithmetic to rather difficult mathematical topics, such as the properties of number systems and vector spaces. Then we would like to suggest what a valuable preparation you now have for further work in mathematics.

Most of the ideas that you have studied in earlier books fall into one of the following categories: problem solving, mathematical systems and their properties, arithmetic and algebraic procedures, geometry, and development of mathematical symbolism. Some topics that you have studied, such as probability, logic, and elementary number theory, do not fit into any one of these categories, but the main portion of your work has been in the five areas mentioned above.

In problem solving, you have progressed from simple problems concerning the number of dimes George has left after he has spent a certain number of them to complicated problems that deal with the speed and direction of a moving object. Your study of mathematical systems has taken you from examples of number systems—the natural, the rational, and the real, for instance—to examples of fields, commutative groups, vector spaces, and rings.

In *Book 1* and *Book 2* of this series, you first reviewed some of the computational skills of arithmetic. Then you acquired new skills in computing with numerals for rational numbers, with decimals, and with numerals for rational approximations. You also learned how to determine square roots of numbers. The algebraic procedures that you have studied include addition, multiplication, subtraction, and division of algebraic expressions and the factoring of polynomials.

In geometry you have gone from elementary ideas related to points, lines, and planes to proofs of properties concerning triangles and to consideration of sets of points in space. You have also learned how sets of points and sets of numbers may be associated with each other in the real-number line, in the real plane, and in a vector space. Finally, you have learned a great deal about the symbolism of mathematics, including set notation, symbols for many geometric ideas and objects, and symbols for ideas in logic.

Now let us outline what you will learn in Part 2 of *Book 3*. In the first unit of this book, you will make use of certain ideas you studied in logic, along with the algebraic skills you have acquired, to develop equivalent conditions and to find solutions of conditions. Here, you will also learn what is meant by the absolute value of a number and you will solve conditions that involve absolute value.

The second unit of this book—unit 22 of the entire series—deals with relations as subsets of Cartesian sets. In this unit you will study functions, which are special kinds of relations that you will consider again and again as long as you study mathematics. Following this introductory unit on relations and functions, you will work in the third unit of this book with some frequently used functions and conditions, such as linear functions, quadratic functions, and quadratic conditions.

In the fourth unit of this book, you will learn to find solutions of systems in which it is necessary to consider two or three conditions simultaneously. Then you will apply your knowledge of systems of conditions to an interesting class of problems known as linear programming problems. Finally, in the last unit, you will take another look at ideas concerning probability, a topic that you first studied in *Book 2*.

By the time you finish this book, you will have covered a great deal of mathematical ground. Perhaps, if we had told you all of this when you began *Book 1*, you would have been frightened at the prospect of beginning! But we hope that the learning process has been relatively painless, usually interesting, and sometimes exciting. We also hope that you have been encouraged to take mathematics courses beyond *Book 3*.

Throughout these books we have tried to convey to you a sense of the structure of mathematics, which is just as important as the details of content that we have just summarized. We want very much for you to have gained an understanding of how mathematical ideas "hang together"—of how one idea follows from another; of how a mathematical system can be built upon earlier ones; of how a theorem can be proved by using ones that were proved earlier; of how ideas from arithmetic and algebra can be related to ideas from geometry. As you continue to study mathematics, such an understanding will be worth as much to you as a knowledge of factual content. If you are now at the end of your formal training in mathematics, such an understanding will be even more valuable than facts in contributing to your appreciation of mathematics and the part it plays in man's thinking.

THE AUTHORS

Unit 21

Equivalent conditions in one variable

Equivalent conditions

By now you have had much experience with conditions and their solution sets. In this unit you will view familiar kinds of conditions in a different way. Then you will study absolute value, which is a new idea, and consider conditions that involve absolute value. Throughout the unit you may assume that the universe for each variable is D unless you are told otherwise.

In this lesson you will study various kinds of conditions for equality. Notice that each condition expressed in D1 is a condition for equality.

A Condition A is formed from the expressions $2x + 9$ and 5 and the idea of equality. You can think of $2x + 9$ and 5 as the "sides" of condition A. Is each side of A a polynomial?

A condition in which both sides are polynomials is a *polynomial condition.*

B How do you know that condition B and condition C are not polynomial conditions?

C What two rational expressions are the sides of condition B?

A condition in which both sides are rational expressions is a *rational condition.*

A $2x + 9 = 5.$

B $3x = 7 + \frac{2}{x}.$

C $x + 4\sqrt{x} = 21.$

D1

Review and extension of basic vocabulary; use of the biconditional to define equivalent conditions

A $2x+9=5$.

B $3x=7+\frac{2}{x}$.

C $x+4\sqrt{x}=21$.

D1

$U=\{0, -1, -2, -3, -4\}$.

D $12+n=9$.

$U=\{2, 4, 6, 8\}$.

E $\frac{1}{2}x+8=3x-2$.

$U=\{0, 1, 3, 5, 7\}$.

F $\frac{1}{6}y^2-\frac{5}{2y}=\frac{2}{y}$.

$U=\{1, 3, 5, \ldots\}$.

G $r^2=4$.

$U=N$.

H $t+3=3+t$.

D2

D How do you know that condition A is a rational condition as well as a polynomial condition?

E How do you know that condition C is not a rational condition?

Notice that the sides of condition C are two algebraic expressions. Such a condition is an *algebraic condition.*

F Which of the sides of condition C is not a rational expression? Which of the sides is a polynomial?

G Why is every polynomial condition also an algebraic condition? Why is every rational condition also an algebraic condition?

You will recall that the universe for a variable is the set of permissible replacements for the variable. Notice that a different universe is given for the variable in each of the conditions expressed in D2.

H What statements do you obtain when you use the members of the universe as replacements for n in condition D? For which replacement do you obtain a true statement?

The number -3 satisfies, or is a solution of, $12+n=9$. Since -3 is the only member of the universe that satisfies condition D, $\{-3\}$ is the solution set of the condition.

I Now consider condition E. What statements do you obtain when you use the members of the universe as replacements for x? Tabulate the solution set of condition E.

J Notice that zero is a member of the universe for y in condition F. Why is zero not a meaningful replacement for y in F?

REMINDER

A meaningful replacement for a variable in an expression is a member of the universe that yields a real number upon replacement of the variable.

See lesson 251, page 219.

K Is 1 a meaningful replacement for y in condition F? Is 5 a meaningful replacement?

L Tabulate the solution set of F.

M Now you will find the solution set of condition G, expressed in D2. Is each member of the universe a meaningful replacement for r in condition G?

N Is 1 a solution of $r^2=4$? Is 3 a solution? Is 5 a solution? How do you know that no member of the specified universe satisfies G?

As you know, the set that has no members is the empty set and can be expressed by the symbol $\{\ \}$. The symbol at the right is also used to express the empty set. D3 shows how to write

$\emptyset$

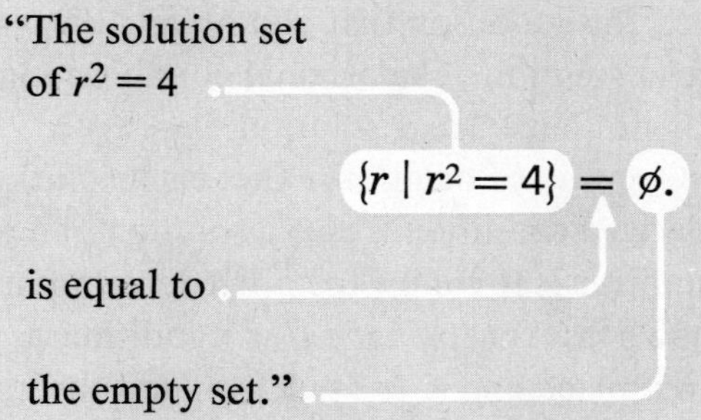

"The solution set of $r^2 = 4$ is equal to the empty set."

$\{r \mid r^2 = 4\} = \phi.$

D3

I $x + 2 = 5.$ $\{3\}$
J $2x + 4 = 10.$ $\{3\}$

D4

I $x + 2 = 5.$ $\{3\}$
K $x + 9 = 12.$ $\{3\}$

D5

I $x + 2 = 5.$ $\{3\}$
L $x - 3 = 0.$ $\{3\}$

D6

and read a sentence containing the new symbol for the empty set.

O Why is $\{r \mid r^2 = 4\} = \phi$ a true statement when $U = \{1, 3, 5, \ldots\}$?

P Look again at D2. What property of addition tells you that each member of the specified universe satisfies condition H? Is the universe for t also the solution set of condition H?

Next you will review the idea of equivalent conditions. Then you will use this idea to help find solution sets of conditions.

In your previous work you have often used properties of the real numbers to derive one condition from another. You have used the properties in such a way that each condition you derived was equivalent to the preceding condition. One purpose of deriving a chain of conditions that are equivalent to a given condition is to obtain a condition like $x = 5$, whose solution set is obvious.

However, it is possible to use properties of real numbers to derive a condition that is not equivalent to the original condition. You can sometimes "gain" solutions when you use a property to derive one condition from another. In the exercises that follow, you will learn how to decide if a condition is equivalent to a given condition.

Study condition I, expressed in D4. Remember that the universe for x is D.

A What statement do you obtain when you replace x by 3 in condition I? Tabulate the solution set of $x + 2 = 5$.

B What condition do you obtain when you multiply each side of $x + 2 = 5$ by 2?

C Look again at D4. What property was used to obtain condition J from condition I? Is $\{3\}$ the solution set of J? How do you know that I and J are equivalent conditions?

D Look at D5. What condition do you obtain when you add 7 to both sides of condition I?

E What property was used to obtain condition K from I?

F ? What is the solution set of K? Does adding 7 to each side of condition I yield a condition that is equivalent to condition I?

G Look at D6. What number was subtracted from each side of condition I to obtain condition L?

H What property was used to obtain condition L from condition I?

I ? When you subtract 5 from each side of condition I, do you obtain an equivalent condition? Explain your answer.

J Look at D7. What property was used to obtain condition M from I?

K Replace x by 3 in condition M. Do you obtain a true statement?

L When you divide each side of condition I by 10, do you obtain an equivalent condition?

M Now multiply each side of condition I by x. Study condition N expressed in D8. What property was used to obtain N from I?

N What statement do you obtain when you replace x in $x^2 + 2x = 5x$ by 0? By 3? Are both 0 and 3 solutions of $x^2 + 2x = 5x$?

O $\{0, 3\}$ is the solution set of condition N. Is N equivalent to I? Explain your answer.

P When you multiply each side of $x + 2 = 5$ by x, you gain a solution because $x^2 + 2x = 5x$ has one more solution than $x + 2 = 5$. Which solution do you gain?

Q Is the solution set of condition I a subset of the solution set of condition N?

Since you can obtain $x^2 + 2x = 5x$ from $x + 2 = 5$ by using a property of real numbers, $x + 2 = 5 \Rightarrow x^2 + 2x = 5x$ is a true statement for each x. This means that there is no x for which $x + 2 = 5$ is true and $x^2 + 2x = 5x$ is false. Therefore, if $x + 2 = 5$ has a solution, then that solution is also a solution of $x^2 + 2x = 5x$. When you multiplied $x + 2$ and 5 by x, you gained the solution 0. When you multiply each side of a polynomial condition by x, the condition that you obtain always has 0 as a solution. The original condition may or may not have 0 as a solution.

One way of being sure that each solution of a derived condition is also a solution of a given condition is to follow the procedure commonly known as "checking." For condition I, you can replace x in $x + 2 = 5$ by 0 and then by 3. Since you obtain a true statement when you replace x in $x + 2 = 5$ by 3, you know that 3 is a solution. Since you obtain a false statement when you replace x in $x + 2 = 5$ by 0, you know that 0 is not a solution.

Another method of determining if each solution of $x^2 + 2x = 5x$ is also a solution of

I	$x + 2 = 5.$	$\{3\}$
M	$\frac{x}{10} + \frac{2}{10} = \frac{5}{10}.$	$\{3\}$

D7

I	$x + 2 = 5.$	$\{3\}$
N	$x^2 + 2x = 5x.$	$\{0, 3\}$

D8

A $\frac{2}{5}x - 30 = 8.$

D9

1	$\frac{2}{5}x - 30 = 8.$	Hypothesis
2	$\frac{2}{5}x - 30 + 30 = 8 + 30.$	Well-defined property of addition
3	$\frac{2}{5}x + 0 = 38.$	Definition of additive inverse
4	$\frac{2}{5}x = 38.$	Identity-element property of addition
5	$\frac{5}{2}(\frac{2}{5}x) = \frac{5}{2}(38).$	Well-defined property of multiplication
6	$x = 95.$	Definition of reciprocal

D10

$x+2=5$ is to try to prove the converse of $x+2=5 \Rightarrow x^2+2x=5x$. Suppose that A and B are conditions. The conditional A $\Rightarrow$ B does not necessarily mean B $\Rightarrow$ A. On the other hand, you can be certain that conditions A and B are equivalent if the biconditional A $\Leftrightarrow$ B is true.

R ? What statement is the converse of the statement $x+2=5 \Rightarrow x^2+2x=5x$? What replacement for x makes $x^2+2x=5x$ true, but makes $x+2=5$ false? Is it possible to prove that $x^2+2x=5x \Rightarrow x+2=5$ is a true statement for each x?

Since you can obtain a false statement from $x^2+2x=5x \Rightarrow x+2=5$, it is not true that each solution of $x^2+2x=5x$ is a solution of $x+2=5$. Therefore, the two conditions are not equivalent.

Let us summarize the above discussion. Given a condition A, you can use properties to prove A $\Rightarrow$ B. This means that, if A has a solution, then that solution is also a solution of B. By proving only A $\Rightarrow$ B, you do not know if A and B are equivalent. You must either check the solutions of B in A or prove B $\Rightarrow$ A in order to determine the solution set of condition A.

By using the procedure just discussed, we can derive equivalent conditions to help us find the solution set of condition A, expressed in D9. First we will prove that, for each x, if $\frac{2}{5}x-30=8$, then $x=95$. This proof is given in D10.

A Study D10 and then look at D11. Which conditional expressed in D11 is proved by the steps given in D10?

B How do you know that, if there is a real number that is a solution of $\frac{2}{5}x-30=8$, then that same real number also satisfies $x=95$?

B $\frac{2}{5}x-30=8 \Rightarrow x=95$.
C $x=95 \Rightarrow \frac{2}{5}x-30=8$.

D11

---

1 $x=95$.
2 $\frac{2}{5}x=\frac{2}{5}(95)$.
3 $\frac{2}{5}x=38$.
4 $\frac{2}{5}x-30=38-30$.
5 $\frac{2}{5}x-30=8$.

D12

D $(\frac{2}{5}x-30=8 \Rightarrow x=95) \wedge (x=95 \Rightarrow \frac{2}{5}x-30=8)$.
E $\frac{2}{5}x-30=8 \Leftrightarrow x=95$.

D13

C ? What real number satisfies $x=95$? Using $\frac{2}{5}x-30=8 \Rightarrow x=95$, can you be sure that 95 also satisfies $\frac{2}{5}x-30=8$?

D Now study the proof given in D12. Justify each step.

E ? The proof given in D12 applies to which conditional expressed in D11? How do you know that 95 must be a solution of $\frac{2}{5}x-30=8$?

F How are the two conditionals expressed in D11 related?

G Look at D13. For each x, how are statements D and E related?

H ? How do you know that statement E is true for each x?

I ? Since statement E is true for each x, we know that $\frac{2}{5}x-30=8$ if and only if $x=95$. Why are $\frac{2}{5}x-30=8$ and $x=95$ equivalent? What is the solution set of $\frac{2}{5}x-30=8$?

J ? In exercises A through I, we proved that $\{95\}$ is the solution set of $\frac{2}{5}x-30=8$. To do this, why did we prove both the conditional $\frac{2}{5}x-30=8 \Rightarrow x=95$ and its converse? How do you know that 95 is the only solution of $\frac{2}{5}x - 30 = 8$?

The conditional $\frac{2}{5}x - 30 = 8 \Rightarrow x = 95$ tells us only one thing: If there is a solution of $\frac{2}{5}x - 30 = 8$, then that solution must be 95, the solution of $x = 95$. To show that 95 is indeed a solution of $\frac{2}{5}x - 30 = 8$, we must also use the conditional $x = 95 \Rightarrow \frac{2}{5}x - 30 = 8$.

Another way to show that 95 is a solution of $\frac{2}{5}x - 30 = 8$ is to replace x by 95 in the condition. Since $\frac{2}{5}(95) - 30 = 8$ is a true statement, 95 is a solution of $\frac{2}{5}x - 30 = 8$. Thus, to prove that $\{95\}$ is the solution set of $\frac{2}{5}x - 30 = 8$, we have a choice of two procedures: We can prove that the biconditional $\frac{2}{5}x - 30 = 8 \Leftrightarrow x = 95$ is true for each x; or we can prove that, for each x, the conditional $\frac{2}{5}x - 30 = 8 \Rightarrow x = 95$ is true, and then check 95 in $\frac{2}{5}x - 30 = 8$.

Now we will find the solution set of condition F, expressed in D14.

K Justify each of conditions G through L, expressed in D14. Some of the conditions need more than one reason for their justification. If condition F has a solution, then what must that solution be?

L To find out whether or not 0 is really a solution of condition F, you can check 0 in the condition. If you replace x in $\frac{1}{x} = 2 + \frac{1}{x}$ by 0, do you obtain a true statement? Is 0 a solution of condition F?

M How do you know that there is no real number that is a solution of condition F?

N Do you think that $0 = x \Rightarrow \frac{1}{x} = 2 + \frac{1}{x}$ for each x? Explain your answer.

In this lesson you studied different kinds of conditions for equality. You also used biconditionals to determine the solution set of a given condition.

D14

F $\frac{1}{x} = 2 + \frac{1}{x}$.

G $\frac{1}{x}(x) = 2x + \frac{1}{x}(x)$.

H $1 = 2x + 1$.

I $1 - 1 = 2x + 1 - 1$.

J $0 = 2x$.

K $\frac{0}{2} = \frac{2x}{2}$.

L $0 = x$.

D15

$U = \{-4, -2, 0, 2, 4\}$.

M $x + 20 = 18$.

N $2\sqrt{12} + a = \frac{48}{a} + 20$.

O $\frac{2}{n} + 10 = n + 11$.

P $y^2 = 100$.

Q $\frac{t^2 - 4}{t + 2} = t - 2$.

R $n + 6 = 10$.

D16

$3x = 6 \Leftrightarrow x = 2$.

Proof I	Proof II
1 $3x = 6$.	1 $x = 2$.
2 $\frac{3x}{3} = \frac{6}{3}$.	2 $3x = 3(2)$.
3 $x = 2$.	3 $3x = 6$.

On your own

Use D15 in connection with exercises 1 through 4.

1 Which conditions are polynomial conditions?

2 Which conditions are rational conditions?

3 Which conditions are algebraic conditions?

4 For each condition, first tell which members of the universe tabulated in the display are meaningful replacements for the variable. Then tabulate the solution set of each condition.

Use D16 in connection with exercises 5 through 10.

5 Proof I is a proof of which conditional?

6 Justify each step of proof I.

7 Proof II is a proof of which conditional?

8 Justify each step of proof II.

9 How do you know that $3x = 6 \Leftrightarrow x = 2$ for each x?

10 Use $3x = 6 \Leftrightarrow x = 2$ to explain why the number 2 is the only solution of $3x = 6$.

11 What biconditional would you have to prove to show that 5 is the only solution of $x + 15 = 20$? Explain your answer.

12 Prove the biconditional that you named for exercise 11. What two conditionals should you prove?

KEEPING SKILLFUL

For each of exercises 1 through 9, give a standard name of the number expressed.

1 25^3	**4** $64^{-\frac{1}{2}}$	**7** $16^{\frac{3}{2}}$
2 $4^{\frac{3}{2}}$	**5** $10{,}000^{\frac{1}{2}}$	**8** $(\frac{1}{12})^{-3}$
3 $(-216)^{\frac{1}{3}}$	**6** $16^{-\frac{3}{4}}$	**9** $512^{\frac{2}{3}}$

For each quotient expressed below, obtain a quotient whose divisor is a polynomial. The universe for each variable is the set of positive real numbers.

10 $\dfrac{x}{\sqrt{x} + 10}$	**15** $\dfrac{5}{\sqrt{c} \cdot \sqrt{y}}$
11 $\dfrac{9}{10\sqrt{x}}$	**16** $\dfrac{1}{\sqrt[5]{-y}}$
12 $\dfrac{2}{\sqrt[3]{x^2}}$	**17** $\dfrac{-3}{8\sqrt{t} + 1}$
13 $\dfrac{4}{6 - \sqrt{x}}$	**18** $\dfrac{8y}{\sqrt{y}\,(y + 4)}$
14 $\dfrac{7x}{\sqrt{2x} + 3}$	**19** $\dfrac{\sqrt{x}}{\sqrt{x} - 7}$

---

21 | **259** Exploring ideas

The linear condition $ax + b = 0$

In this lesson you will study an important kind of condition that is known as a linear condition for equality. You will also learn a convenient method for finding the solutions of conditions of this kind.

A Each condition expressed in D1 involves only one variable. How do you know that each of these conditions is a polynomial condition?

Condition A consists of the polynomials $5x + 7$ and 0. Because $5x + 7$ is a first-degree polynomial, condition A is a first-degree polynomial condition.

B Look again at D1. Condition B is a second-degree polynomial condition. What is the degree of each of conditions C, D, and E?

A first-degree polynomial condition is often called a *linear condition*. The standard form of a linear condition for equality in one variable is $ax + b = 0$, where $a \neq 0$.

> **linear condition for equality in one variable.** A condition of the form $ax + b = 0$, where $a \neq 0$.

A $5x + 7 = 0.$
B $\frac{1}{4}x^2 - 20 = 0.$
C $10x^4 = 0.$
D $\sqrt{6}x - 3.8 = 0.$
E $15x^3 - 5x^2 + 10x - 5 = 0.$

D1

A $5x + 7 = 0$.
B $\frac{1}{4}x^2 - 20 = 0$.
C $10x^4 = 0$.
D $\sqrt{6}x - 3.8 = 0$.
E $15x^3 - 5x^2 + 10x - 5 = 0$.

D1

F $\frac{2}{3}x + 9 = 0$.
G $3x = 15$.
H $8x + 6 = 2x + 5$.

D2

I $x(x + 4) = 2(\frac{1}{2}x^2 - 4x + 6)$.
J $x^2 + 4x = x^2 - 8x + 12$.
K $4x = -8x + 12$.
L $12x = 12$.
M $12x - 12 = 0$.

D3

C Which conditions expressed in D1 are linear conditions?

D What replacements have been made for a and b in $ax + b = 0$ to obtain each linear condition expressed in D1?

E Look at D2. Which condition is of the form $ax + b = 0$?

F Use properties of real numbers to derive $3x - 15 = 0$ from condition G. $3x - 15 = 0$ and $3x = 15$ are equivalent conditions. How can $3x - 15 = 0$ be put in the form $ax + b = 0$?

G Derive $6x + 1 = 0$ from condition H.

H The development in D3 shows how to derive $12x - 12 = 0$ from condition I. Justify each of conditions J through M. How can $12x - 12 = 0$ be put in the form $ax + b = 0$?

You can see that a condition of the form $ax + b = 0$ can be derived from each of conditions G and H, expressed in D2, and from condition I, expressed in D3. If a condition can be put into the form $ax + b = 0$, where $a \neq 0$, then it is a linear condition for equality in one variable.

Next we will use properties of real numbers to prove a theorem concerning the solutions of linear conditions for equality. The theorem is expressed below.

For each a *and* b, *the condition* $\mathrm{ax + b = 0}$, *where* $\mathrm{a \neq 0}$, *has exactly one solution, and that solution is* $\frac{-\mathrm{b}}{\mathrm{a}}$.

I The first part of the proof of the theorem expressed above is given in D4. Justify each step.

J ? The proof given in D4 is a proof of what conditional? If $ax + b = 0$ has a solution, then what must that solution be?

K ? From a proof of $ax + b = 0 \Rightarrow x = \frac{-b}{a}$, can you be certain that $\frac{-b}{a}$ is a solution of $ax + b = 0$?

L To prove that $\frac{-b}{a}$ is a solution of $ax + b = 0$, where $a \neq 0$, replace x by $\frac{-b}{a}$ in $ax + b = 0$. What statement do you obtain? For each a and b, is $a\left(\frac{-b}{a}\right) + b = 0$ a true statement? Remember that $a \neq 0$.

M Is $\frac{-b}{a}$ a solution of $ax + b = 0$? How do you know that $\frac{-b}{a}$ is the only solution of the condition?

We will use the theorem that we have just proved to find the solution of a particular linear condition. Study condition N, expressed in D5.

1 $ax + b = 0.$
2 $ax + b + (-b) = 0 + (-b).$
3 $ax + \big(b + (-b)\big) = -b.$
4 $ax + 0 = -b.$
5 $ax = -b.$
6 $\frac{1}{a}(ax) = \frac{1}{a}(-b).$
7 $\left(\frac{1}{a} \cdot a\right)x = \frac{-b}{a}.$
8 $1x = \frac{-b}{a}.$
9 $x = \frac{-b}{a}.$

D4

N The development in D5 shows how to put condition N into the form $ax + b = 0$. Justify conditions O through U.

Since, for $-6x + 30 = 0$, the replacement for a is -6 and the replacement for b is 30, we obtain $\frac{-30}{-6}$ from $\frac{-b}{a}$. Therefore, we say that $\frac{-30}{-6}$, or 5, is the *value* of $\frac{-b}{a}$ for $-6x + 30 = 0$.

O How do you know that $\{x \mid -6x + 30 = 0\} = \{5\}$? How do you know that 5 is the only solution of condition N, the original condition?

When a linear condition is in standard form, it is convenient to use $ax + b = 0 \Leftrightarrow x = \frac{-b}{a}$ to obtain the solution. When a linear condition is not in standard form, however, it is just as convenient to use properties of real numbers to obtain a condition of the form $x = k$. For example, to solve condition N, we could have continued our work until we derived the condition $x = 5$. We could then have checked 5 in the original condition. In this case we would have derived the conditions expressed in D6.

P Notice that condition T is expressed again in D6. Justify conditions V and W. The conditions expressed in D5 and D6 prove what conditional?

Q Now show that 5 is a solution of condition N. Do this by checking 5 in condition N. How do you know that 5 is the only solution of condition N?

As you acquire more skill in solving conditions, fewer steps will be necessary. In fact, you could probably solve condition N in only three or four steps. No matter how many steps you use, however, you should always be able to justify each step.

N $\frac{2x}{3} - \frac{x-2}{2} = \frac{x}{6} - (4 - x).$

O $6\left(\frac{2x}{3} - \frac{x-2}{2}\right) = 6\left(\frac{x}{6} - (4 - x)\right).$

P $6\left(\frac{2x}{3}\right) - 6\left(\frac{x-2}{2}\right) = 6\left(\frac{x}{6}\right) - 6(4 - x).$

Q $4x - 3(x - 2) = x - (24 - 6x).$

R $4x - 3x + 6 = x - 24 + 6x.$

S $x + 6 = 7x - 24.$

T $-6x + 6 = -24.$

U $-6x + 30 = 0.$

D5

T $-6x + 6 = -24.$

V $-6x = -30.$

W $x = 5.$

D6

For each of exercises R through U, find the solution of the given condition.

R $11\frac{1}{4} - 2x = x - 4\frac{1}{2}$.

S $1 - (x - 2) = 4 - (2x + 11)$.

T $3(5 - 3y) = 8y - 2$.

U $\frac{7 - 2n}{3} = \frac{2n + 12}{4}$.

In this lesson you have learned that linear conditions for equality are a special kind of polynomial condition. You also have proved that $\frac{-b}{a}$ is the unique solution of the linear condition for equality $ax + b = 0$, where $a \neq 0$.

On your own

Tabulate the solution set of each of the conditions expressed below.

1 $x + 2 = 6$.
2 $7m - 4m = 12$.
3 $-3z = 9$.
4 $w + \frac{1}{5} = \frac{1}{3}$.
5 $.78 + u = .5$.
6 $4y - \frac{1}{2}y = 2y + 3$.
7 $y - \frac{3}{4} = \frac{1}{2}$.
8 $3x - 5x = -8$.
9 $3\frac{2}{3}y - 11 = 0$.
10 $2(z - 3) + 7 = 4z$.
11 $\frac{3}{5}(x - 2) - \frac{2}{3}(7 - 2x) = 2$.
12 $\frac{4}{7} - \frac{2w - 3}{2} = \frac{w + 5}{2}$.
13 $\frac{y}{2} + \frac{y}{3} = 10$.
14 $15 - (7 - 5x) = 2x + (5 - 3x)$.
15 $8n - (7 - n) = 3(n - 2) - 13$.
16 $2(z + 1) = 4 - (3z - 8)$.
17 $\frac{r - 5}{2} = \frac{r - 8}{3}$.
18 $\frac{x}{2} + \frac{x + 1}{3} = 7$.
19 $(y + 1)(y + 2) = (y + 3)(y + 4)$.

The linear conditions $ax + b < 0$ and $ax + b > 0$

You will find that linear conditions for inequality are closely related to linear conditions for equality. Therefore, the procedures you studied in lesson 259 will be utilized when you are solving linear conditions for inequality in this lesson.

A Each condition expressed in D1 is a condition for inequality. Which conditions involve the idea of "less than"? Which involve the idea of "greater than"?

You know that $ax + b = 0$ is the standard form of a linear condition for equality in one variable. $ax + b < 0$ and $ax + b > 0$, where $a \neq 0$, are standard forms of linear conditions for inequality in one variable.

B Look again at D1. How can you obtain condition A from $ax + b < 0$? How can you obtain condition B from $ax + b < 0$? How can you obtain condition C from $ax + b > 0$?

C Since $-3x + 7 > 0$ has the same meaning as $0 < -3x + 7$, you can think of $-3x + 7 > 0$ as a standard form of condition D. Why can you also think of $3x - 7 < 0$ as a standard form of condition D?

D ? Condition E includes the polynomial expression $\frac{4}{5}(10 + 15x) - 5x$. Simplify the ex-

linear condition for inequality in one variable. A condition of either the form $ax + b < 0$ or the form $ax + b > 0$, where $a \neq 0$.

A $2x+5<0$.
B $30x<0$.
C $-5x+\frac{1}{2}>0$.
D $0<-3x+7$.
E $\frac{4}{5}(10+15x)-5x<0$.
F $8(x-2)+\frac{1}{2}(10x+4)<0$.
G $(x+8)(x+6)-x^2>0$.
H $(x+10)^2-(x-3)^2<0$.

D1

I $3(5x+1)>2(\frac{1}{2}x+5)$.
J $15x+3>x+10$.
K $14x+3>10$.
L $14x-7>0$.

D2

M $\frac{4x+7}{5}>\frac{10x-3}{2}$.
N $10\left(\frac{4x+7}{5}\right)>10\left(\frac{10x-3}{2}\right)$.
O $2(4x+7)>5(10x-3)$.
P $8x+14>50x-15$.
Q $-42x+29>0$.

D3

pression. Explain why E is a linear condition for inequality.

E Put each of conditions F, G, and H in a standard form.

There are two standard forms of any linear condition for inequality in one variable: the form $ax+b<0$ and the form $ax+b>0$, where $a\neq 0$.

F The development in D2 shows how you can derive a condition in standard form from the condition $3(5x+1)>2(\frac{1}{2}x+5)$. Notice that first we simplify each side of condition I. Justify condition J.

G Explain why the sum property of "less ? than" for real numbers justifies condition K expressed in D2.

> REMINDER
> Sum property of "less than":
> The universe for each variable is D.
> For each a, b, and c,
> if $a<b$, then $a+c<b+c$.
> *See lesson 223, page 86.*

H What property of real numbers justifies condition L?

I Why can you think of condition L as a standard form of condition I? Why is condition I a linear condition for inequality?

Put each of the conditions expressed in exercises J through M in a standard form.

J $5(9x+6)+\frac{1}{2}(4x+6)>8$.
K $\frac{2}{3}(27x-6)<5x$.
L $10(-2x+3)+4x>3(2x)-6$.
M $(x-2)^2<(x-2)(x+7)$.

N The development in D3 shows how a condition in standard form can be derived from condition M. What is the least common multiple of 5 and 2? What property of "less than" justifies condition N?

> REMINDER
> Positive-multiplier property of "less than": The universe for each variable is D. For each a, b, and c, if $a<b$ and $c>0$, then $ac<bc$.
> *See lesson 223, page 86.*

O Justify each of conditions O, P, and Q, expressed in D3.

P Look again at D3. Is $-42x+29>0$ a standard form of condition M? How do you know that $\frac{4x+7}{5}>\frac{10x-3}{2}$ is a linear condition for inequality?

Put each of the conditions expressed in exercises Q through V either in the form $ax+b<0$ or in the form $ax+b>0$.

Q $\frac{2x-5}{3}<\frac{7}{3}$.

R $\frac{x}{3}+\frac{x}{4}>\frac{x}{12}+6$.

S $\frac{x}{5}-2x<\frac{1}{10}$.

T $\frac{3x+1}{2}-5x<\frac{4x}{3}+10$.

U $\frac{x-3}{8}>\frac{2x+5}{2}$.

V $\frac{x+2}{6}<\frac{x-3}{2}$.

Now we will use properties of real numbers to prove a biconditional concerning linear conditions for inequality that can be put in the form $ax+b>0$, where $a>0$. The biconditional is expressed below.

For each $a>0$ *and for each* b *and* x, $ax+b>0 \Leftrightarrow x>\frac{-b}{a}$.

A The proof given in D4 is a proof of what conditional?

B Justify steps 1, 2, and 3 of the proof given in D4.

C You know that $ax+b>0$ is a linear condition when $a\neq 0$. Suppose that $a>0$. Is $\frac{1}{a}>0$? If $\frac{1}{a}>0$, what property of "less than" justifies step 4 of the proof? Justify step 5.

D ? Now you know that, for each $a>0$ and for each b and x, $ax+b>0\Rightarrow x>\frac{-b}{a}$. Can you be sure that each solution of $x>\frac{-b}{a}$ is also a solution of $ax+b>0$?

E The proof given in D5 is a proof of what conditional?

M $\frac{4x+7}{5}>\frac{10x-3}{2}$.

N $10\left(\frac{4x+7}{5}\right)>10\left(\frac{10x-3}{2}\right)$.

O $2(4x+7)>5(10x-3)$.

P $8x+14>50x-15$.

Q $-42x+29>0$.

D3

$$ax+b>0\Rightarrow x>\frac{-b}{a}.$$

1 $ax+b>0$.

2 $ax+b+(-b)>0+(-b)$.

3 $ax>-b$.

4 $\frac{1}{a}(ax)>\frac{1}{a}(-b)$.

5 $x>\frac{-b}{a}$.

D4

$$x>\frac{-b}{a}\Rightarrow ax+b>0.$$

1 $x>\frac{-b}{a}$.

2 $ax>a\left(\frac{-b}{a}\right)$.

3 $ax>-b$.

4 $ax+b>-b+b$.

5 $ax+b>0$.

D5

F What property of "less than" justifies step 2 of the proof given in D5? Justify steps 3, 4, and 5 of the proof.

G ? You have proved that, for each $a > 0$ and for each b and x, $ax + b > 0 \Rightarrow x > \frac{-b}{a}$ and $x > \frac{-b}{a} \Rightarrow ax + b > 0$. What biconditional have you proved? How do you know that the solutions of $x > \frac{-b}{a}$ are the only solutions of $ax + b > 0$? When $a > 0$, is $\{x \mid ax + b > 0\} = \left\{x \mid x > \frac{-b}{a}\right\}$?

H Put $5x + 7 > -2x$ in the form $ax + b > 0$, where $a > 0$. What is the value of $\frac{-b}{a}$? Is $\{x \mid 5x + 7 > -2x\} = \{x \mid x > -1\}$?

Next we will prove a biconditional concerning linear conditions for inequality that can be put in the form $ax + b < 0$, where $a > 0$. The biconditional that we will prove is expressed below.

For each a > 0 *and for each* b *and* x, ax + b $< 0 \Leftrightarrow$ x $< \frac{-\text{b}}{\text{a}}$.

I To prove $ax + b < 0 \Leftrightarrow x < \frac{-b}{a}$, you must prove two conditionals. What are they?

J If you replace "greater than" by "less than" in the steps given in D4, you will have a proof of $ax + b < 0 \Rightarrow x < \frac{-b}{a}$. Justify each step of this new proof.

K If you replace "greater than" by "less than" in the steps given in D5, you will have a proof of $x < \frac{-b}{a} \Rightarrow ax + b < 0$. Justify each step of this new proof.

L ? You have proved that, for each $a > 0$ and for each b and x, $ax + b < 0 \Rightarrow x < \frac{-b}{a}$ and $x < \frac{-b}{a} \Rightarrow ax + b < 0$. What biconditional have you proved? How do you know that the solutions of $x < \frac{-b}{a}$ are the only solutions of $ax + b < 0$? Is $\{x \mid ax + b < 0\} = \left\{x \mid x < \frac{-b}{a}\right\}$? Is $\{x \mid ax + b < 0\}$ an infinite set?

M Put $3(5x + \frac{2}{3}) + x < 10$ in the form $ax + b < 0$. What is the value of $\frac{-b}{a}$? Give a standard description of the solution set of the condition $3(5x + \frac{2}{3}) + x < 10$.

N Can you use $ax + b > 0 \Leftrightarrow x > \frac{-b}{a}$, where $a > 0$, to find the solutions of $-4n - 12 > 0$? Explain your answer.

O What property of "less than" tells you that $4n + 12 < 0$ is equivalent to $-4n - 12 > 0$? Is $\{n \mid -4n - 12 > 0\} = \{n \mid n < -3\}$?

REMINDER

Negative-multiplier property of "less than": The universe for each variable is D. For each a, b, and c, if $a < b$ and $c < 0$, then $ac > bc$.

See lesson 238, page 159.

P ? Use properties of real numbers to prove that, for each $a < 0$ and for each b and x, $\{x \mid ax + b > 0\} = \left\{x \mid x < \frac{-b}{a}\right\}$.

Q Can you use $ax + b < 0 \Leftrightarrow x < \frac{-b}{a}$, where $a > 0$, to find the solution set of $-2x + 8 < 0$?

R If $-2x + 8 < 0$, then $-1(-2x + 8) > -1(0)$. This means that $2x - 8 > 0$ is equivalent to $-2x + 8 < 0$. Is $\{x \mid -2x + 8 < 0\} = \{x \mid x > 4\}$?

S ? Use properties of real numbers to prove that, for each $a < 0$ and for each b and x, $\{x \mid ax + b < 0\} = \left\{x \mid x > \frac{-b}{a}\right\}$.

A $\frac{w}{6} - \frac{2w}{3} < \frac{w-9}{3}$.

B $6\left(\frac{w}{6} - \frac{2w}{3}\right) < 6\left(\frac{w-9}{3}\right)$.

C $6\left(\frac{w}{6}\right) - 6\left(\frac{2w}{3}\right) < 2(w-9)$.

D $w - 4w < 2w - 18$.

E $-3w < 2w - 18$.

F $-5w < -18$.

G $\frac{-1}{5}(-5w) > \frac{-1}{5}(-18)$.

H $w > \frac{18}{5}$.

D6

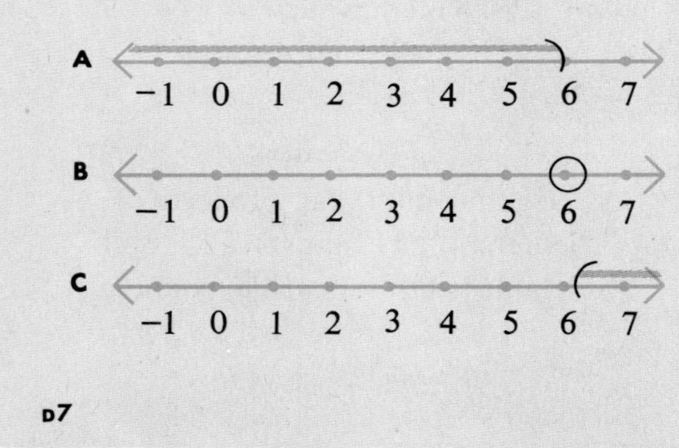

D7

From the theorems that you have just proved, you know that $\left\{x \mid x < \frac{-b}{a}\right\}$ is the solution set of $ax + b < 0$, where $a > 0$, and it is the solution set of $ax + b > 0$, where $a < 0$. Also, $\left\{x \mid x > \frac{-b}{a}\right\}$ is the solution set of $ax + b > 0$, where $a > 0$, and it is the solution set of $ax + b < 0$, where $a < 0$.

Put each condition expressed in exercises T through Y in standard form. Then give a standard description of the solution set of the original condition.

T $3x - 4 > x + 48$.

U $\frac{-y}{4} > \frac{1}{2}$.

V $\frac{7}{6}n - \frac{5}{3} < -4$.

W $2(-2y + 8) - y < 1$.

X $\frac{3x}{5} - \frac{3x}{10} > \frac{x}{4} - \frac{1}{10}$.

Y $\frac{x-7}{2} < \frac{3-2x}{5}$.

In the preceding exercises, you used properties of real numbers to help you put linear conditions for inequality in standard form. Then you used the appropriate biconditional to determine the solution set of the original condition. It is often more convenient to derive a condition of the form $x < k$ or the form $x > k$ from the original condition.

A The development in D6 shows how $w > \frac{18}{5}$ can be derived from condition A. Justify each of conditions B through H.

B Is $\frac{w}{6} - \frac{2w}{3} < \frac{w-9}{3}$ equivalent to $w > \frac{18}{5}$? Give a standard description of the solution set of the original condition.

For each condition expressed in exercises C, D, and E, derive a condition either of the form $x < k$ or of the form $x > k$. Use as many (or as few) steps as you wish, but be sure you can justify each step. Then give a standard description of the solution set of the original condition.

C $\frac{5}{8}x - \frac{3}{4}x < \frac{1}{8} - \frac{1}{6}x$.

D $8(y - 2) - 5(3y + 4) > 6$.

E $-17.5 < 8.1 - n$.

F Use properties of real numbers to derive a condition of the form $x = k$ from $-(-\frac{4}{9}x) = \frac{8}{3}$. Tabulate the solution set of $-(-\frac{4}{9}x) = \frac{8}{3}$.

G Use the solution set of $-(-\frac{4}{9}x) = \frac{8}{3}$ to help describe the solution sets of $-(-\frac{4}{9}x) < \frac{8}{3}$ and $-(-\frac{4}{9}x) > \frac{8}{3}$, respectively.

H Look at the graphs in D7. Which graph represents the locus of $-(-\frac{4}{9}x) = \frac{8}{3}$? The locus of $-(-\frac{4}{9}x) > \frac{8}{3}$? The locus of $-(-\frac{4}{9}x) < \frac{8}{3}$?

In this lesson you studied different methods of solving linear conditions for inequality.

On your own

For each of exercises 1 through 10, first put the condition in standard form, if necessary. Then give a standard description of the solution set of the condition.

1 $8x+6>0.$

2 $3x-30<0.$

3 $-24y+12<0.$

4 $-2.5n<25.$

5 $-2x-20>-20.$

6 $-x+3.9>4.2x.$

7 $\frac{5}{3}(15x-7)>2(8-10x).$

8 $-(-\frac{3}{7}x)<-\frac{3}{14}.$

9 $11-5(3m-2)>3(m-5).$

10 $\frac{3}{2}n+\frac{5}{3}<\frac{1}{2}n+\frac{14}{3}.$

For each condition expressed in exercises 11 through 18, derive an equivalent condition of the form $x<k$ or the form $x>k$.

11 $x+5>-20.$

12 $12<2x-26.$

13 $5x-7<2x-1.$

14 $\frac{4}{3}y-3>\frac{3}{2}y-5.$

15 $3.1s-2.75<7.75-s.$

16 $\dfrac{t+5}{11}>\dfrac{t-1}{9}.$

17 $3(5-x)-4(5+x)<16.$

18 $\dfrac{r+2}{3}>\dfrac{1-r}{4}-\dfrac{1}{6}.$

For each condition expressed in exercises 19 through 25, tabulate the solution set, if possible. Otherwise, give a standard description of the solution set. Then make a graph of the solution set.

19 $4n+3(\frac{2}{3}n-2)=\frac{3}{4}(12n+8).$

20 $\dfrac{y}{3}+\dfrac{y-2}{9}<\dfrac{y-1}{3}.$

21 $x(2x+10)=(2x+5)(x-3)-7.$

22 $(x+5)^2-(x+3)(x+2)>4(x+5).$

23 $\dfrac{m+2}{3}+2m=\dfrac{m-5}{4}.$

24 $y(y-3)+15<(y+7)^2.$

25 $\dfrac{x-6}{5}-\dfrac{x+2}{4}>\dfrac{3x+7}{2}.$

21 **261** Exploring ideas

Compound linear conditions

You can apply the information that you have learned about simple linear conditions for equality and inequality in one variable to finding the solutions of compound linear conditions in one variable.

A Look at D1. Condition A is a compound linear condition in one variable. What connective is used in A? What does the connective tell you about the solution set of A?

B Explain how to derive $x>-2$ from the simple condition $8x+3>-11+x$. Explain how to derive $x<3$ from $2(x+4)<x+11$.

C How do you know that condition B is equivalent to A? Is $\{x|x>-2 \wedge x<3\}$ the solution set of A?

D Is $4 \in \{x|x>-2\}$? Is $4 \in \{x|x<3\}$? How do you know that 4 is not a member of $\{x|x>-2 \wedge x<3\}$? Name three members of $\{x|x>-2 \wedge x<3\}$.

E The intersection of $\{x|x>-2\}$ and $\{x|x<3\}$ is the set that contains only those numbers that are in both $\{x|x>-2\}$ and $\{x|x<3\}$. Explain why 2 is a member of $\{x|x>-2\} \cap \{x|x<3\}$. Is the intersection of $\{x|x>-2\}$ and $\{x|x<3\}$ the same set as $\{x|x>-2 \wedge x<3\}$?

A $8x+3>-11+x \wedge 2(x+4)<x+11.$

B $x>-2 \wedge x<3.$

C $-2<x<3.$

D1

A $8x+3>-11+x \wedge 2(x+4)<x+11$.
B $x>-2 \wedge x<3$.
C $-2<x<3$.

D1

$-3 \quad -2 \quad -1 \quad 0 \quad 1 \quad 2 \quad 3$

$\{x \mid 8x+3>-11+x \wedge 2(x+4)<x+11\}$

D2

D $\frac{3(x-2)}{4}+\frac{x}{2}<\frac{-1}{4} \vee \frac{1}{3}+\frac{2x}{5}<\frac{x}{2}$.

1 $4\left(\frac{3(x-2)}{4}\right)+4\left(\frac{x}{2}\right)<4\left(\frac{-1}{4}\right)$.

2 $3(x-2)+2x<-1$.
3 $3x-6+2x<-1$.
4 $5x-6<-1$.
5 $5x<5$.
6 $x<1$.

D3

E $x<1 \vee 3\frac{1}{3}<x$.

D4

F Each member of $\{x \mid x>-2 \wedge x<3\}$ is greater than what number? Each member is less than what number?

G Look again at D1. What does condition C require? Is $\{x \mid -2<x<3\}=\{x \mid x>-2 \wedge x<3\}$?

H Is the symbol $\{x \mid -2<x<3\}$ a standard description of the solution set of condition A?

As you know, the solution set of a condition that can be put in the form $a<x<b$, where $a<b$, is an open interval. The replacements for a and b are the limits of the interval.

I Explain why the solution set of condition A is an open interval. What are the limits of this interval?

J Now look at the graph in D2. How is the locus of $8x+3>-11+x \wedge 2(x+4)<x+11$ indicated? Are points -2 and 3 in this locus? Is the locus an infinite set?

For each condition expressed in exercises K, L, and M, tabulate the solution set, if possible. Otherwise, give a standard description of the solution set. Then make a graph of the locus.

K $3(x-4)>2x-15 \wedge 4(3x-1)<2$.
L $2(a-2)-(3a-4)=8-(3a+8) \wedge \frac{3}{7}a<12$.
M $3n<3(n+3)-6n \wedge \frac{1}{2}(1-n)+n=8$.
N Which of the conditions expressed in exercises K, L, and M has an open interval as its solution set?

Next you will study compound linear conditions that involve the connective "or."

A Study condition D, expressed in D3. What does the connective "or" tell you about the solution set of the compound condition?

B You will first solve the simple condition $\frac{3(x-2)}{4}+\frac{x}{2}<\frac{-1}{4}$. The steps in D3 show how to derive $x<1$ from this simple condition. Justify steps 1 through 6. After you have multiplied both $\frac{3(x-2)}{4}+\frac{x}{2}$ and $\frac{-1}{4}$ by 4, do you obtain a condition that does not involve division?

C Is each member of $\{x \mid x<1\}$ a solution of condition D?

D Now solve the other simple condition in condition D. What is the least number by which you can multiply $\frac{1}{3}+\frac{2x}{5}$ and $\frac{x}{2}$ to obtain a condition that does not involve division?

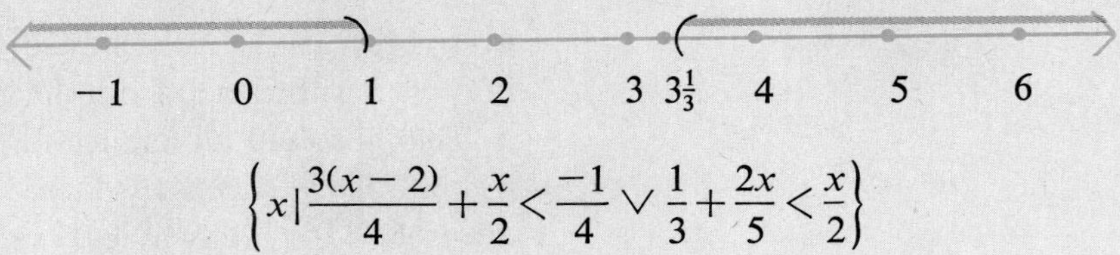

$$\left\{x \middle| \frac{3(x-2)}{4}+\frac{x}{2}<\frac{-1}{4} \vee \frac{1}{3}+\frac{2x}{5}<\frac{x}{2}\right\}$$

D5

E Is each member of $\{x \mid 3\frac{1}{3} < x\}$ a solution of condition D?

F How do you know that D is equivalent to condition E, expressed in D4? Give a standard description of the solution set of D.

G The union of $\{x \mid x < 1\}$ and $\{x \mid 3\frac{1}{3} < x\}$ contains only the members of $\{x \mid x < 1\}$ and the members of $\{x \mid 3\frac{1}{3} < x\}$. Why are -4 and 4 both members of $\{x \mid x < 1\} \cup \{x \mid 3\frac{1}{3} < x\}$? Is $\{x \mid x < 1\} \cup \{x \mid 3\frac{1}{3} < x\} = \{x \mid x < 1 \vee 3\frac{1}{3} < x\}$?

H The graph of the locus of condition D is shown in D5. Is the graph of the locus of each simple condition in D also shown?

Condition F, expressed in D6, is a compound condition whose principal connective is "and." Notice, however, that each component of condition F involves the connective "or." To solve F, you should first solve the simple conditions in each of the components.

I Show how to derive $x = 3$ from $.7x = .4x + .9$ and $x < 3$ from $15x < 40 - (x - 8)$. Which component of condition F is equivalent to $x = 3 \vee x < 3$?

J Show how to derive $x = -1$ from $10x - 2 = 46 + 58x$ and $x > -1$ from $x - 4x < 2 - x$. How do you know that F is equivalent to condition G, expressed in D7?

You will recall that the symbol $\leqq$ is read "less than or equal to." Therefore, $x \leqq a$ has the same meaning as $x = a \vee x < a$. Similarly, the symbol $\geqq$ is read "greater than or equal to," and $x \geqq a$ has the same meaning as $x = a \vee x > a$.

F $(.7x = .4x + .9 \vee 15x < 40 - (x - 8)) \wedge (10x - 2 = 46 + 58x \vee x - 4x < 2 - x)$.

D6

G $(x = 3 \vee x < 3) \wedge (x = -1 \vee x > -1)$.

H $(x \leqq 3) \wedge (x \geqq -1)$.

I $(-1 \leqq x) \wedge (x \leqq 3)$.

J $-1 \leqq x \leqq 3$.

D7

K Is $x = 3 \vee x < 3$ the same as $x \leqq 3$? Is $x = -1 \vee x > -1$ the same as $x \geqq -1$? Look again at D7. Is H equivalent to G? Is I equivalent to H?

L Condition I requires that each member of the solution set be greater than or equal to what number? It also requires that each member be less than or equal to what number?

M Condition J requires that each member of the solution set be greater than or equal to -1 and less than or equal to 3. Is J equivalent to I?

N How do you know that $\{x \mid -1 \leqq x \leqq 3\}$ is the solution set of F, expressed in D6?

The solution set of a condition that can be put in the form $a \leqq x \leqq b$, where $a < b$, is a closed interval. The replacements for a and b are the limits of the interval.

O Look again at D6 and D7. When condition F is put in the form $a \leqq x \leqq b$, what are the replacements for a and b? Is the solution set of F a closed interval? What are the limits?

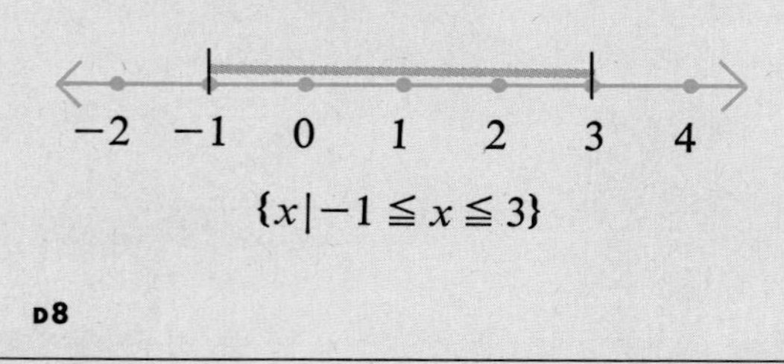

D8

K $x \approx_1 8$.

D9

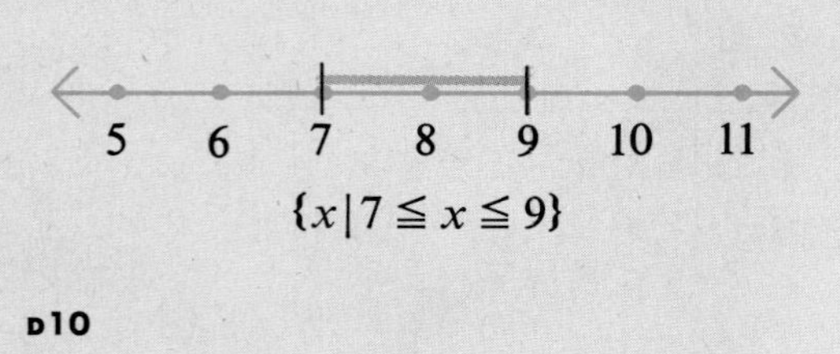

D10

P The graph of the locus of $-1 \leqq x \leqq 3$ is shown in D8. Are points -1 and 3 in this locus?

For each condition expressed in exercises Q through T, give a standard description of the solution set. Then make a graph of the locus.

Q $-10x > \dfrac{20 + 20x}{2} \vee \dfrac{2x}{3} + \dfrac{9}{2} < 1 + 3x$.

R $10x \geqq 25$.

S $\frac{1}{3}x < \frac{1}{3}(2x - \frac{2}{3}) + \frac{4}{9} \vee 7\frac{1}{2}x > -10$.

T $(-6 \leqq 3x) \wedge \big(x - (-20) \leqq 24\big)$.

U Which of the conditions expressed in exercises Q through T has a closed interval as its solution set?

The solution sets of conditions that involve the idea of "approximately equal to" are also closed intervals. Look at D9. Condition K requires that each solution be approximately equal to 8 with a tolerance of 1. This means that the absolute difference of each solution and 8 must be less than or equal to 1. Remember that the absolute difference of two numbers is the difference obtained when the lesser number is subtracted from the greater number.

A The absolute difference of 7.3 and 8 is $8 - 7.3$. Is $8 - 7.3 \leqq 1$? Does 7.3 satisfy condition K? Explain why 8.03 satisfies K.

B The greatest number that satisfies $x \approx_t k$ is $k + t$. Does $8 + 1$ satisfy K? Is 9 the greatest member of $\{x \mid x \approx_1 8\}$?

C The least number that satisfies $x \approx_t k$ is $k - t$. What is the least number that satisfies $x \approx_1 8$?

D You have learned that the solution set of $x \approx_t k$ is the set of numbers greater than or equal to $k - t$ and less than or equal to $k + t$. What closed interval is the solution set of $x \approx_1 8$? Does the graph in D10 show the locus of $x \approx_1 8$?

E Put $x \approx_{.4} 5$ in the form $a \leqq x \leqq b$. Then make a graph of the locus.

In this lesson you solved compound linear conditions in one variable that involve the connectives "and" and "or." You also studied conditions whose solution sets are intervals.

On your own

For each of exercises 1 through 10, tabulate the solution set of the given condition, if possible. Otherwise, give a standard description of the solution set. Then, if the solution set is an interval, tell what kind of interval it is and name the limits. Finally, make a graph of the locus of the condition.

1 $\frac{2}{3}n < 10 \wedge 2(3n - 6) > 16 - n$.

2 $\dfrac{x - 6}{5} < \dfrac{2x}{3} - \dfrac{7}{5} \wedge 5 - (x - 3) = 2x - 5$.

3 $\dfrac{1 - 2t}{4} < \dfrac{1}{4} \wedge 5(t - 1) < 0$.

4 $5 - 3y > 3 \vee \dfrac{y}{2} + 1 > y$.

5 $2s - 8s > 4 - 8s \wedge \dfrac{s - 1}{2} - \dfrac{1 + 2s}{3} < s - \dfrac{5}{6}$.

6 $n \approx_{.4} 8$.

7 $\frac{2a}{3} + \frac{3}{4} > \frac{13}{12} \wedge .5a - .08 < .8 + .06a$.

8 $3(5x - 4) > 2(4 - 3x) + 1 \vee \frac{1}{2}(5 - 4x) > 8x$.

9 $5(7 - 2x) - x > -3x - 5 \vee \frac{2x}{3} - 4 > \frac{x}{5} + 10$.

10 $x \approx_2 14 \vee x \approx_3 16$.

APPLYING MATHEMATICS

For each of the following problems, write a sentence that expresses a condition and then give the answer to the problem. Use 3.14 as an approximation of π.

1 A city park is in the shape of a triangle. The west boundary of the park is perpendicular to the north boundary. The length of the west boundary is 2.2 mi. The length of the north boundary is 1.3 mi. What is the area of the park in square miles?

2 Theoretically, the temperature at which all molecular activity ceases is −273°C. What is this temperature expressed on the Fahrenheit scale?

3 One minute after take-off, a jet plane had reached an altitude of $\frac{1}{2}$ mi. and was over a city that is 8 mi. from the take-off point. The jet plane's path of ascent made what angle with the horizontal?

4 When the planet Pluto is closest to the sun, the distance between it and the sun is 2.76×10^9 mi. What is this distance in kilometers?

5 Mr. Slater borrowed $1700 from his father. At the end of two years he repaid the loan plus $178.50 interest. What was the rate of interest per year?

6 The height of a square regular pyramid is 592 ft. The length of a side of the base is 870 ft. What is the volume of the pyramid in cubic feet?

7 110 volts of pressure will produce 5500 watts of power with a current of 50 amperes. With the same amount of current, how many more volts of pressure are required to produce 6000 watts of power?

8 Clark practices weight lifting with two bar bells that weigh 75 lb. and 100 lb., respectively. Raising the 100-lb. bar bell a distance of 4 ft. requires how many more foot-pounds of work than raising the 75-lb. bar bell the same distance?

9 Rectangle RMNS has an area of 1296 square centimeters. The length of the rectangle is 48 centimeters. Parallelogram RJKL has the same area as the rectangle. The measure of the base of parallelogram RJKL is $\frac{1}{3}$ of the width of the rectangle. What is the measure in centimeters of an altitude of parallelogram RJKL?

10 An express elevator moves to the top floor of a skyscraper at a rate of 1400 ft. per minute. What is the speed of the elevator in miles per hour?

11 A certain gondola car contains a 60-ton mixture of iron ore, which is made up of two grades. One grade of ore is 20% iron, and the other grade is 40% iron. The entire mixture is 24% iron. How many tons of each grade of ore are included in the mixture?

12 Although the earth is not perfectly spherical in shape, we say that the measure of a "radius" of the earth at the equator is approximately 4000 mi. What is the volume in cubic miles of a sphere whose radius is 4000 miles long?

13 In January, Mr. Slattery had $6080 in a savings account. The interest on the account is compounded semiannually at a rate of 2% per 6-month period. How much money will Mr. Slattery have in his account at the end of the year if he makes no deposits and no withdrawals?

CHECKING UP

If you have trouble with this test, you can find help in lessons 258 through 261.

Test 240

1 What is the standard form of a linear condition for equality in one variable?

2 What number is not a meaningful replacement for x in $\frac{4}{2x-5} - 3 = 7 - 3x$?

3 What condition do you obtain when you multiply each side of $\frac{1}{2}x + \frac{1}{3} < \frac{1}{4}x + \frac{5}{6}$ by 12?

4 What condition do you obtain when you divide each side of $4(x-3) + 10 = 8 + 2x$ by 2?

5 What condition do you obtain when you subtract 5 from each side of $4x + 5 = 32$?

6 What condition do you obtain when you multiply each side of $1.5x + 2 = 3.4$ by 10?

7 Think of $-3x + 5 = 0$ as being of the form $ax + b = 0$. What is the value of $\frac{-b}{a}$?

8 Tabulate the solution set of $x + 7 = 7$.

9 Tabulate the solution set of $2.9x - 4.5 = 3x - 5$.

10 Tabulate the solution set of $\frac{2}{3}x + 4 = 3 + \frac{3}{4}x$.

11 Solve $5x + 7 = 4(2x - 3) + 9$.

12 What x satisfies $\frac{2x}{3} = \frac{4x-2}{7}$?

13 Derive a condition of the form $x < k$ from $2.8x - 1 < 2.3x - .25$.

14 What are the limits of the interval that is the solution set of $2(2x - 1) > 3x - 5 \wedge 7x - 1 < 3(x + 1)$?

15 What integers are in the interval that is the solution set of $-4.5 < x < .5$?

16 Make a graph of $3(4 - x) < 7 - 2x$.

17 Make a graph of $x \leqq 2 \vee x \geqq 5$.

18 Put $\frac{3x}{4} - \frac{3-2x}{3} > x - \frac{3}{2}$ into the form $ax + b > 0$.

21 | 262 Exploring ideas

Absolute value

In this lesson you will learn what is meant by the absolute value of a real number. You will also derive some properties that concern absolute value.

The real-number line pictured in D1 will help you understand the idea of absolute value. Remember that point 0 is the origin of the number line.

A The origin is one endpoint of $\overline{CF}$. What is the coördinate of point C? What is the coördinate of the origin? What is $m(\overline{CF})$?

> REMINDER
>
> The measure of a segment is the absolute difference of the coördinates of the endpoints of the segment. If the coördinate of A is 0 and the coördinate of B is -2, then $m(\overline{AB}) = 0 - (-2)$, or 2.
>
> *See lesson 98, page 427, Book 1.*

B Is the origin an endpoint of each segment named below? Find the measure of each segment.

$\overline{AF}$ $\overline{BF}$ $\overline{DF}$ $\overline{EF}$

C ? Think of each segment named in exercise B as determined by the origin and point x, where $x < 0$. Does $-x$ represent the measure of a segment determined by point x and point 0, where $x < 0$? Give an example to explain your answer.

D The number 0 and a number greater than 0 are the coördinates of the endpoints of each

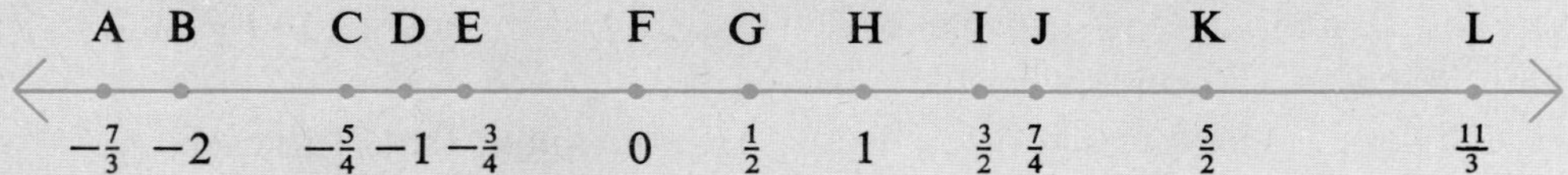

D1

"The absolute value of negative three is equal to three."

$|-3| = 3.$

D2

absolute value of a real number. If $x \geqq 0$, then the absolute value of x is x. If $x < 0$, then the absolute value of x is $-x$.

segment named below. Find the measure of each segment.

$\overline{FG}$ $\overline{FH}$ $\overline{FI}$ $\overline{FJ}$ $\overline{FK}$ $\overline{FL}$

E If $x > 0$, then does x represent the measure of a segment that is determined by the origin and point x? Use a segment named in exercise D to help explain your answer.

You can think of the *absolute value* of a real number x as the measure of a segment whose endpoints are point x and the origin. Since point $-\frac{5}{4}$ and the origin are the endpoints of $\overline{CF}$, and $m(\overline{CF}) = \frac{5}{4}$, the absolute value of $-\frac{5}{4}$ is $\frac{5}{4}$. Notice that, since the measure of a segment is always a positive number, the absolute value of x, where $x \neq 0$, is positive.

F Use $\overline{FG}$ to help explain why the absolute value of $\frac{1}{2}$ is $\frac{1}{2}$. Use the real-number line pictured in D1 to help find the absolute value of each number named below.

$-\frac{7}{3}$ -2 -1 $-\frac{3}{4}$ 1 $\frac{3}{2}$ $\frac{7}{4}$ $\frac{5}{2}$ $\frac{11}{3}$

G You know that the measure of a segment that is determined by point x and point 0 is x if $x > 0$. If $x > 0$, what is the absolute value of x?

H You also know that the measure of a segment determined by point x and point 0 is $-x$ if $x < 0$. If $x < 0$, what is the absolute value of x?

I Find the absolute value of each number named below.

-10 10 $-\frac{30}{6}$ $(8-6)$ $(6-8)$ 7^2 $(-4)^3$

D2 shows how to write and read a sentence that concerns the absolute value of a number.

J Is $|-\frac{5}{4}| = \frac{5}{4}$? Is $|\frac{1}{2}| = \frac{1}{2}$?

K If $x \geqq 0$, is $|x| = x$? When is $|x| = -x$?

Find a standard name of each number expressed in exercises L through Q. For example, a standard name of $|-5+1|$ is the numeral 4.

L $|-5+1|$ **N** $|(-10)^2|$ **P** $|\sqrt{4}|$

M $|-\frac{4}{5}-(-\frac{2}{3})|$ **O** $|(-\frac{1}{2})(\frac{3}{5})|$ **Q** $|(\sqrt{5})^2|$

Several important properties of real numbers involve the idea of absolute value.

A $\sqrt{(-3)^2}$ is the principal, or the positive, square root of $(-3)^2$. What is a standard name of $\sqrt{(-3)^2}$? Is $\sqrt{(-3)^2} = |-3|$? Explain why $\sqrt{10^2} = |10|$ and $\sqrt{(-6)^2} = |-6|$.

B In unit 20 you learned that, if $x \geqq 0$, then $\sqrt{x^2} = x$. You also know that, if $x \geqq 0$, then $|x| = x$. If $x \geqq 0$, is $\sqrt{x^2} = |x|$? Explain your answer.

C If $x < 0$, is $\sqrt{x^2} = -x$? If $x < 0$, is $|x| = -x$? Explain why, if $x < 0$, then $\sqrt{x^2} = |x|$.

In exercises B and C, you showed that $\sqrt{x^2} = |x|$ when $x \geqq 0$ and when $x < 0$. Therefore, the statement expressed below is a theorem of real numbers.

For each x, $\sqrt{x^2} = |x|$.

D Explain why $|-5|^2 = 5^2$. Is $|8|^2 = 8^2$? Is $|-\frac{1}{2}|^2 = (\frac{1}{2})^2$?

E From the definition of absolute value of a real number, you know that, when $x < 0$, $|x| = -x$. If $x < 0$, explain why $|x|^2 = (-x)^2$. Is $(-x)^2 = x^2$? If $x < 0$, is $|x|^2 = x^2$?

F You also know that, when $x \geqq 0$, $|x| = x$. If $x \geqq 0$, explain why $|x|^2 = x^2$.

In exercises E and F above, you showed that $|x|^2 = x^2$ when $x < 0$, and also when $x \geqq 0$. Therefore, the statement expressed below is a theorem of real numbers.

For each x, $|x|^2 = x^2$.

G Is $|-\frac{3}{4}| = \frac{3}{4}$? Is $|-(-\frac{3}{4})| = \frac{3}{4}$? Explain why $|-\frac{3}{4}| = |-(-\frac{3}{4})|$. How do you know that $|-2.35| = |-(-2.35)|$? How do you know that $|-38| = |-(-38)|$?

Now we will derive a property that relates $|x|$ and $|-x|$.

H You have already derived the property that, for each x, $|x| = \sqrt{x^2}$. Hence, for each $-x$, $|-x| = \sqrt{(-x)^2}$. Is $\sqrt{(-x)^2} = \sqrt{x^2}$?

I Now you know that $|x| = \sqrt{x^2}$ and $|-x| = \sqrt{x^2}$. Explain why $|-x| = |x|$.

In exercises H and I, you showed that the statement expressed below is a theorem of real numbers.

For each x, $|-x| = |x|$.

J Is $|-\frac{2}{3}| \cdot |\frac{1}{2}| = \frac{2}{3} \cdot \frac{1}{2}$? Is $|-\frac{2}{3}| \cdot |\frac{1}{2}| = \frac{1}{3}$? Explain your answers.

K How do you know that $|-\frac{2}{3} \cdot \frac{1}{2}|$ is the absolute value of $-\frac{1}{3}$? Show that $|-\frac{2}{3} \cdot \frac{1}{2}| = |-\frac{2}{3}| \cdot |\frac{1}{2}|$.

$|x| \cdot |y|$ is the product of the absolute values of two numbers, and $|xy|$ is the absolute value of the product of two numbers. Now you will learn how $|x| \cdot |y|$ and $|xy|$ are related.

L You know that, for each x, $|x| = \sqrt{x^2}$. Therefore, for each xy, $|xy| = \sqrt{(xy)^2}$. Is $\sqrt{(xy)^2} = \sqrt{x^2y^2}$? Is $\sqrt{x^2y^2} = \sqrt{x^2}\sqrt{y^2}$? Explain why $|xy| = \sqrt{x^2}\sqrt{y^2}$.

M You know that, for each x, $|x| = \sqrt{x^2}$ and, for each y, $|y| = \sqrt{y^2}$. Is $|x| \cdot |y| = \sqrt{x^2}\sqrt{y^2}$?

N In exercises L and M, you showed that $|xy| = \sqrt{x^2}\sqrt{y^2}$ and $|x| \cdot |y| = \sqrt{x^2}\sqrt{y^2}$. Is $|xy| = |x| \cdot |y|$? How do you know that the statement expressed below is a theorem of real numbers?

For each x *and* y, $|xy| = |x| \cdot |y|$.

Use the property expressed above to find a standard name of each product expressed in exercises O through T.

O $|\frac{1}{2}| \cdot |-2|$

P $|-5| \cdot |\frac{1}{3}|$

Q $|\frac{1}{5}| \cdot |\frac{10}{3}| \cdot |-\frac{9}{2}|$

R $|\sqrt{144}| \cdot |\sqrt{\frac{1}{9}}|$

S $|-\frac{8}{3}| \cdot |\frac{27}{2}| \cdot |-\frac{3}{4}|$

T $|2+4| \cdot |5-9|$

Now you know what the absolute value of a real number is. You have also derived several properties that involve absolute value.

On your own

Find a standard name of each number expressed below.

1 $|-7|$

2 $|-\frac{3}{8}|$

3 $|100|$

4 $|-563|$

5 $|\frac{1}{3} - \frac{2}{5}|$

6 $|\frac{2}{5}| \cdot |-\frac{1}{3}|$

7 $|(-6)^2|$

8 $|-(6^2)|$

9 $|\sqrt{121}|$

10 $|-18-(-6)|$

11 $|\frac{1}{2}\sqrt{\frac{16}{36}}| + |-5|$

12 $|-3\sqrt{2} + 4\sqrt{2}|$

13 $2|-6| + 3|6|$

14 $\frac{2}{3}|-7+(-8)|$

15 $\frac{2}{3}|-7| + \frac{2}{3}|-8|$

16 $|-8| + |2\frac{1}{3}| + |-15\frac{2}{3}|$

For each of exercises 17 through 30, tell whether the sentence expresses a true statement or a false statement. If the statement is true, tell what property justifies it.

17 $\sqrt{144} = |144|$.
18 $|-4| = -4$.
19 $|-6|^2 = 36$.
20 For each x, $\sqrt{x^4} = |x^2|$.
21 $|-5+3| = |-5| + |3|$.
22 $|\frac{2}{3}| = |-2| \cdot |-\frac{1}{3}|$.
23 $|-18| = |-(-18)|$.
24 $\sqrt{25} = |5|$.
25 For each x, $2|x| + 3|x| = 5|x|$.
26 For each a and b, $\sqrt{\frac{a^2b^2}{4}} = \left|\frac{ab}{2}\right|$.
27 For each a and b, $|a-b| = |a| - |b|$.
28 For each a and b, $|a^2b^2| = |a^2| \cdot |b^2|$.
29 For each n, $|3n| = 3|n|$.
30 For each a and b, $|a| \div |b| = |a \div b|$.

KEEPING SKILLFUL

For each of the following exercises, find the indicated sum, difference, or product.

1 $(5x^2 + 8x - 5) + (3x^2 - 12x + 25)$
2 $(16x + 25y) - (85x + 155y)$
3 $(24a^3 + a^2 - 6a + 15) + (-16a^2 - 7a - 15)$
4 $(18h^2y^3)(21hy^4)$
5 $(.68a^3 - .25a^2 + .7a) - (-a^3 - .82a^2 + 1.25)$
6 $(.75y^3 - .16y) + (1.25y^3 - .16y^2 + .18a)$
7 $-8ax^4(2ax^3 - 3ax^2 + 4x)$
8 $(125a - 65b - 124c) - (65a - 125b + 15)$
9 $(14c^3 + 15c^2 - 8d) +$
$(-18c^3 + c^2 - 25c + 5d)$
10 $(\frac{1}{5}t^2 - \frac{1}{4}t + 64) - (\frac{1}{2}t^2 + 3t - 16)$
11 $-\sqrt{3}x^2y^2(\sqrt{3}x^4y - x^3y + \sqrt{3})$
12 $(\frac{1}{4}x^4 - \frac{1}{3}y + \frac{1}{12}) + (x^4 + \frac{2}{3}y - \frac{5}{12}) + (\frac{1}{6}x^4 + \frac{2}{3})$
13 $72ca(6c^2 - 4ca + 2a - 1)$
14 $(\frac{8}{9}x^2 + 1\frac{2}{9}x + 65) - (x^2 - x - 100)$
15 $(-24x^{10}y^4z^2)(2x^{12}y^3z^2a)$
16 $(2.7a^4 - 25) + (3.2a^4 - a^3 + a^2) +$
$(.7a - 35)$
17 $.5x^3y^2(3x^2y + 3.5xy^2 - 16)$
18 $(72c^2 - 85c + 12d) - (-18c^2 - 15c + d)$
19 $\frac{3}{4}a^2(\frac{3}{8}x^4 - \frac{2}{3}x^3 - \frac{2}{3}x^2 - x - \frac{3}{4})$

21 **263** Exploring ideas

Conditions involving absolute value

The idea of absolute value may occur in conditions, such as $|x| = 10$ and $|-x| + 5 = 7$. Now you will learn to solve conditions of this kind.

A Does 3 satisfy $|x| = 3$? Does -3 satisfy $|x| = 3$? Tabulate $\{x \mid |x| = 3\}$.

B Does 3 satisfy $x = 3 \lor x = -3$? Does -3 satisfy $x = 3 \lor x = -3$? Tabulate the solution set of $x = 3 \lor x = -3$.

C How do you know that $|x| = 3$ is equivalent to $x = 3 \lor x = -3$?

We can show that any condition of the form $|x| = k$, where $k \geqq 0$, is equivalent to a condition of the form $x = k \lor x = -k$.

D Look at D1. Does k satisfy condition A? Does $-k$ satisfy A? Remember that $k \geqq 0$.

E Tabulate the solution set of $|x| = k$.

F Does k satisfy condition B? Does $-k$ satisfy B? Tabulate the solution set of B.

G How do you know that condition B is equivalent to condition A? Does the paragraph below express a property of real numbers?

The universe for k *is the set of non-negative real numbers. For each* k, $\{x \mid |x| = k\} = \{x \mid x = k \lor x = -k\}$.

A $|x| = k$.
B $x = k \lor x = -k$.

D1

H Use the property just expressed to find the solutions of $|x| = 25$. Use the property to find the solutions of $|x| = \frac{4}{5}$.

You can use the property to find the solution set of each condition expressed in D2.

I Explain why $2x = 10 \vee 2x = -10$ is equivalent to condition C. What numbers satisfy $2x = 10 \vee 2x = -10$? Tabulate the solution set of C.

J Explain why $x + 3 = 8 \vee x + 3 = -8$ is equivalent to condition D. What numbers satisfy $x + 3 = 8 \vee x + 3 = -8$? Tabulate the solution set of D.

K What compound condition involving the connective "or" is equivalent to condition E? What numbers satisfy the compound condition? Tabulate the solution set of E.

For each of exercises L through O, first find an equivalent condition that involves the connective "or." Then tabulate the solution set of the original condition.

L $|3x + 2| = 14$. **N** $|6x - 8x| = 4$.
M $|5(x + 2)| = 25$. **O** $|5 - x| = 9$.

C $|2x| = 10$.
D $|x + 3| = 8$.
E $|6 - x| = 5$.

D2

F $\frac{2}{3}|3x| + 1 = 7$.

D3

P Now look at D3. How can $\frac{2}{3}|3x| = 6$ be obtained from condition F? If $\frac{2}{3}|3x| = 6$, how do you know that $|3x| = 9$?

Q If $|3x| = 9$, is $3x = 9 \vee 3x = -9$? Explain why $3x = 9 \vee 3x = -9$ is equivalent to condition F.

R Use $3x = 9 \vee 3x = -9$ to help you tabulate the solution set of F.

S The graph in D4 represents the locus of condition F. What points are in this locus?

Solve each condition expressed below and make a graph of the locus of the condition.

T $|x| + 5 = 6$. **V** $\frac{1}{2}|x + 6| = 4$.
U $2|x| - 1 = 4$. **W** $3|x| + 2|x| = 15$.

X Study condition G, expressed in D5. For each x, is $\sqrt{x^2} = |x|$? How do you know that $|x| = 16$ is equivalent to G?

Y Why is $x = 16 \vee x = -16$ equivalent to condition G? Tabulate $\{x \mid \sqrt{x^2} = 16\}$.

Z Tabulate the solution set of $\sqrt{x^2} = \frac{2}{3}$. Tabulate the solution set of $\sqrt{x^2} = 8$.

Conditions for inequality also may involve the idea of absolute value.

A In lesson 262 you learned that $|x|$ is the measure of a segment determined by point x and point 0. The condition $|x| \leqq 2$ requires that the measure of a segment determined by point x and point 0 must be less than or equal to what number?

B A graph of the locus of $|x| \leqq 2$ is shown in D6. Explain why point 2 and point -2 are in the locus. Why is every point between point 2

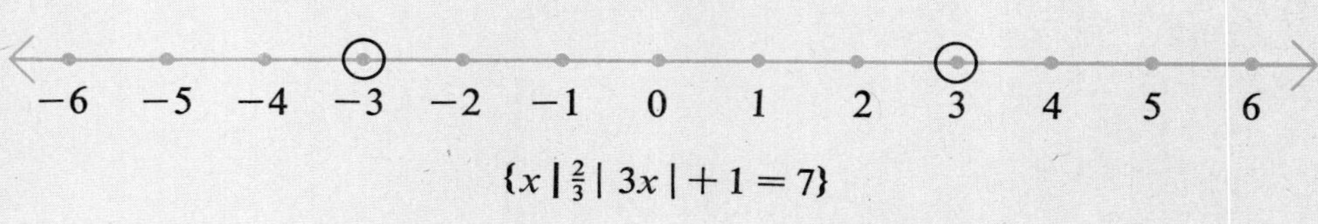

$\{x \mid \frac{2}{3}|3x| + 1 = 7\}$

D4

G $\sqrt{x^2} = 16$.

D5

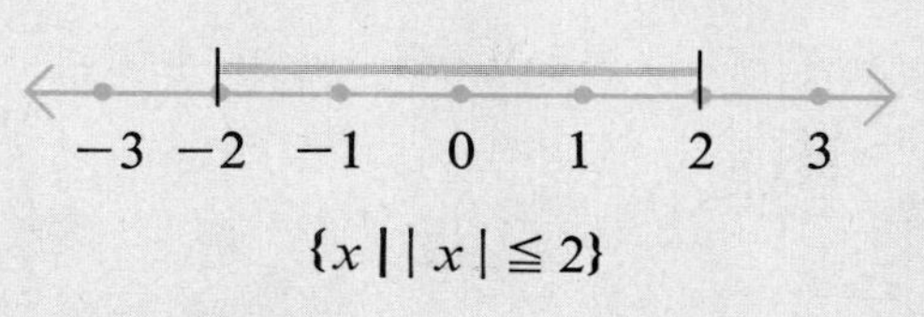

$\{x \mid |x| \leqq 2\}$

D6

−3 −2 −1 0 1 2 3

$\{x \mid |x| < 2\}$

D7

H $|2x + 2| \leqq 6$.

I $-6 \leqq (2x + 2) \leqq 6$.

J $-6 \leqq 2x + 2 \wedge 2x + 2 \leqq 6$.

D8

1 $-6 \leqq 2x + 2$.	4 $2x + 2 \leqq 6$.
2 $-8 \leqq 2x$.	5 $2x \leqq 4$.
3 $-4 \leqq x$.	6 $x \leqq 2$.

D9

and point -2 in the locus of $|x| \leqq 2$? Explain why the points to the left of point -2 and the points to the right of point 2 are *not* in the locus.

C Look again at D6. Is $\{x \mid |x| \leqq 2\}$ the set that contains 2, -2, and all real numbers between 2 and -2?

D Is $\{x \mid |x| \leqq 2\} = \{x \mid -2 \leqq x \leqq 2\}$? The solution set of $|x| \leqq 2$ is what kind of interval? What two numbers are the limits of this interval?

E The locus of $|x| < 2$ is represented in D7. Why are points 2 and -2 not in the locus?

F Look again at D7. $\{x \mid |x| < 2\}$ is the set of all real numbers between what two numbers?

G Is $\{x \mid |x| < 2\} = \{x \mid -2 < x < 2\}$? The solution set of $|x| < 2$ is what kind of interval? What two numbers are the limits of this interval?

In exercises A through G, you learned that the solution set of $|x| \leqq 2$ is the closed interval $\{x \mid -2 \leqq x \leqq 2\}$ and the solution set of $|x| < 2$ is the open interval $\{x \mid -2 < x < 2\}$. In a similar manner, we could develop the properties that are expressed below.

The universe for k *is the set of non-negative real numbers. For each* k, $\{x \mid |x| \leqq k\} = \{x \mid -k \leqq x \leqq k\}$.

The universe for k *is the set of non-negative real numbers. For each* k, $\{x \mid |x| < k\} = \{x \mid -k < x < k\}$.

H Is $\{x \mid -5 \leqq x \leqq 5\}$ the solution set of $|x| \leqq 5$? How do you know? Explain why $\{x \mid -5 \leqq x \leqq 5\}$ is also the solution set of $5 \geqq |x|$.

I How do you know that $\{x \mid -5 < x < 5\}$ is the solution set of $|x| < 5$?

J Make a graph of the locus of $5 > |x|$. How is the locus of $5 > |x|$ different from the locus of $5 \geqq |x|$?

Now study condition H, expressed in D8. You know that, for each $k \geqq 0$, $|x| \leqq k \Leftrightarrow -k \leqq x \leqq k$. Therefore, $|2x + 2| \leqq 6 \Leftrightarrow -6 \leqq (2x + 2) \leqq 6$. In this way, condition I is derived from H. Now, using the idea that $-k \leqq x \leqq k$ is the same as $-k \leqq x \wedge x \leqq k$, you can derive condition J from I. Thus, conditions H, I, and J are equivalent.

Now look at D9. Steps 1, 2, and 3 show how to obtain $-4 \leqq x$ from $-6 \leqq 2x + 2$. Steps 4, 5, and 6 show how to obtain $x \leqq 2$ from the condition $2x + 2 \leqq 6$.

K How do you know that $-4 \leqq x \leqq 2$ is equivalent to each of the conditions expressed in D8? The solution set of $|2x+2| \leqq 6$ is what kind of interval? Name the limits of this interval.

L Look at D10. Explain how to derive $\frac{1}{2}|6x| < 3$ from condition K. If $\frac{1}{2}|6x| < 3$, how do you know that $|6x| < 6$?

M Is $-6 < 6x < 6 \Leftrightarrow |6x| < 6$ a true statement for each x? How do you know? Explain why $-6 < 6x < 6$ is equivalent to condition K.

N $-6 < 6x < 6$ is the conjunction of what two simple conditions? How do you know that $-1 < x < 1 \Leftrightarrow -6 < 6x < 6$?

O Is $\{x \mid -1 < x < 1\}$ the solution set of condition K? What kind of interval is this solution set? Name the limits of the interval.

For each condition expressed below, give a standard description of the interval that is its solution set. Then tell what kind of interval the solution set is and name the limits.

P $|x-3| \leqq 1$.

Q $11 > 2|x| + 7$.

R $3|x| + 7|x| < 20$.

S $\frac{1}{2}|4x| \leqq 8$.

H $|2x+2| \leqq 6$.

I $-6 \leqq (2x+2) \leqq 6$.

J $-6 \leqq 2x+2 \wedge 2x+2 \leqq 6$.

D8

K $\frac{1}{2}|6x| - 2 < 1$.

D10

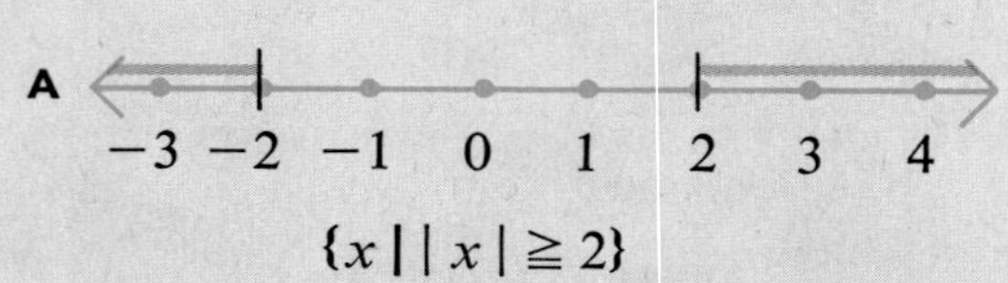

$\{x \mid |x| \geqq 2\}$

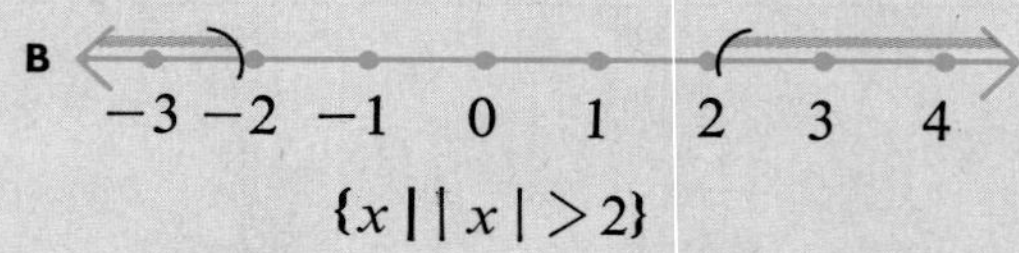

$\{x \mid |x| > 2\}$

D11

C $\frac{1}{2}|3x| + 2 > 5$.

D12

You have considered conditions of the forms $|x| \leqq k$ and $|x| < k$. Next you will examine several conditions of the forms $|x| \geqq k$ and $|x| > k$.

A Look at D11. Graph A represents the locus ? of $|x| \geqq 2$. Graph B represents the locus of $|x| > 2$. Why does each locus contain every point to the right of point 2 and every point to the left of point -2? Explain why the points between point 2 and point -2 are in neither locus.

B Explain why point 2 and point -2 are in the locus of $|x| \geqq 2$ but not in the locus of $|x| > 2$.

C Look again at graph A. Is $\{x \mid |x| \geqq 2\}$ equal to $\{x \mid x \geqq 2 \vee x \leqq -2\}$?

D Look again at graph B. Is $\{x \mid |x| > 2\}$ equal to $\{x \mid x > 2 \vee x < -2\}$?

It is clear that the solution set of $|x| \geqq 2$ is $\{x \mid x \geqq 2 \vee x \leqq -2\}$ and the solution set of $|x| > 2$ is $\{x \mid x > 2 \vee x < -2\}$. In a similar manner, we could develop properties about any condition of the form $|x| \geqq k$ and any condition of the form $|x| > k$. These properties are expressed below.

The universe for k *is the set of non-negative real numbers. For each* k, $\{x \mid |x| \geqq k\} = \{x \mid x \geqq k \vee x \leqq -k\}$.

The universe for k *is the set of non-negative real numbers. For each* k, $\{x \mid |x| > k\} = \{x \mid x > k \vee x < -k\}$.

Use the properties just expressed to explain why each of sentences E through H expresses a true statement.

E $\{x \mid |x| \geqq \frac{1}{2}\} = \{x \mid x \geqq \frac{1}{2} \vee x \leqq -\frac{1}{2}\}$.

F $\{x \mid |x| > 7\} = \{x \mid x > 7 \vee x < -7\}$.

G $\{x \mid \frac{2}{3} < |x|\} = \{x \mid x > \frac{2}{3} \vee x < -\frac{2}{3}\}$.

H $\{x \mid 1.8 \leqq |x|\} = \{x \mid x \geqq 1.8 \vee x \leqq -1.8\}$.

I Study condition C, expressed in D12. Explain how $\frac{1}{2}|3x| > 3$ can be obtained from C. If $\frac{1}{2}|3x| > 3$, explain why $|3x| > 6$.

You know that, for each $k \geqq 0$, $|x| > k \Leftrightarrow x > k \vee x < -k$. For this reason, $|3x| > 6 \Leftrightarrow 3x > 6 \vee 3x < -6$.

J Explain how $x > 2$ can be obtained from $3x > 6$ and how $x < -2$ can be obtained from $3x < -6$. How do you know that the solution set of condition C is $\{x \mid x > 2 \vee x < -2\}$?

K Explain why $\{x \mid |x| \leqq 2\}$ is the complement of the solution set of condition C.

> REMINDER
>
> The complement of a given subset of a universe is the set that contains all the members of the universe, and only those members, that do not belong to the given subset.
>
> *See lesson 112, page 20, Book 2.*

L Show that $\{y \mid y \geqq 1 \vee y \leqq -1\}$ is the solution set of $7 + 3|2y| \geqq 13$.

M Express a condition that involves the idea of absolute value and whose solution set is $\{x \mid x \geqq 3 \vee x \leqq -3\}$.

Until now, this lesson has concerned such conditions as $|x| = k$, $|x| < k$, and $|x| > k$, where k is replaced by a non-negative real number. You can also obtain conditions involving absolute value if you replace k by a negative number. Now you will work with conditions in which $k < 0$.

N ? Explain why the solution set of $|x| = -3$ is the empty set.

O ? Tabulate the solution set of $|x| < -3$. Does every real number satisfy the condition $|x| > -3$?

P Tabulate the solution set of $|x| \leqq -5$. What real numbers satisfy the condition $|x| \geqq -5$?

In this lesson you studied several properties that involve conditions of the forms $|x| = k$, $|x| < k$, $|x| \leqq k$, $|x| > k$, and $|x| \geqq k$. You also found solution sets of such conditions.

On your own

For each of exercises 1 through 14, tell whether the statement expressed is true or false.

1 $\{x \mid |x| < 7\} = \{x \mid x < 7\}$.

2 $\{x \mid |x| < -30\} = \emptyset$.

3 $\{x \mid |x| = \sqrt{\frac{1}{4}}\} = \{\frac{1}{2}\}$.

4 $\{x \mid |x| < 45\} = \{x \mid -45 < x < 45\}$.

5 $\{x \mid \sqrt{x^2} = \frac{1}{4}\} = \{x \mid |x| = \frac{1}{4}\}$.

6 $\{x \mid x = 100\}$ is a subset of $\{x \mid |x| = 100\}$.

7 $\{x \mid x < -12\}$ is a subset of $\{x \mid |x + 4| > 8\}$.

8 $\{x \mid 10 \geqq |x|\} = \{x \mid x \geqq 10 \vee x \leqq -10\}$.

9 $\{x \mid x \geqq 1\} = \{x \mid -1 \leqq x \leqq 1\}$.

10 $\{x \mid 13x - 21 < 5\} = \{x \mid |x| < 2\}$.

11 $\{x \mid |x| = 4\} = \{4, -4\}$.

12 $\{x \mid |x| < 2\} \cap \{x \mid -3 < x < 1\} = \{x \mid -2 < x < 1\}$.

13 $\{x \mid \sqrt{x^2} > 8\} = \{x \mid x > 8 \wedge x < -8\}$.

14 $\{x \mid |x| \leqq 7\} = \{x \mid x > 7 \vee x < -7\}$.

Tabulate the solution set of each condition expressed in exercises 15 through 24.

15 $\sqrt{x^2} = \frac{4}{9}$.

16 $|x - 28| = 32$.

17 $|3 + x| = 48$.

18 $\frac{2}{5}|x| = 150$.

19 $3|x| = 300$.

20 $|x| - 12\frac{2}{5} = 18\frac{1}{5}$.

21 $\frac{1}{2}|x| + 9 = 25$.

22 $\frac{1}{2}|x + 10| = 8$.

23 $|x - 6| = 10 \wedge |2x| \geqq 8$.

24 $|x| = 9 \wedge x < 0$.

For each condition expressed in exercises 25 through 30, give a standard description of the interval that is its solution set.

25 $|x| < 10$.
26 $|x+5| < 17$.
27 $|x - 1\frac{5}{7}| \leqq 2\frac{3}{7}$.
28 $|3x+1| \leqq 13$.
29 $2|x|+7 < 63$.
30 $\sim(|x| > 5)$.

Make a graph of the locus of each condition expressed in exercises 31 through 34.

31 $|3x| = 12$.
32 $|x| - 4 > 0$.
33 $|x+7| \leqq 10$.
34 $|5x - 5| > 20$.

KEEPING SKILLFUL

For each of exercises 1 through 18, find the product.

1 $(m+8)(n-20)$
2 $(x+5y)(x-5y)$
3 $(4a+3b)(3a-b)$
4 $(50a+2)^2$
5 $(y^2-4)(y-5)$
6 $(18a+4b)(2a-4b)$
7 $(\frac{1}{17}+a)(\frac{1}{17}+a)$
8 $(24-y)(16-x)$
9 $(\frac{1}{8}a-24)(\frac{1}{3}a-6)$
10 $(.5+7a)(.5-7a)$
11 $(\frac{1}{4}x-20)^2$
12 $45(\frac{1}{5}y^3y^2)(\frac{1}{3}a^2y)$
13 $(.75a-4)(.85b+20)$
14 $25x^3(x^2y)(x^3y^2y)$
15 $(c^4d^3-4)(c^4d^3+4)$
16 $(\frac{1}{5}x-15)(\frac{2}{3}w-45)$
17 $(14ac-25)(ac+4)$
18 $(24-x^2)(24+x^2)$

Tabulate the solution set of each condition expressed below.

19 $34y = 204$.
20 $4(x-4) - 6(x+4) = 10$.
21 $\frac{a-3}{4} = \frac{a-12}{8}$.
22 $\frac{2}{3}(y+18) + 26 = 44$.
23 $8a - a(4-a) = a^2 + 4$.
24 $3.5y - .6y = .2y + 1.8$.
25 $(c+3)(c+4) = (c+6)(c+7)$.
26 $\frac{3}{4} + \frac{x-4}{2} = \frac{2x+5}{2}$.
27 $10(d-10) + 8 = 14d$.
28 $15\frac{1}{2}y + 3\frac{1}{2}y = 6y - 5$.

21 264 Exploring problems

Linear conditions in problem solving

In your earlier work in mathematics, you learned to use conditions of the forms $ax+b=0$, $ax+b<0$, and $ax+b>0$ to solve problems. In this unit you have learned that such conditions are linear conditions in one variable, and you are ready to develop such conditions to solve more complicated problems.

Read the problem in D1.

A How do you know that Mr. Abbott invested \$850, part at $3\frac{1}{2}\%$ and part at 4%?

B Suppose that we use x as a variable for the number of dollars invested at $3\frac{1}{2}\%$. We would like to use another expression in x to represent the number of dollars invested at 4%. Explain why $850 - x$ represents the number of dollars invested at 4%.

C Use the interest formula, $i = prt$, to explain why $500(.05)(2)$ is the interest earned in two years by an investment of \$500 at 5%. What does $x(.035)(2)$ represent? What does $(850-x)(.04)(2)$ represent?

D What is the total amount of interest that Mr. Abbott received after two years? How do you know that the sentence below in color expresses a condition for the problem in D1?

$$500(.05)(2) + x(.035)(2) + (850-x)(.04)(2) = 115.$$

E Look at D2. Condition A is the condition for the problem in D1. Justify each of conditions B through E.

Mr. Abbott invested \$1350. He invested \$500 of this amount at a rate of 5% per year. Part of the remainder he invested at $3\frac{1}{2}$%, and part he invested at 4%. The total interest that his investments earned in two years was \$115. How much did Mr. Abbott invest at $3\frac{1}{2}$% and how much did he invest at 4%?

D1

A $500(.05)(2) + x(.035)(2) + (850 - x)(.04)(2) = 115.$

B $50 + .07x + 68 - .08x = 115.$

C $118 - .01x = 115.$

D $-.01x = -3.$

E $x = 300.$

D2

A freight train traveling at a rate of 32 miles per hour left a station $2\frac{1}{4}$ hr. earlier than a passenger train that traveled in the same direction at a rate of 48 miles per hour. In how many hours did the passenger train overtake the freight train?

D3

John sold a total of 16 one-year subscriptions to two magazines and collected more than \$66. The subscription price of one of the magazines was \$3.50 per year, and the price of the other was \$4.50 per year. What is the greatest number of \$3.50 subscriptions that John could have sold?

D4

F Tabulate the solution set of the condition for the problem in D1. How do you know that Mr. Abbott invested \$300 at a rate of $3\frac{1}{2}$%?

G We used $850 - x$ to represent the number of dollars invested at 4%. Was $(850 - 300)$ dollars, or \$550, invested at 4%?

H You can verify your answers. After two years, is the total interest on \$500 invested at 5%, \$300 invested at $3\frac{1}{2}$%, and \$550 invested at 4% equal to \$115?

Now read the problem in D3.

I Let x represent the number of hours that the freight train had traveled when the passenger train overtook it. What is the rate of the freight train? Use the formula $d = rt$ to explain what $32x$ represents.

J What is the rate of the passenger train? Why does $x - 2\frac{1}{4}$ represent the number of hours that it took the passenger train to overtake the freight train? Does $x - 2\frac{1}{4}$ also represent the number of hours that the passenger train had traveled when it overtook the freight train? What does $48(x - 2\frac{1}{4})$ represent?

K Does $32x$ represent the same distance as $48(x - 2\frac{1}{4})$? Why does the sentence below in color express a condition for the problem?

$$32x = 48(x - 2\tfrac{1}{4}).$$

L Derive $x = 6\frac{3}{4}$ from the condition expressed above. Then tabulate $\{x \mid 32x = 48(x - 2\frac{1}{4})\}$.

M You used $x - 2\frac{1}{4}$ to represent the number of hours that it took the passenger train to overtake the freight train. How do you know that it took $6\frac{3}{4} - 2\frac{1}{4}$, or $4\frac{1}{2}$, hours for the passenger train to overtake the freight train?

Next you will study problems that involve linear conditions for inequality in one variable.

Read the problem in D4.

A Let x represent the number of \$3.50 subscriptions. You know that John sold 16 sub-

John sold a total of 16 one-year subscriptions to two magazines and collected more than \$66. The subscription price of one of the magazines was \$3.50 per year, and the price of the other was \$4.50 per year. What is the greatest number of \$3.50 subscriptions that John could have sold?

D4

The length of a rectangle is $1\frac{1}{2}$ times its width. If each dimension were increased by 3 units, the perimeter of the new rectangle would be greater than 10 times the length of the original rectangle. What is the width of the original rectangle in units?

D5

scriptions altogether. What does $16 - x$ represent?

B $3.50x$ represents the number of dollars that John collected from the sale of x subscriptions priced at \$3.50 each. How can you represent the amount that he collected from the sale of $(16 - x)$ subscriptions priced at \$4.50 each?

C What does $3.50x + 4.50(16 - x)$ represent? Why does the sentence below in color express a condition for the problem in D4?

$$3.50x + 4.50(16 - x) > 66.$$

D Show that $\{x | x < 6\}$ is the solution set of $3.50x + 4.50(16 - x) > 66$.

E Is $5\frac{1}{2}$ an element of $\{x | x < 6\}$? Can you use $5\frac{1}{2}$ to get an answer to the problem?

F ? Can you use a number other than a positive integer to get an answer to the problem? Is $x \in I_p$ another simple condition for the problem?

The sentence below in color expresses a compound condition for the problem in D4.

$$3.50x + 4.50(16 - x) > 66 \wedge x \in I_p.$$

G Tabulate the set of positive integers that is the solution set of the compound condition for the problem. What is the greatest number of \$3.50 subscriptions that John could have sold?

Now read the problem in D5. Let x represent the width of the original rectangle. Since we are using conditions in only one variable, and since the length of the original rectangle is $1\frac{1}{2}$ times the width, we can use $1\frac{1}{2}x$ to represent the length.

H You know that each dimension of the new rectangle is 3 units greater than the corresponding dimension of the original rectangle. What does $1\frac{1}{2}x + 3$ represent? What does $x + 3$ represent? What does $2(1\frac{1}{2}x + 3) + 2(x + 3)$ represent?

I What do you know about the perimeter of the new rectangle and the length of the original rectangle? Explain why the sentence below in color expresses a condition for the problem in D5.

$$2(1\tfrac{1}{2}x + 3) + 2(x + 3) > 10(1\tfrac{1}{2}x).$$

J ? Show how $\frac{6}{5} > x$ can be derived from the condition expressed above. Explain why only positive numbers that are members of $\{x | \frac{6}{5} > x\}$ can be used to get an answer to the problem in D5. What is another simple condition for the problem?

The sentence below in color expresses a compound condition for the problem.

$$2(1\tfrac{1}{2}x + 3) + 2(x + 3) > 10(1\tfrac{1}{2}x) \wedge x > 0.$$

K Give a standard description of the solution set of the compound condition for the problem in D5.

A feed dealer plans to mix corn that sells for \$1.14 per bushel with wheat that sells for \$1.74 per bushel to obtain a mixture that will sell for at least \$1.50 per bushel. How many bushels of corn should the dealer put in a mixture of 200 bushels?

D6

Larry has fewer than 30 pennies, nickels, and dimes. The number of nickels is 2 times the number of pennies, and the number of dimes is 3 times the number of pennies. Altogether, Larry has more than 82 cents. How many pennies does Larry have?

D7

If 3 is added to twice a given number, the absolute value of the sum is not greater than 15. What is the number?

$$\sim(|2x+3| > 15).$$

D8

Now we can give the answer to the problem. The width of the original rectangle is greater than 0 units and less than $\frac{6}{5}$ units.

Read the problem in D6.

L If x represents the number of bushels of corn in the mixture, what does $1.14x$ represent?

M You know that the mixture contains 200 bushels in all. What does $200 - x$ represent? What does $1.74(200 - x)$ represent? What does $1.14x + 1.74(200 - x)$ represent?

N Does 1.50(200) refer to the selling price of the mixture of corn and wheat? Why is $1.14x + 1.74(200 - x) \geqq 1.50(200)$ a condition for the problem in D6? Why is $x > 0$ also a condition for the problem?

The sentence below in color expresses a compound condition for the problem in D6.

$$1.14x + 1.74(200 - x) \geqq 1.50(200) \wedge x > 0.$$

O Show that $\{x \mid 0 < x \leqq 80\}$ is the solution set of the condition expressed above. You can use this set to get the answer to the problem.

The dealer must put more than 0 bushels of corn and at most 80 bushels of corn in the mixture.

Read the problem in D7.

P Let x represent the number of pennies that Larry has. What does $2x$ represent? What does $3x$ represent? What does $x + 2x + 3x$ represent? Explain why $x + 2x + 3x < 30$ is a simple condition for the problem in D7.

Q Explain why $1x$ represents the value of x pennies in cents. How should you represent the value of $2x$ nickels in cents? How should you represent the value of $3x$ dimes?

R What does $x + 5(2x) + 10(3x)$ represent? What is another simple condition for the problem in D7?

S Explain why $x \in I_p$ is also a condition for the problem in D7.

The sentence below in color expresses a compound condition for the problem.

$$(x + 2x + 3x < 30) \wedge \big(x + 5(2x) + 10(3x) > 82\big) \wedge (x \in I_p).$$

T Tabulate the solution set of the condition expressed above. Then give the answer to the problem in D7.

Read the problem in D8. Notice that this problem deals with numbers only, and also that it involves the idea of absolute value.

If 3 is added to twice a given number, the absolute value of the sum is not greater than 15. What is the number?

$$\sim(|2x+3|>15).$$

D8

A The condition for the problem is also expressed in D8. What does x represent? Why should you use $|2x+3|$ in the condition rather than $|2x|+3$ or $2|x+3|$? How do you know that $|2x+3|>15$ is not the condition for the problem?

B Is $\sim(|2x+3|>15) \Leftrightarrow |2x+3| \leqq 15$ a true statement? How do you know?

C What compound condition that involves "and" is equivalent to $|2x+3| \leqq 15$?

D Show that $\{x \mid -9 \leqq x \leqq 6\}$ is the solution set of $\sim(|2x+3|>15)$.

Now you can answer the problem in D8.

The number is greater than or equal to -9 and less than or equal to 6.

In this lesson you used simple and compound linear conditions in one variable to solve problems.

On your own

For each problem, first write a sentence that expresses the condition. The condition should involve only one variable. Next tabulate the solution set of the condition, if possible. Otherwise, give a standard description of the solution set. Then give the answer to the problem.

1 Mr. Locke invested $420 at a rate of interest that yields more than $21 per year. At what rate of interest did he invest the $420?

2 Two men, who are 15 miles apart, start walking toward each other at the same time. The first man walks at a rate of 3 miles per hour, and the second man at a rate of 4 miles per hour. In how many hours will they meet?

3 Ernie had 60 Hungarian stamps in his collection; David had 45 Hungarian stamps. After Ernie had bought some, but not all, of David's Hungarian stamps, he had more than 6 times as many as David. How many Hungarian stamps did Ernie buy from David?

4 Of the 28 students in Jill's mathematics class, $\frac{1}{2}$ of the boys and $\frac{1}{4}$ of the girls are members of the science club. In all, 10 members of the class belong to the science club. How many boys and how many girls are in Jill's mathematics class?

5 Mr. Schwartz invested part of $500 at a rate of 4% and the remainder at a rate of 5%. After 2 years, his total interest was $41.50. How much had Mr. Schwartz invested at each rate?

6 Mrs. Olson baked some cupcakes and gave 6 of them to a neighbor. Then she donated $\frac{5}{6}$ of the remaining cupcakes to a bake sale. If she had 6 cupcakes left, how many cupcakes did she bake?

7 Lewis has 10 coins in nickels and dimes. If he had 2 more nickels and 3 more dimes, he would have $1.05. How many dimes does Lewis have?

8 Mr. Bishop drove 235 miles in 5 hours. For part of the trip he drove on an expressway at an average rate of 55 miles per hour. His average rate for the rest of the trip was 35 miles per hour. For how many hours did Mr. Bishop drive on the expressway?

9 A merchant wants to make a mixture of candy to sell for $.38 per pound out of candy that sells for $.35 per pound and candy that sells for $.45 per pound. How many pounds of $.45 candy should he use in a 100-pound mixture?

10 The length of a rectangle is 4 units greater than twice its width. If the width were increased by 2 units, the area of the new rectangle would be 40 square units greater than

the area of the original rectangle. What is the width of the original rectangle in units?

11 If $\frac{1}{3}$ of a given number is subtracted from $\frac{1}{2}$, the difference is $\frac{3}{4}$ of the difference of the given number and $\frac{1}{3}$. What is the given number?

12 Twice the absolute value of a number is less than 24. What is the number?

KEEPING SKILLFUL

For each condition expressed below, give a standard description of the solution set.

1 $6x + 20 > 0.$ 5 $25t + 40 < 0.$
2 $3\frac{1}{2}a + 10\frac{1}{2} < 0.$ 6 $-6.4y + 4 > 0.$
3 $17s + 5 > 0.$ 7 $1\frac{1}{2}x + 3\frac{1}{4} > 0.$
4 $-80b + 60 < 0.$ 8 $-.26y + .52 < 0.$

For each condition expressed below, give a standard description of the solution set. Then make a graph of the locus of the condition.

9 $\frac{y}{4} + \frac{y}{6} > \frac{y}{2} + 1.$
10 $(x + 2)^2 - 6x < x^2 + 6.$
11 $.3n + 1.5(.5n + .3) > 3(.4n - 1).$
12 $\frac{x-2}{4} + \frac{x+5}{4} < \frac{2x+5}{2}.$
13 $\frac{x+3}{6} + \frac{x-4}{3} > \frac{x}{4}.$

SPECIAL CHALLENGE

A permutation of three objects is an ordered triple. Consider the permutations of these three objects: a triangle, a square, and a circle. One possible permutation is (triangle, square, circle), or (△, □, ⊙).

A How many permutations are there of three objects taken three at a time?

B Now think about changing (△, □, ⊙) into (△, ⊙, □). Under this change, or *transformation*, the second component of (△, □, ⊙) becomes the third component of (△, ⊙, □). What happens to the first and third components of (△, □, ⊙) under this transformation?

Let the symbol T_1 (read "T sub-one") be the name of the transformation that maps (△, □, ⊙) onto (△, ⊙, □). T_1 can be described by a symbol such as the one at the right, which is a 3-by-3 grid consisting of three horizontal rows and three vertical columns. Notice that there is exactly one X in each row and in each column.

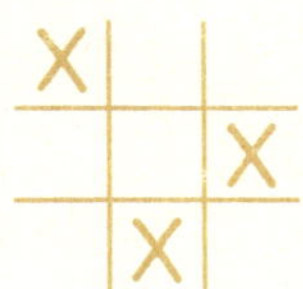

C D1 shows how a 3-by-3 grid describes T_1. Notice that the rows are numbered from top to bottom and the columns are numbered from left to right. The X in the second row and the third column indicates that the second component of (△, □, ⊙) becomes a third component under T_1. What does the X in the first row and the first column indicate? What does the X in the third row and the second column indicate?

D Onto what permutation does T_1 map the permutation (⊙, △, □)? Onto what permutation does T_1 map (□, ⊙, △)?

Since there are six permutations of three objects taken three at a time, six transformations

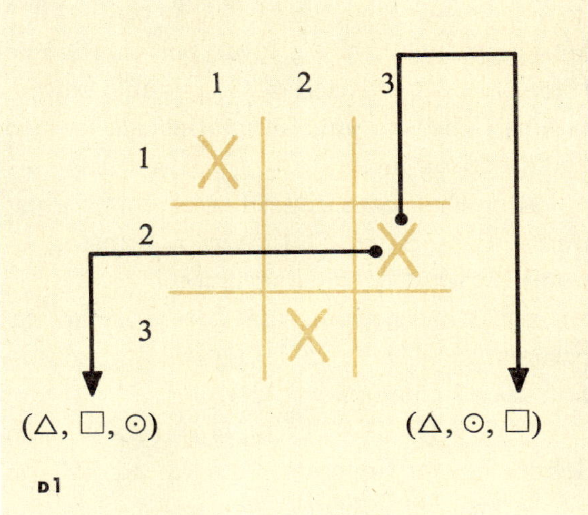

D1

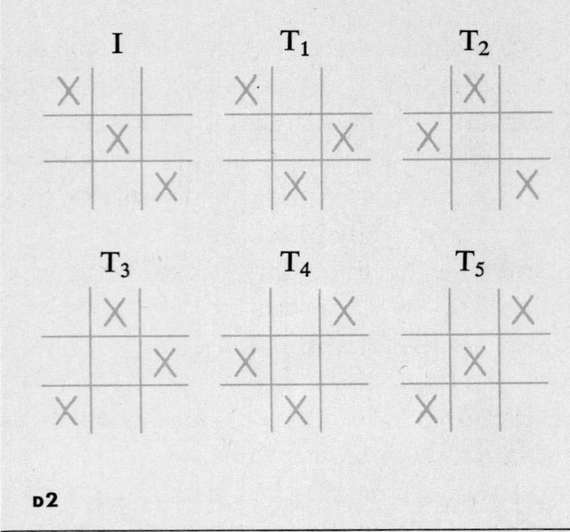

D2

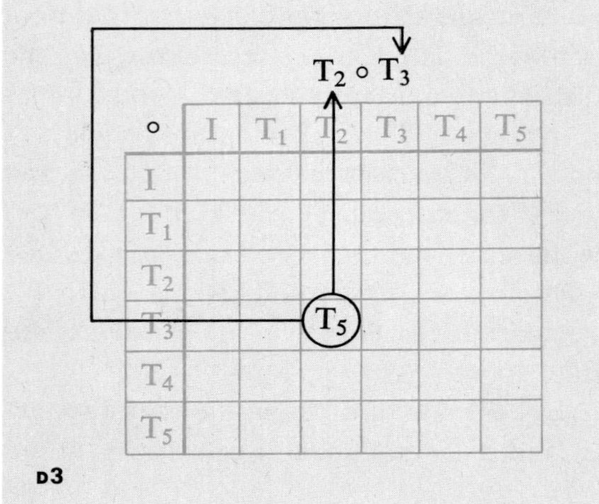

D3

are necessary to map a given permutation of three objects onto each of the possible permutations. The six transformations are named and described in D2.

E Onto what permutation does transformation I map (△, □, ⊙)? Why is transformation I the identity transformation?

F Onto what permutation does T_4 map the permutation (△, ⊙, □)? Onto what permutation does T_2 map (⊙, □, △)?

Let $G = \{I, T_1, T_2, T_3, T_4, T_5\}$. We can define a binary operation "followed by" on set G. We will indicate "followed by" by the symbol ∘. Consider $T_2 \circ T_3$. Let us see what effect $T_2 \circ T_3$ has on (□, ⊙, △).

G Onto what permutation does T_2 map the permutation (□, ⊙, △)? Onto what permutation does T_3 map (⊙, □, △)?

H From exercise G, you see that $T_2 \circ T_3$ maps (□, ⊙, △) onto (△, ⊙, □). What single transformation maps (□, ⊙, △) onto (△, ⊙, □)?

Since T_5 and $T_2 \circ T_3$ have the same effect on (□, ⊙, △), the statement $T_2 \circ T_3 = T_5$ is true.

I Onto what permutation does $T_2 \circ T_3$ map (△, □, ⊙)? Onto what permutation does T_5 map (△, □, ⊙)?

J What single transformation has the same effect as $T_3 \circ T_2$? What can you conclude from your answer?

K Copy and complete the "followed by" table in D3. Is "followed by" closed in set G?

L What is the identity element of "followed by" in set G? What single transformation has the same effect as $T_4 \circ I$? As $I \circ T_4$?

M For each element in set G, what is its inverse under the operation "followed by"?

N What single transformation has the same effect as $T_4 \circ T_2$? As $T_1 \circ (T_4 \circ T_2)$?

O What single transformation has the same effect as $T_1 \circ T_4$? As $(T_1 \circ T_4) \circ T_2$?

Exercises N and O illustrate the fact that set G is associative under "followed by."

P Set G, along with the operation of "followed by," has all but one of the five properties required of a commutative group. Which property does it lack?

Set G, along with the operation of "followed by," forms a *non-commutative group.* This kind of system is often used in solving problems related to science and business.

Q Use a 4-by-4 grid to describe the transformation that maps (a, b, c, d) onto (b, d, c, a).

R What grid describes the transformation that maps (3, 2, 5, 1, 4) onto (1, 2, 3, 4, 5)?

APPLYING MATHEMATICS

For each problem, first write a sentence that expresses a condition involving one variable. Then give the answer to the problem.

1 280 votes, at most, were cast in a class election. The winning candidate received 30 more votes than the losing candidate. How many votes did the losing candidate receive?

The amount of money that is paid as earnings per share of stock is called a *dividend*. The per cent that the dividend is of the value of the stock is the *dividend rate*.

2 Miss Kelly had \$570 invested in a certain stock for two years. The dividend rate for the second year was $1\frac{1}{2}$ times the dividend rate for the first year. Miss Kelly received a total of \$42.75 in dividends for the two years. What was the dividend rate for each year?

3 In the first lap of a skating race, Carol skated at a rate of 10 yd. per second and Mary skated at a rate of 7 yd. per second. Mary started the race $1\frac{1}{2}$ sec. before Carol. In how many seconds did Carol overtake Mary?

4 Kevin weighs 50 lb. more than his brother and 40 lb. less than his father. Together, Kevin and his brother weigh 30 lb. more than their father. How many pounds does each boy weigh?

5 In a certain city, 5% of the residents are retired. In a nearby city, 2% of the residents are retired. The two cities have a combined population of 150,000. Of these 150,000 persons, 3% are retired. What is the population of each city?

6 Last year Mr. Walch made a rectangular skating rink that was 3 times as long as it was wide. If he makes the rink 3 ft. wider this year, he will increase its area by 135 sq. ft. What was the length and what was the width in feet of the rink that he made last year?

7 Mr. Rossi has two drums filled with oil. One drum contains 30 gal. and can be emptied at a rate of 2 gal. per minute. The other drum contains 42 gal. and can be emptied at a rate of 3 gal. per minute. Suppose that he begins to empty both drums at the same time. In how many minutes will the two drums contain the same amount of oil?

8 Mr. True has been offered a job that pays \$100 per week and a commission of 4% on all sales. He has also been offered a second job that pays \$80 per week and a commission of 12% on all sales. How many dollars' worth of sales would he have to make to earn more money at the second job than at the first job?

9 At 7 o'clock one morning, the cash register in a restaurant contained fewer than 20 bills. There were 4 more one-dollar bills than five-dollar bills. There were 4 fewer ten-dollar bills than five-dollar bills. Altogether, there was more than \$50 in the register. How many bills of each kind were in the register?

10 A candy-store owner has 2 part-time employees and 3 full-time employees. The hourly wage of a full-time employee is 60 cents more than that of a part-time employee. For a day in which each of the employees worked 8 hr., the store owner paid a total of \$50.40 in wages. What is the hourly wage of a part-time employee?

11 A scholarship committee has more than \$10,000 to distribute as scholarships worth \$2000, \$1000, and \$500. They must grant $\frac{2}{3}$ as many \$1000 scholarships as \$500 scholarships, and $\frac{1}{3}$ as many \$2000 scholarships as \$500 scholarships. Altogether, they must grant fewer than 13 scholarships. How many scholarships of each kind can the committee grant?

12 If 3 times the absolute value of a certain number is added to 16, the result is greater than 40. What is the given number?

CHECKING UP

The small numerals within parentheses tell what pages to turn to for help if you need it.

Test 241

Tell what words or symbols best complete exercises 1 through 11.

1 The absolute value of -9 is ~~~~. (273)

2 Two conditions that have the same ~~~~ are equivalent. (255)

3 The sum of $|7|$ and $|-11|$ is ~~~~. (273)

4 You obtain ~~~~ when you divide each side of $3x+6=15$ by 3. (256)

5 You can obtain $7=7x$ if you add ~~~~ to each side of $7-2x=5x$. (255)

6 When you divide each side of $-2x>8$ by -2, you obtain ~~~~. (265)

7 A standard name of $|-\sqrt{25}|$ is ~~~~. (273)

8 The number ~~~~ is not a meaningful replacement for x in $3+\frac{4}{5(x+7)}=9$. (258)

9 A standard form of $5(2x-1)=3(x-1)-1$ is ~~~~. (259)

10 The value of $\frac{-b}{a}$ for $3x-7<0$ is ~~~~. (262)

11 The limits of the interval determined by $|x+3|\leqq 5$ are ~~~~ and 2. (277)

Test 242

12 What is the absolute value of zero? (273)

13 What is a standard name of $|32|-|-32|$? (273)

14 What do you obtain when you subtract $\frac{2}{3}x$ from each side of $x>\frac{2}{3}x+8$? (255)

15 What do you obtain when you multiply each side of $3-x<2-5x$ by -1? (265)

16 Tabulate the set of positive integers that are solutions of $3x+2<14$. (266)

17 Let x represent a number. How can you represent 5 less than this number? (283)

18 Solve $21.5x-45.4=3.5x-4.7x$. (260)

19 Derive a condition of the form $x<k$ from $\frac{7-4x}{3}+5x>2x+3(3+x)$. (266)

20 Tabulate the solution set of $|2x-5|=7$. (276)

21 Make a graph of $7-2x<12$. (266)

Test 243

From the list below each exercise, choose the item that correctly completes the exercise.

22 ~~~~ is a polynomial condition. (253)

a $18-2\sqrt{x}=72$ **c** $\frac{x^2}{8}-3x=\sqrt{5}$

b $13x+5=\frac{1}{x}$ **d** $2x-\frac{4}{x-2}=18$

23 For each $a>0$ and for each b and x, $ax+b>0 \Leftrightarrow$ ~~~~. (264)

a $x>\frac{-a}{b}$ **c** $x<\frac{-b}{a}$

b $x>\frac{-b}{a}$ **d** $x<\frac{-a}{b}$

24 ~~~~ is not a member of the solution set of $|3x+8|>10$. (278)

a -10 **b** -5 **c** 5 **d** 10

25 The condition ~~~~ determines an open interval. (277)

a $|x+2|>10$ **c** $|3+2x|<7$

b $14<|6-x|$ **d** $9-|x|<5$

26 $96x=108$ is not equivalent to ~~~~. (255)

a $54=\frac{48}{x}$ **c** $8x=\frac{108}{12}$

b $96x+7=115$ **d** $90x=54\sqrt{4}-6x$

27 A standard form of $5x-18<2x+4(x-5)$ is ~~~~. (262)

a $11x+2<0$ **c** $x-2>0$

b $x+3>0$ **d** $5x-8<0$

28 The solution set of $\frac{2(x-7)}{5}+1<x-6$ is ~~~~. (264)

a $\{x|x>7\}$ **c** $\{x|x<5\}$

b $\{x|x<2\}$ **d** $\{x|x>-3\}$

29 The solution set of $|3x+5|-8 \leqq 14$ is ~~~~. (277)

a $\{x \mid x \leqq \frac{17}{3}\}$

b $\{x \mid -\frac{17}{3} \leqq x \leqq \frac{17}{3}\}$

c $\{x \mid -9 \leqq x \leqq \frac{17}{3}\}$

d $\{x \mid x \leqq -9 \wedge x \leqq \frac{17}{3}\}$

30 $\frac{13}{7} < 4 - \frac{2x}{3}$ is equivalent to ~~~~. (266)

a $84 - 14x < 39$

b $14x < 39 - 84$

c $84 - 39 > 14x$

d $13 < 28 - 2x$

31 The condition ~~~~ is not equivalent to $\frac{4x-3}{12} + 5x = 7x + 2$. (261)

a $20x + 27 = 0$

b $64x - 3 = 84x + 24$

c $4x - 3 + 60x = 12(7x + 2)$

d $20x = 27$

Test 244

For each of problems 32 through 35, write a sentence that expresses a condition. Then give the answer to the problem.

32 At Kearney High School, $\frac{2}{7}$ of the boys participate in after-school sports. 84 boys participate in after-school sports. How many boys are enrolled in Kearney High School? (280)

33 Warren and Ed together weigh 279 lb. Ed weighs $\frac{4}{5}$ as much as Warren. How many pounds does Warren weigh? (280)

34 To enclose a rectangular garden, Mr. Hall used 120 ft. of fencing. The length of the garden is 10 ft. greater than the width. How wide is the garden in feet? (280)

35 Mr. Douglas owns a sporting goods store. He paid $4.00 apiece for some fishing reels, and he sold all but 5 of them at $6.00 apiece. He gave away the 5 reels as door prizes. He sold the reels for $114 more than he had paid for them. How many reels did Mr. Douglas buy? (280)

CHECKING UP

The small numerals within parentheses tell what pages to turn to for help if you need it.

Test 245

Write "T" for each sentence below that expresses a true statement. Write "F" for each sentence that expresses a false statement.

1 The square of every even integer is divisible by 4. (146)

2 For each x and y, $x < y$ gives you the same information as $x > y$. (85)

3 A property that we prove is called a theorem. (80)

4 For each y, $(10y - 3) - (y + 6)$ is equal to $9y + 3$. (189)

5 For each x and y, $x^2 + y^2 = (x + y)^2$. (200)

6 The locus of any condition of the form $y = \frac{k}{x}$ is a hyperbola. The universe for k is the set of non-zero real numbers. (104)

7 For each x, if $x > 5$, then $5 - x < 0$. (91)

8 $(3 \times \sqrt{3})^2 = 3^2 \times (\sqrt{3})^2$. (173)

9 $4 > 4 \vee 4 < 9$. (120)

10 Two vectors that are directed segments and that have the same starting point have no sum. (20)

Test 246

Tell what words or symbols best complete exercises 11 through 20.

11 Point ~~~~ is the terminal point of $\overrightarrow{DN}$. (7)

12 The ~~~~ of a right triangle is the side opposite the right angle. (15)

13 The difference of x and 5 is the same as the sum of x and ~~~~. (82)

14 Multiplication of integers ~~~~ over addition of integers. (211)

15 $ax^2 + bx + c$, where $a \neq 0$, is the standard form of a ~~~~ polynomial in one variable. (181)

16 A monomial or the sum of monomials is a ~~~. (180)

17 A conditional has the same truth value as its ~~~. (128)

18 A standard name of $16^{\frac{3}{4}}$ is ~~~. (243)

19 The idea of force includes both ~~~ and direction. (26)

20 In problems that involve vectors that are members of D × D, mathematicians refer to a member of D as a ~~~. (55)

Test 247

From the list below each exercise, choose the item that correctly completes the exercise.

21 The numeral ~~~ does not name a natural number. (66)

a $7-9$ **b** $25+18$ **c** 14×7 **d** $58 \div 2$

22 $\overrightarrow{XY}$ and $\overrightarrow{YZ}$ are ~~~ vectors of $\overrightarrow{XZ}$. (29)

a resultant **c** component
b vertical **d** parallel

23 It is true that ~~~. (85)

a $-5 < -5$ **c** $5 < -5$
b $0 < -5$ **d** $-5 < 0$

24 The expression ~~~ is equal to $5 - y$. (189)

a $y-5$ **c** $-(-5+y)$
b $-(5+y)$ **d** $-y-5$

25 Set R is a proper subset of set S. Therefore, for each x, ~~~. (125)

a if $x \in S$, then $x \in R$
b if $x \in R$, then $x \in S$
c if $x \in R$, then $y \in R$
d if $x \in S$, then $y \in R$

26 ~~~ is not an integral operation. (244)

a addition **c** multiplication
b subtraction **d** division

27 The real number 3 is not a solution of ~~~. (254).

a $2x - 5 = \frac{1}{2}(x+7) - (x+1)$
b $3(8-x) + 9 = 4(3x-1) - 8$
c $5x + 7(x-2) - 10 = 4x + 1$
d $x^2 + 8x - 6(13 - 3x) = x^2$

28 The ~~~ is not required of a field. (68)

a distributive property
b sum property of "less than"
c closure property
d commutative property

29 A factored form of $25x^2 - 20x + 4$ is ~~~. (200)

a $(5x-2)(5x-2)$ **c** $(5x+2)(5x+2)$
b $(25x-1)(x-4)$ **d** $(5x-2)(5x+2)$

30 Set ~~~ forms a commutative group under multiplication. (54)

a I **b** R_p **c** D × D **d** N

Test 248

For each of problems 31 through 38, write a sentence that expresses a condition. Then give the answer to the problem.

31 Roger is twice as old as Ted. In five years, Ted will be $\frac{2}{3}$ as old as Roger will be. How old is each of the boys now? (108)

32 The price of Mr. Campion's new car was \$3250. In addition, he paid a sales tax of $3\frac{1}{2}\%$. How much did the car cost him? (280)

33 Mr. Wise drove from his home to Oakville at an average rate of 55 mi. per hour. He drove home again at an average rate of 45 mi. per hour. He drove a total of 8 hr. How many miles is Oakville from Mr. Wise's home? (280)

34 The area of a rectangular room is 544 sq. ft. Its width is 17 ft. How long is the room in feet? (280)

35 In △ABC, ∠C is a right angle, $\angle A^\circ = 34$, and $m(\overline{AB}) = 48$. What is $m(\overline{BC})$? (29)

36 The measure of an edge of a cube is 1 yd. What is the volume in cubic inches? (108)

37 Water weighs approximately 62.4 lb. per cubic foot. A rectangular swimming pool is 40 ft. long and 20 ft. wide. If the pool is filled to an average depth of 4 ft., what is the weight of the water in pounds? (108)

38 The sum of 3 consecutive integers is 39. What are the integers? (280)

Unit 22

Relations and functions

A relation as a subset of a Cartesian set

In *Book 2* you learned that a set of ordered pairs is a relation. The relations that you studied were determined by such conditions as $y = kx$, $y = kx^2$, $y = \frac{k}{x}$, and $y = \frac{k}{x^2}$. In this unit you will learn more about relations. You will also study special relations that are known as functions.

A Tabulate the set of days in the week. We will call this set A.

B Suppose that B is the set whose members are the integers from 1 through 29. How many members are in B?

C Think about the Cartesian set A × B. Name three members of this set.

D How many members of A × B have Monday as a first component?

E How many members of A × B have 29 as a second component?

> REMINDER
>
> A Cartesian set is the set of all ordered pairs that can be formed by matching each member of one set in turn with each member of a second set.
>
> *See lesson 31, page 127, Book 1.*

F ? How can you use the fundamental counting property to determine the number of members in A × B?

D1 shows a page from a calendar for the month of February in a certain leap year. From this calendar we can obtain a set of ordered pairs that are formed in the following way: In each ordered pair, the first component is a day of the week; the second component is an integer for a date in February that falls on that day of the week. We will call this set M.

S	M	T	W	T	F	S
						1
2	3	4	5	6	7	8
9	10	11	12	13	14	15
16	17	18	19	20	21	22
23	24	25	26	27	28	29

D1

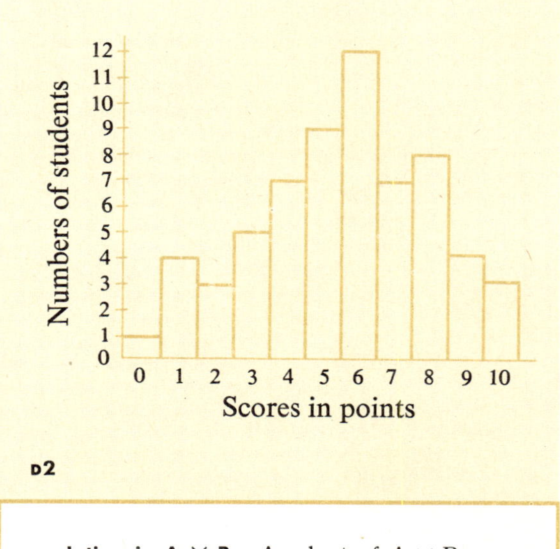

D2

relation in A × B. A subset of A × B.

G Is (Monday, 3) a member of M? Does M contain (Saturday, 19)? Explain your answers.

H Which ordered pair indicates that Feb. 13 falls on Thursday? Which ordered pairs indicate that a Tuesday could be Feb. 4, Feb. 11, Feb. 18, or Feb. 25?

I How many members are in M? Does M contain each member of A × B, described in exercise C? Is M a subset of A × B? Explain your answers.

We can say that set M is a *relation in A × B*. A relation in a Cartesian set is a subset of the Cartesian set.

J Is set M a relation in B × A? Explain your answer.

K How many members of M have Tuesday as a first component? How many members of M have Saturday as a first component?

L Are there two or more members of M that have the same first component?

The graph in D2 is a histogram. It shows the numbers of students who received various scores on a 10-point examination. The numerals at the bottom of the graph indicate the possible scores in points. The numerals at the left of the graph indicate the numbers of students who received certain scores.

M How many students scored 10 points in the examination? Which score was received by 12 students?

N Use the histogram in D2 to tabulate the set of ordered pairs that are formed in the following way: In each ordered pair, the first component indicates a number of points scored; the second component indicates the number of students who received that score. Call this set K.

O Think about the Cartesian set formed from {0, 1, 2, . . ., 10} and {0, 1, 2, . . ., 12}. Is K a relation in this Cartesian set? Is K a relation in I × I? Is it also a relation in D × D?

P In K are there two or more ordered pairs that have the same first component? What is the second component of the ordered pair whose first component is 3?

So far, we have shown that a relation in a Cartesian set may be selected from the Carte-

$S = \{-3, -2, 1, 5\}$.

D3

A $y > x$.
B $y = x + 4$.

D4

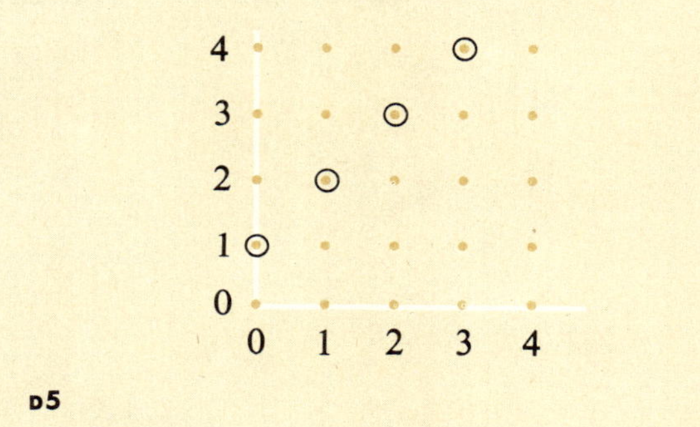

D5

sian set with the aid of a chart or a graph. Next you will use conditions to select subsets of Cartesian sets.

A Set S is tabulated in D3. Is S a subset of the set of integers? Is it a subset of the set of real numbers? Tabulate $S \times S$.

B The universe for (x, y) is $S \times S$. Tabulate $\{(x, y) \mid y = x\}$. Is this solution set a relation in $S \times S$? Is it also a relation in $I \times I$? In $D \times D$?

You can see that $y = x$ selects, as its solution set, a certain relation from $S \times S$. Any relation that is selected from a Cartesian set and is the solution set of a condition is a relation *determined* by the condition.

C Now suppose that the universe for (x, y) is $D \times D$. Can you tabulate $\{(x, y) \mid y = x\}$ in this case? Give the names of three members of $\{(x, y) \mid y = x\}$.

D Is the set described in exercise C a relation ? in $S \times S$? In $I \times I$? In $D \times D$? Explain your answers.

E Explain why a given condition may be said to determine more than one relation.

F Look at D4. The universe for (x, y) is $D \times D$. Is $(-3, 2)$ a member of the solution set of condition A? Is $(0, -6)$ a member? Is $(\sqrt{5}, 10)$ a member? Is $(\frac{1}{2}, \frac{1}{4})$ a member?

G Give the names of four members of the solution set of condition A that are not mentioned in exercise F.

H Is the solution set of A a finite set?

I Is each member of $D \times D$ also a member of the solution set of A? Is each member of the solution set of A also a member of $D \times D$?

J When the universe is $D \times D$, does A determine a relation in $D \times D$? In $I \times I$? Explain your answers.

K In the relation determined by $y > x$, how many ordered pairs have 3 as a first component? How many ordered pairs have $\sqrt{2}$ as a first component? In this relation, are there any ordered pairs that have the same first component?

L Now consider condition B, expressed in D4. Which of the ordered pairs expressed below are members of $\{(x, y) \mid y = x + 4\}$ when the universe for (x, y) is $D \times D$?

$(2, -2)$ $(4, 0)$ $(0, 4)$ $(3, 7)$ $(-5, -1)$

M Is the solution set of B finite? Is each member of the solution set a member of $D \times D$?

N How do you know that B determines a relation in $D \times D$?

O How many members of the relation determined by $y = x + 4$ have 2 as a first component? How many members have -6 as a first component?

You can often discover facts about a relation by studying its graph.

A D5 shows a graph of relation F in $M \times M$. $M = \{0, 1, 2, 3, 4\}$. Tabulate relation F.

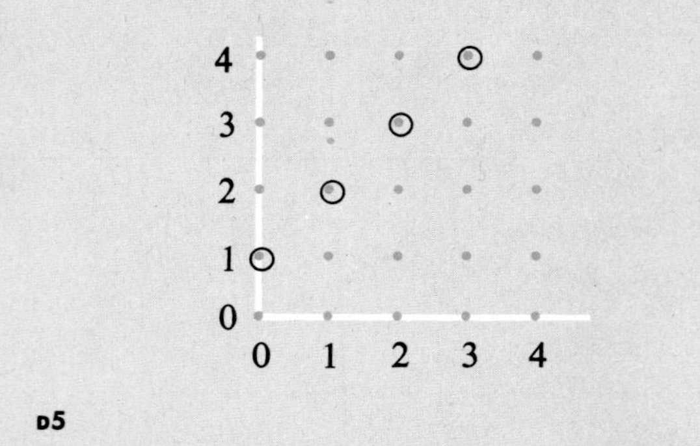

D5

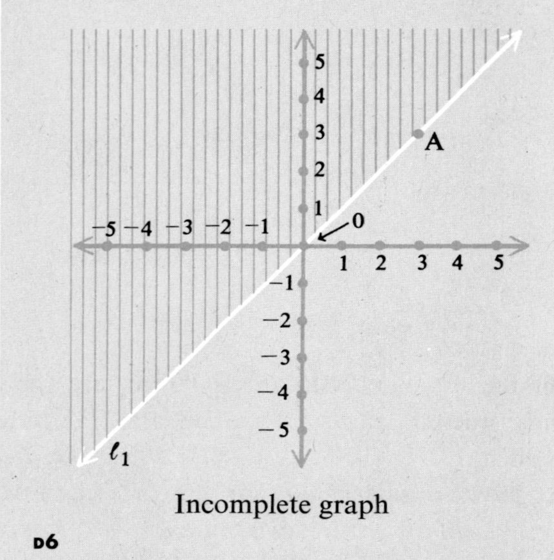

Incomplete graph

D6

C = {(0, 0), (1, 2), (2, 4)}.
D = {(2, 0), (3, 1), (4, 2), (5, 3)}.
E = {(0, 2), (0, 3), (0, 4), (0, 5),
(1, 3), (1, 4), (1, 5),
(2, 4), (2, 5), (3, 5)}.

D7

B Is F also a relation in I × I? In D × D?

C In F, are there two or more ordered pairs that have the same first component?

D For each ordered pair in F, the second component is how much greater than the first component?

E If the universe for (x, y) is M × M, does the condition $y = x + 1$ determine relation F? Explain your answer.

F Now look at D6, which shows a graph of relation J in D × D. Line ℓ_1 is shown in white to indicate that it is not part of the locus of J. Point A is associated with (3, 3). Does J contain (3, 3)? Does J contain (0, 0)?

G Does J contain any (x, y) in which $y = x$? In which $y < x$? In which $y > x$?

H ? When the universe for (x, y) is D × D, what is a condition that determines relation J?

I ? In relation J, are there two or more ordered pairs that have the same first component? Give examples to explain your answer.

If a relation is determined by a condition, you can often discover the condition by inspecting the ordered pairs in the relation.

J Look at D7. Relations C, D, and E are relations in B × B, where B = {0, 1, 2, 3, 4, 5}. Tabulate B × B.

K Study relation C. For each ordered pair, by what number can you multiply the first component to obtain the second component?

L If the universe for (x, y) is B × B, what is a condition that determines relation C?

M Study relation D. For each ordered pair, is the first component a factor of the second component? Is the first component greater than the second component? How can the second component be obtained from the first component?

N If the universe for (x, y) is B × B, what is a condition that determines relation D?

O If the universe for (x, y) is B × B, what is a condition that determines E?

Now you know that a relation in A × B is a subset of A × B. You also know that various kinds of relations can be obtained from charts, graphs, and conditions and that it is possible to find conditions that determine certain given relations.

On your own

1 Tabulate the relation that contains all ordered pairs formed in the following way: Each first component is a month of the year; each second component is the number of days that are in that month in a leap year.

2 Tabulate the relation that can be obtained from the chart below. Each first component should be a chemical element. Each second component should be the atomic number of that element.

Element	Oxygen	Chlorine	Krypton	Radon
Atomic number	8	17	36	86

3 Tabulate the relation that contains all ordered pairs formed in this way: Both components are members of $\{1, 2, 3, \ldots, 10\}$; each first component is a factor of the second component.

4 In the formula $F = \frac{9}{5}C + 32$, F represents a number of degrees Fahrenheit, and C represents a number of degrees centigrade. A relation in which each first component is a centigrade temperature and each second component is a Fahrenheit temperature can be determined by $F = \frac{9}{5}C + 32$. Tabulate the members of this relation that have the following first components.

0 50 75 100 125 150

5 Describe a physical situation that might determine a relation that contains, among others, the following ordered pairs.

(1, 1) (2, 8) (3, 27) (4, 64)

6 $A = \{\frac{1}{2}, 1, 2, 3, 4\}$. Tabulate $A \times A$.

Tabulate the relation determined by each condition expressed in exercises 7 through 12. The universe for (x, y) is $A \times A$, which you tabulated for exercise 6. Then tell if the relation is in $I \times I$ or in $D \times D$, as well as in $A \times A$.

7 $y = x$. 9 $y = 2x$. 11 $y = x^2$.
8 $y = x + 2$. 10 $y < x$. 12 $y < x + 1$.

For each relation tabulated below, give a condition that determines the relation when the universe for (x, y) is $A \times A$.

13 $\{(1, 2), (2, 3), (3, 4)\}$
14 $\{(\frac{1}{2}, 2), (1, 4)\}$
15 $\{(4, 1), (2, \frac{1}{2})\}$
16 $\{(2, 1), (3, 2), (4, 3)\}$
17 $\{(\frac{1}{2}, 1), (\frac{1}{2}, 2), (\frac{1}{2}, 3), (\frac{1}{2}, 4), (1, 2),$
$(1, 3), (1, 4), (2, 3), (2, 4), (3, 4)\}$
18 $\{(\frac{1}{2}, 2), (1, 2), (2, 2), (3, 2), (4, 2)\}$
19 $\{(\frac{1}{2}, 3), (1, 4)\}$

KEEPING SKILLFUL

For each exercise below, tabulate the solution set of the given condition, if possible. Otherwise, give a standard description of the solution set.

1 $3c + 8 > 50$. 6 $-4\frac{1}{2}x + 8 < 16$.
2 $1.6 < 5x + .2$. 7 $25y - 40y = -5 + 30$.
3 $3\frac{1}{4}w - 16 = 0$. 8 $-s + 3.7 > 7.2 + .3s$.
4 $4(n - 2) > 10$. 9 $\frac{1}{2}y - 4 < 2\frac{1}{2}y + 6$.
5 $8c + 40 > 0$. 10 $.5(z - 4) + .75 = 8$.
11 $(x + 7)^2 - (x + 4)(x + 1) < 6(x + 8)$.
12 $8n + 4(\frac{3}{5}n - 2) < 5(1\frac{1}{5}n - 8)$.
13 $\dfrac{6 + x}{4} + 5x > \dfrac{x + 8}{4}$.
14 $16 - (8 + 4y) = 32 + 6(y + 4)$.
15 $(a + 4)(a + 8) = (a + 3)^2$.
16 $(x + 9)^2 - (x + 1)(x + 2) > 24(x + 2)$.
17 $6x + 5 = 29 \wedge 16x + 2 > 48$.
18 $24c - 3\frac{1}{2} = 2c + 4\frac{1}{2} \vee$
$3(c + 8) - 2(c + 4) > 0$.
19 $5 + 2(x + 4) = -9 \wedge$
$25x - (4x + 1) < x + 5$.
20 $\dfrac{x + 4}{12} + x < 2 \wedge 2(x + 5) > 10$.

22 **266** Exploring ideas

Domain and range of a relation

In this lesson you will pay special attention to the set of first components and the set of second components of the ordered pairs in a relation.

A Look at D1. Notice that the members of set A are continents and the members of set B are cities. Tabulate A × B.

B ? Set R is a relation in A × B that consists of all the ordered pairs that can be formed in the following way: Each first component is a continent; each second component is a city on that continent. Tabulate R.

C Tabulate the set of first components of the elements of R. Does this set of first components contain every member of A? Is it a subset of A?

{North America, South America, Africa, Europe} is the *domain* of R. The domain of a relation in A × B is the set that consists of all the first components of the elements of the relation. The domain is a subset of A.

D Tabulate the set that contains all the second components of relation R. Is this set of second components a subset of B?

{Chicago, Paris, New York, Buenos Aires, Nairobi} is the *range* of R. The range of a relation in A × B is the set that consists of all the second components of the elements of the relation. The range is a subset of B.

E Is North America in the domain of R? What elements of the range of R are paired with North America to form elements of R?

F Are there two or more elements of R with the same first component?

G ? Explain why a relation in a finite Cartesian set must have a finite domain and a finite range.

Now look at the chart in D2, which summarizes the results of an experiment concerning the volume of 1 gram of water at various centigrade temperatures.

H Use the chart in D2 to help you tabulate relation K, in which each first component is a temperature and each second component is the volume of 1 gram of water at that temperature.

A = {North America, South America, Africa, Europe, Antarctica}.
B = {Chicago, Paris, Honolulu, New York, Buenos Aires, Sidney, Nairobi}.

D1

Temperature in degrees centigrade	4	12	15	19	22
Volume in cubic centimeters	1.0000	1.0002	1.0004	1.0006	1.0008

D2

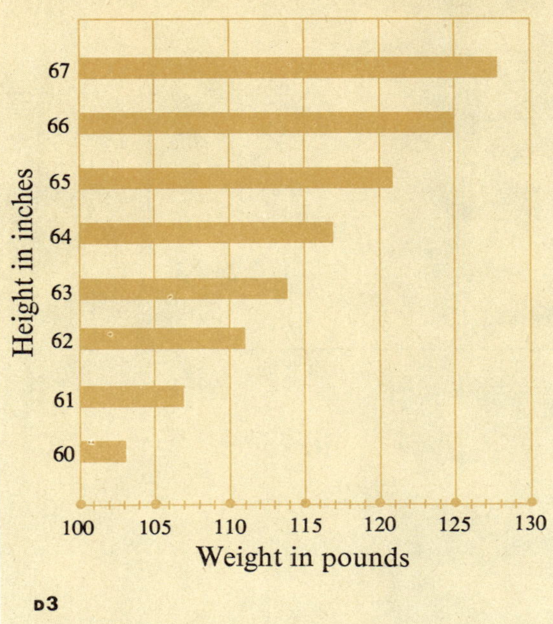

D3

$E = \{1, 2, 3, 4, 5, 6\}$.
$F = \{2, 4, 6, 8\}$.

D4

do main of a relation in A × B (dō mān′). The subset of A that consists of all the first components of the elements of the relation.

range of a relation in A × B. The subset of B that consists of all the second components of the elements of the relation.

I Tabulate the domain of K. Tabulate the range.

The bar graph in D3 gives average weights for 15- and 16-year-old girls of various heights.

J Use the graph in D3 to help you tabulate relation T, in which each first component is a height and each second component is the weight corresponding to that height.

K Tabulate the domain of relation T. Tabulate the range.

Next you will consider the domain and the range of relations that are determined by conditions.

A Look at D4. Tabulate $E \times F$.

B Set M is the relation determined by $y = 2x$ when the universe for (x, y) is $E \times F$. Tabulate M.

C How do you know that M is a relation in $E \times F$?

D Tabulate the domain of M. Is this domain a subset of E? Is it a proper subset of E?

E Tabulate the range of M. Is the range a subset of F? Is it a proper subset of F?

F ? Relation P is determined by $y = 2x$ when the universe for (x, y) is $D \times D$. How is relation P different from relation M, which you tabulated for exercise B?

G Is relation P a relation in $E \times F$? Is P a relation in $D \times D$?

H ? If you could replace x in $y = 2x$ by each real number in turn, would you obtain a corresponding real number for y? Describe the domain of P.

I ? How do you know that the range of P is D?

J Now consider the relation determined by $y = \frac{4}{x}$ when the universe for (x, y) is $E \times F$. Tabulate this relation. Tabulate the domain and the range of the relation.

K ? Think about the relation determined by $y = \frac{4}{x}$ when the universe for (x, y) is $D \times D$. Why does the domain of this relation contain every real number except 0? Why does the range contain every real number except 0?

By now it should be clear that a given condition may determine more than one relation because it is possible to have more than one universe for the ordered pair of variables.

From now on, when we refer to the relation determined by a condition, we will mean only the relation that is the solution set of the condition when the universe is D × D. If we wish to consider any other relation determined by a condition, we will specify a particular universe or a particular domain.

L Think about the relation determined by $y = \sqrt{x+3}$. Why is the domain of this relation the set of real numbers that are greater than or equal to -3? Why does the range contain only the non-negative real numbers?

You should conclude from exercise L that, if the universe is D × D, the domain of a relation in D × D consists of the members of D that are meaningful replacements for x.

You can also determine the domain and the range of a relation by studying a graph of the relation.

M D5 shows a graph of a relation in a finite Cartesian set. Does the locus of the relation contain any points with 0 as a first coördinate? With 2 as a first coördinate? What numbers are the first coördinates of the points in the locus of the relation? Are these numbers the elements of the domain?

N Name the second coördinates of the points in the locus represented in D5. Tabulate the range of the relation.

O The graph in D6 is a graph of a relation in D × D. Does the locus of the relation contain a point with $-\sqrt{3}$ as a first coördinate? With -700 as a first coördinate? With 0 as a first coördinate? With $\sqrt{4097}$ as a first coördinate?

P Is there any real number that is not the first coördinate of some point in the locus represented in D6? What is the domain of the relation?

Q Is there any real number that is not the second coördinate of some point in the locus

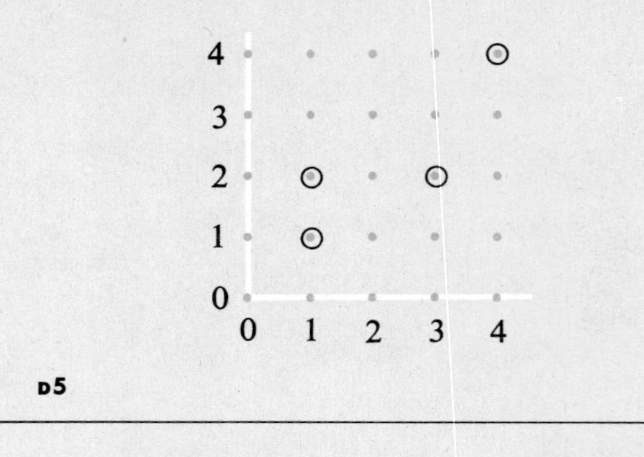

D5

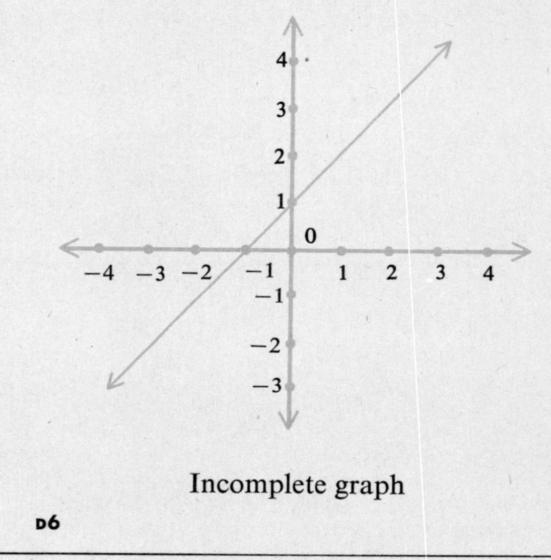

Incomplete graph

D6

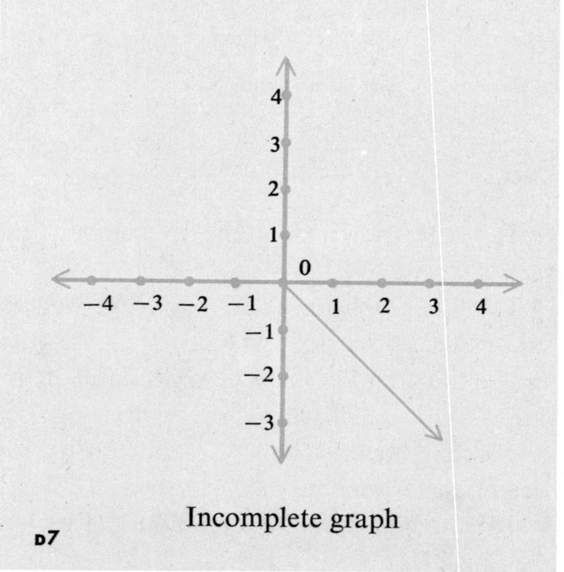

Incomplete graph

D7

represented in D6? What is the range of the relation?

R D7 shows a graph of another relation in D × D. Does the locus of this relation contain any point with a negative real number as a first coördinate? Is 0 a first coördinate of a point in the locus? Is each positive real number a first coördinate of a point in the locus?

S Describe the domain of the relation whose graph is shown in D7.

T What real numbers are the second coördinates of the points in the locus represented in D7? Describe the range of the relation.

Now you know that the domain of a relation in A × B is the subset of A that contains all the first components of the elements of the relation and that the range is the subset of B that contains all the second components of the elements of the relation.

On your own

In each of exercises 1 through 10, a condition that determines a relation and the domain of the relation are given. In each case, the relation is a set of (x, y). Tabulate the relation. Then tabulate its range.

1 $y = x - 2$. Domain = $\{-1, 0, 6, 8, 9\}$.
2 $y = x - 2$. Domain = $\{-6, -\frac{2}{3}, \frac{3}{4}, 7\}$.
3 $x = y - 1$. Domain = $\{-1, 0, 1, 3\frac{1}{2}, 9\frac{2}{5}\}$.
4 $2y = 4x$. Domain = $\{1, 2, 3, 4, 5\}$.
5 $y = -x$. Domain = $\{-3, 0, \sqrt{5}\}$.
6 $2x - 3 = y$. Domain = $\{-6, -\frac{1}{2}, 5, 7\}$.
7 $x^2 = y$. Domain = $\{-\frac{1}{3}, -2, 0, 8\}$.
8 $\frac{y}{x} = -2$. Domain = $\{-\frac{1}{2}, -1, \sqrt{2}\}$.
9 $y = x^4 - 1$. Domain = $\{-1, 0, \sqrt{3}, 3\}$.
10 $y = \sqrt{x}$. Domain = $\{0, \frac{1}{9}, 9, 49, 269\}$.

For each of exercises 11 through 22, describe the domain and the range of the relation determined by the condition. The universe for (x, y) is specified in each case.

11 $y = 3x$. U = D × D.
12 $x + y = 7$. U = N × N.
13 $y = 2x$. U = R × R.
14 $y = x^2$. U = D × D.
15 $y = 2x - 5$. U = D × D.
16 $y = \sqrt{x}$. U = D × D.
17 $y > x$. U = N × N.
18 $y = x + 2$. U = C × C.
19 $y = -x$. U = N × N.
20 $\frac{y}{x} = 1$. U = D × D.
21 $y = \sqrt{x - 2}$. U = D × D.
22 $y = (x + 1)^2$. U = D × D.

KEEPING SKILLFUL

For each of exercises 1 through 22, find a standard name of the number expressed.

1 $|1000|$
2 $|-50|$
3 $|\frac{1}{4} - \frac{1}{2}|$
4 $|-65|$
5 $|.5| \cdot |-.7|$
6 $|(-8)^2|$
7 $|-\frac{1}{3} - \frac{1}{12}|$
8 $|-.625|$
9 $|(-5)^2|$
10 $|\sqrt{169}|$
11 $3|\sqrt{4}|$
12 $|\sqrt{121}| + |-5|$
13 $|-49| + |\sqrt{49}|$
14 $|2000 - 3125|$
15 $|-5\sqrt{10} + 6\sqrt{10}|$
16 $4|-8| + 2|-4|$
17 $\frac{1}{5}|-10 + (-8)|$
18 $\frac{2}{5}|-10| + \frac{3}{5}|-15|$
19 $|.6| + |-.6| + |1.2|$
20 $|.6| \cdot |.3| \cdot |-.3|$
21 $|-\frac{1}{4}| \cdot |-\frac{1}{3}| \cdot |-\frac{1}{6}|$
22 $|3 + 4| \cdot |6 - 10|$

For each exercise below, tabulate the solution set of the given condition, if possible. Otherwise, give a standard description of the solution set.

23 $|x| = 125$.
24 $|d| > 260$.
25 $\sqrt{x^2} = 256$.
26 $|y + 2| < 4.8$.
27 $|y + 4| < 10$.
28 $|3c + 3| \leqq 12$.
29 $|x - 3| \leqq 25$.
30 $|x + 30| = 40$.
31 $.6|d + 4| = 12$.
32 $|c| \geqq 14.9$.
33 $|3(c + 2)| = 20$.
34 $20|x| + 5|x| = 100$.

22 267 Exploring ideas

Functions

You have observed that in a relation each element of the domain may be paired with one or more elements of the range. In this lesson we will be especially concerned with the *number* of range elements that are paired with each member of the domain.

In lesson 265 you formed A × B, where A is the set of days in the week and B is the set of integers from 1 through 29. Then you used the calendar shown in D1 to determine a relation M in A × B. You will recall that, in each member of M, the first component is a day of the week and the second component is an integer for a date in February that falls on that day of the week. Thus, the members of M are (Saturday, 1), (Sunday, 2), (Monday, 3), and so on.

A What set is the domain of M? What set is the range?

B If you refer to a member of M that has Friday as a first component, do you necessarily mean (Friday, 7)? If you refer to a Friday in February, do you necessarily mean February 7? Explain your answers.

C In relation M, is each member of the domain paired with exactly one member of the range?

Now suppose that you use the calendar shown in D1 to determine a relation K in B × A. In each member of K, the first component is an integer for a date in February and the second component is the day of the week on which that date falls. Thus, the members of K are (1, Saturday), (2, Sunday), (3, Monday), and so on.

D Relation K has how many members? What set is the domain? What set is the range?

E If you refer to a member of K that has 19 as a first component, do you necessarily mean (19, Wednesday)? If you refer to the 19th of February, do you necessarily mean a Wednesday? Explain your answers.

F In relation K, is each member of the domain paired with exactly one member of the range?

Exercises A through F point out a significant difference between relation K and relation M. Any given member of the domain of M is the first component of 4 or 5 different ordered pairs, but each member of the domain of K is the first component of *exactly one* ordered pair. This means that, if you know what ordered pairs belong to K and if you know the first component of a pair, then you also know that there is only one possibility for the second

S	M	T	W	T	F	S
						1
2	3	4	5	6	7	8
9	10	11	12	13	14	15
16	17	18	19	20	21	22
23	24	25	26	27	28	29

D1

$R_1 = \{(0, 1), (1, 2), (2, 3), (3, 4)\}$.
$R_2 = \{(0, 2), (0, 3), (0, 4), (1, 3), (1, 4), (2, 4)\}$.

D2

function (fungk′shən). A relation in which each element of the domain is paired with exactly one element of the range.

component. This characteristic of K makes it a special kind of relation that is known as a *function*. A relation is a function if and only if each element of the domain is paired with exactly one element of the range.

Now you can investigate other relations to decide if they are functions.

G J = {0, 1, 2, 3, 4}. Tabulate J × J.

H R_1, which is a relation in J × J, is tabulated in D2. How do you know that R_1 is the relation determined by $y = x + 1$ when the universe for (x, y) is J × J?

I Tabulate the domain of R_1. Tabulate the range. How many elements of R_1 have a first component of 0? Of 1? Of 2? Of 3?

J How do you know that R_1 is a function?

K Look again at D2. R_2 is another relation in J × J. What is a condition for inequality that determines R_2?

L Tabulate the domain and the range of R_2.

M ? How do you know that R_2 is a relation that is not a function?

So far, we have considered only functions that are relations in finite Cartesian sets. Now we will consider infinite functions and their graphs. Look at D3. Since we are usually considering (x, y) pairs, we often refer to the first axis as the x-axis and to the second axis as the y-axis. Notice that the axes represented in D3 are labeled as the x-axis and the y-axis, respectively.

A Think about the relation that is determined by $y = x + 1$ when the universe for (x, y) is D × D. Which line represented in D3 is the locus of this relation?

B What is the domain of the relation determined by $y = x + 1$? What is the range?

C ? Think of replacing x in $y = x + 1$ by each member of the domain in turn. For each replacement of x, how many replacements for y

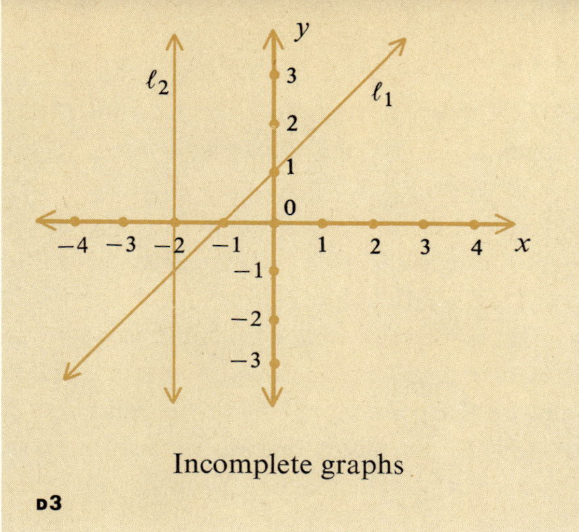

Incomplete graphs

D3

would you obtain? How do you know that $y = x + 1$ determines a function?

D Notice that a vertical line, ℓ_2, also is represented in D3. How do you know that ℓ_2 is the locus of $x = -2$?

E Describe the first component of each (x, y) that satisfies $x = -2$.

F How do you know that the function determined by $y = x + 1$ contains exactly one member of $\{(x, y) \mid x = -2\}$?

G In how many points does ℓ_1 intersect ℓ_2?

H Think of all the conditions of the form $x = k$, where k is a real number. How do you know that, for each k, the relation determined by $y = x + 1$ contains exactly one member of $\{(x, y) \mid x = k\}$?

I Describe the locus of any condition of the form $x = k$.

J ? Look again at D3. Explain why any vertical line intersects ℓ_1 in exactly one point.

K Now think about the relation determined by $y > x + 1$. How is the locus of this relation different from the locus of the relation determined by $y = x + 1$?

L If you replace x by -2 in $y > x + 1$, do you obtain exactly one replacement for y?

M How do you know that $y > x + 1$ determines a relation that is not a function?

N How many members of the relation determined by $y > x + 1$ are also members of $\{(x, y) \mid x = -2\}$?

O Is there at least one vertical line that intersects the locus of $y > x + 1$ in more than one point? Explain your answer.

P If a relation is not a function, is there at least one vertical line that intersects its locus in more than one point? How do you know?

Q How do you know that no vertical line can intersect the locus of a function in more than one point?

In the exercises that follow, you will consider several more relations in $D \times D$ to decide whether or not they are functions.

A $R_3 = \{(0, 1), (1, 1)\}$. Tabulate the domain of R_3. Tabulate the range.

B Is R_3 a function? Explain your answer.

C $R_4 = \{(1, 0), (1, 1)\}$. How do you know that R_4 is not a function?

D Make a graph of R_4 in $D \times D$. Give the condition for a vertical line that intersects the locus of R_4 in more than one point.

D4 shows a graph of the relation determined by $y = x^2$. As you know, $y = x^2$ is of the form $y = kx^2$. Hence, the locus of $y = x^2$ is a special kind of curve called a parabola.

E If you could replace x in $y = x^2$ by each real number in turn, would you obtain a corresponding replacement for y? How do you know that D is the domain of $\{(x, y) \mid y = x^2\}$?

F Explain why replacing x by each real number in turn would always yield a non-negative real number as a replacement for y. What set is the range of the relation determined by $y = x^2$?

G How many members of $\{(x, y) \mid y = x^2\}$ have 1 as a first component? How many points are in the intersection of the parabola and the vertical line that is the locus of $x = 1$?

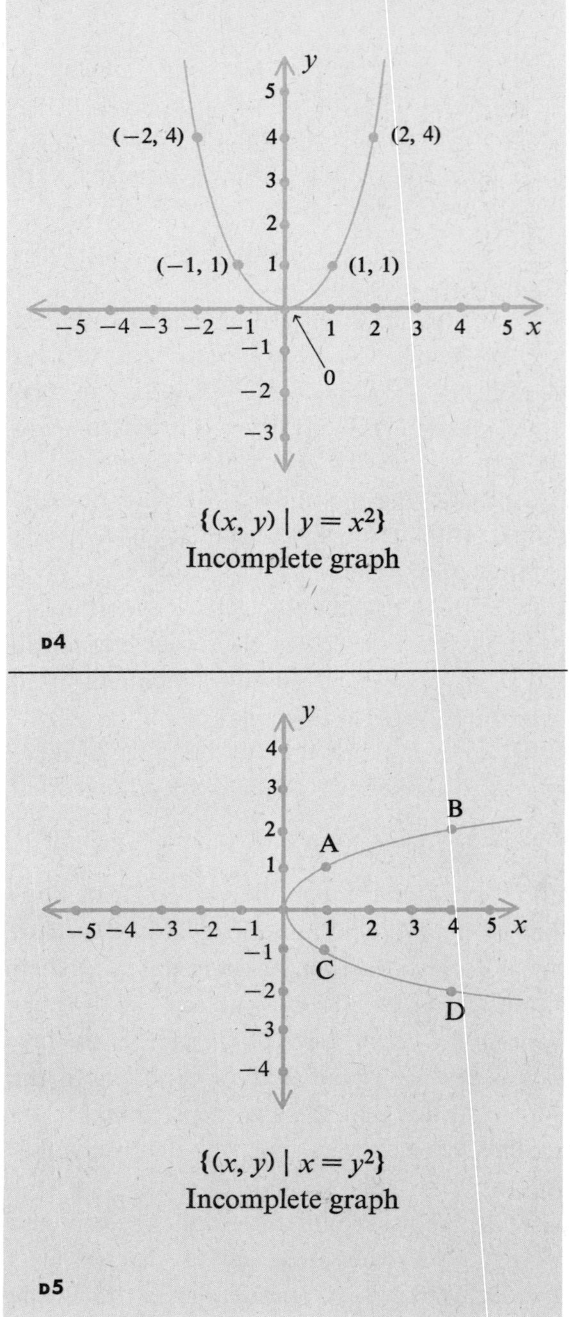

$\{(x, y) \mid y = x^2\}$
Incomplete graph

D4

$\{(x, y) \mid x = y^2\}$
Incomplete graph

D5

H How many members of $\{(x, y) \mid y = x^2\}$ have $3\frac{1}{2}$ as a first component? How many points are in the intersection of the parabola for $y = x^2$ and the vertical line that is the locus of $x = 3\frac{1}{2}$?

I How many points are in the intersection of the parabola and the vertical line that is the locus of $x = 5000$?

J Is $\{(x, y) \mid y = x^2\}$ a function? Is there a vertical line in the real plane that intersects the locus of $y = x^2$ in more than one point?

K Now look at the graph in D5. Point A is associated with (1, 1). What point is associated with (4, 2)? With (1, −1)? With (4, −2)?

L Does each (x, y) mentioned in exercise K satisfy $x = y^2$?

M The graph in D5 is a graph of the relation determined by $x = y^2$. How do you know that the set of non-negative real numbers is the domain of $\{(x, y) \mid x = y^2\}$? What is the range of $\{(x, y) \mid x = y^2\}$?

N If you replace x by 4 in $x = y^2$, what two replacements do you obtain for y? How many points are in the intersection of the locus of $x = y^2$ and the vertical line that is the locus of $x = 4$?

O How do you know that $\{(x, y) \mid x = y^2\}$ is not a function?

In this lesson you learned how to determine whether or not a relation is a function. You know that, in a function, each element of the domain is paired with exactly one element of the range. You also know that no vertical line can intersect the locus of a function in more than one point.

On your own

Tabulate the relation described in each of exercises 1 through 8. Then tell whether or not the relation is a function. The universe for (x, y) is A × B, where A = {0, 1, 2, 4} and B = {0, 3, 4}.

1 $\{(x, y) \mid x + y < 4\}$

2 $\{(x, y) \mid x + y < 2\}$

3 $\{(x, y) \mid y = x\}$

4 $\{(x, y) \mid y > x\}$

5 $\{(x, y) \mid y < x\}$

6 $\{(x, y) \mid y = \frac{3}{4}x\}$

7 $\{(x, y) \mid y > \frac{3}{4}x\}$

8 $\{(x, y) \mid y < \frac{3}{4}x\}$

For each exercise below, make a graph of the relation. If the relation is not a function, give the condition for a vertical line that intersects the locus of the relation in more than one point. The universe for (x, y) is given in each case.

9 $\{(x, y) \mid x = y\}$ U = D × D.

10 $\{(x, y) \mid x + 1 = 7\}$ U = D × D.

11 $\{(x, y) \mid x + y = 3\}$ U = D × D.

12 $\{(x, y) \mid y < x\}$ U = D × D.

13 $\{(x, y) \mid x < y + 2\}$ U = D × D.

14 $\{(x, y) \mid y = x^2\}$ U = I × I.

15 $\{(x, y) \mid x = y^2\}$ U = I × I.

16 $\{(x, y) \mid x = y^2\}$ U = N × N.

17 $\{(x, y) \mid |x| = 2\}$ U = D × D.

18 $\{(x, y) \mid |y| = 2\}$ U = D × D.

Use the graph in D6 in connection with exercises 19 through 27. The circle represented in D6 is the locus of $x^2 + y^2 = 4$.

19 Give the coördinates of points M, N, P, and Q, represented in D6.

20 Express four true statements to show that the coördinates of points M, N, P, and Q are members of $\{(x, y) \mid x^2 + y^2 = 4\}$.

21 In which quadrant is point $(\sqrt{3}, 1)$? Is $(\sqrt{3}, 1)$ a member of $\{(x, y) \mid x^2 + y^2 = 4\}$?

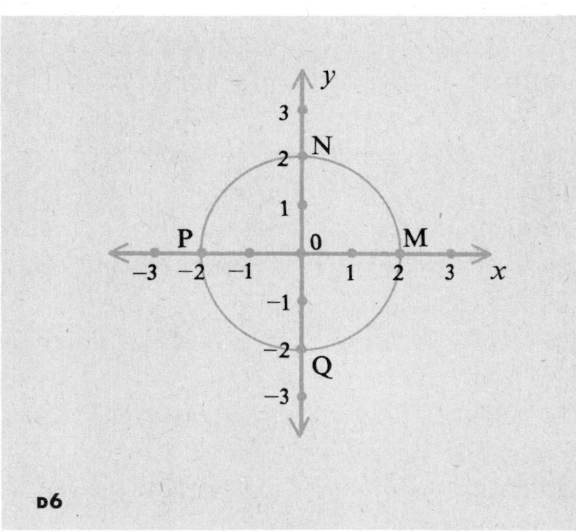

D6

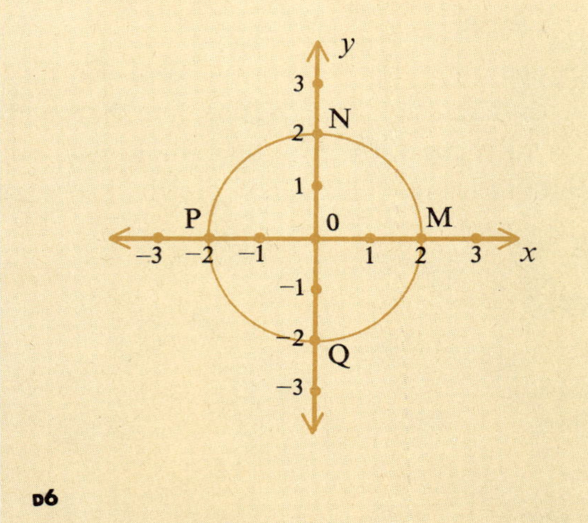

D6

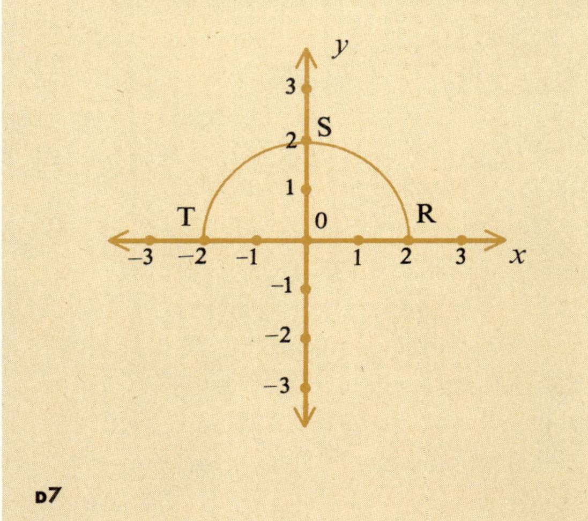

D7

22 In which quadrant is point $(\sqrt{3}, -1)$? Is $(\sqrt{3}, -1)$ a member of $\{(x, y) \mid x^2 + y^2 = 4\}$?
23 The vertical line that is the locus of $x = \sqrt{3}$ intersects the circle for $x^2 + y^2 = 4$ in how many points?
24 Is $\{(x, y) \mid x^2 + y^2 = 4\}$ a function? How do you know?
25 Explain why $\{x \mid -2 \leqq x \leqq 2\}$ is the domain of $\{(x, y) \mid x^2 + y^2 = 4\}$.
26 Name the closed interval that is the range of $\{(x, y) \mid x^2 + y^2 = 4\}$.
27 Name the limits of the interval that is the range of $\{(x, y) \mid x^2 + y^2 = 4\}$.

Use the graph in D7 in connection with exercises 28 through 35. The semicircle represented in D7 is the locus of $y = \sqrt{4 - x^2}$.
28 Give the coördinates of points R, S, and T, represented in D7.
29 Express three statements to show that the coördinates of points R, S, and T are members of $\{(x, y) \mid y = \sqrt{4 - x^2}\}$.
30 What replacement for y do you obtain when you replace x in $y = \sqrt{4 - x^2}$ by 0? Remember that the symbol $\sqrt{4 - x^2}$ refers only to the principal square root.
31 In how many points does the locus of $x = 0$ intersect the semicircle?
32 What y do you obtain when you replace x in $y = \sqrt{4 - x^2}$ by $\sqrt{3}$?
33 In how many points does the locus of $x = \sqrt{3}$ intersect the semicircle?
34 Is $\{(x, y) \mid y = \sqrt{4 - x^2}\}$ a function?
35 What closed interval is the domain of $\{(x, y) \mid y = \sqrt{4 - x^2}\}$? What is the range?

KEEPING SKILLFUL

For each of exercises 1 through 12, find the quotient of the numbers named. The first number named is the dividend.

1 $300\frac{1}{4}, -5\frac{1}{2}$
2 $-.019, .125$
3 $54485, 85$
4 $-16\frac{1}{3}, -7$
5 $-1716, 132$
6 $250, 6\frac{1}{4}$
7 $-149.38, -271.6$
8 $12\frac{3}{5}, -4\frac{1}{5}$
9 $-\frac{8}{9}, -4\frac{1}{2}$
10 $-135, .65$ (Hundredths)
11 $75.6, 60.4$ (Tenths)
12 $-132.9, -.82$ (Tenths)

For each of exercises 13 through 18, find the quotient.

13 $\dfrac{16a^2b^4}{3x^2y^2} \div \dfrac{8ab}{3x^2y}$
14 $\dfrac{144ay^3z^4}{3d^2e^4} \div \dfrac{12y^2z^2}{9d^2e}$
15 $\dfrac{3x - 15}{4} \div \dfrac{x - 5}{2}$
16 $\dfrac{a^4b^2}{2b + 14} \div \dfrac{ab}{2}$
17 $(2x^3 - 13x^2 - 12x + 35) \div (x - 7)$
18 $(3y^4 - 9y^3 + 7y^2 - 17y + 30) \div (y - 2)$

22 268 **Exploring ideas**

Functional notation

It is customary in mathematics to use a special kind of notation in connection with functions. The purpose of the special notation is to emphasize the fact that a function is a relation in which exactly one element of the range corresponds to each element of the domain.

A Look at the tabulation in D1. Notice the letter that has been used to name the set of (x, y). How do you know that set f is a function?

From now on, we will use small letters, such as "f" and "g," to name sets that are functions.

B Tabulate the domain of function f. Tabulate the range.

C What member of the range of function f corresponds to 1 in the domain?

The symbol at the right represents the member of the range of function f that corresponds to x in the domain. D2 shows how to read this symbol.

$$f(x)$$

D If you replace x by 1 in $f(x)$, you obtain $f(1)$. How do you know that $f(1)$ is equal to 5?

E Which range element is $f(3)$? Which range element is $f(4)$?

The element of the range of a function that corresponds to a given element of the domain is sometimes called the *image* of the domain element. Thus, in the function f, $f(x)$ is the image of x.

F Look again at D1. Which range element is the image of 1? Which range element is the image of 2?

$f = \{(1, 5), (2, 6), (3, 7), (4, 9)\}$.

D1

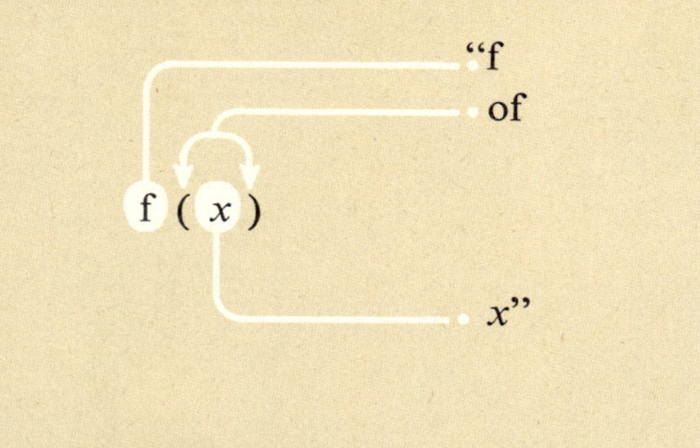

D2

$S = \{2, 3, 4\}$. $T = \{4, 6, 8, 10\}$.

A $b = 2a$.

$g = \{(a, b) \mid b = 2a\}$.

D3

Since $f(x)$ is the image of x, you may use the symbol at the right for each ordered pair in function f. When you use the symbol $(x, f(x))$, rather than the symbol (x, y), you are using *functional notation*.

$$(x, f(x))$$

Next you will see how functional notation is used in connection with conditions.

G Look at D3, in which sets S and T are tabulated. $S \times T$ is the universe for (a, b) in condition A. Tabulate the relation in $S \times T$ that is determined by condition A. Then tabulate the domain and the range of the relation.

H How do you know that $\{(a, b) \mid b = 2a\}$ is a function? In D3, what letter is used to name this function?

Because the second component of each (a, b) in function g is the range element that corresponds to an element a in the domain of function g, you can use the symbol at the right to express the second component. In other

$$g(a)$$

S = {2, 3, 4}. T = {4, 6, 8, 10}.

A $b = 2a$.

$g = \{(a, b) \mid b = 2a\}$.

D3

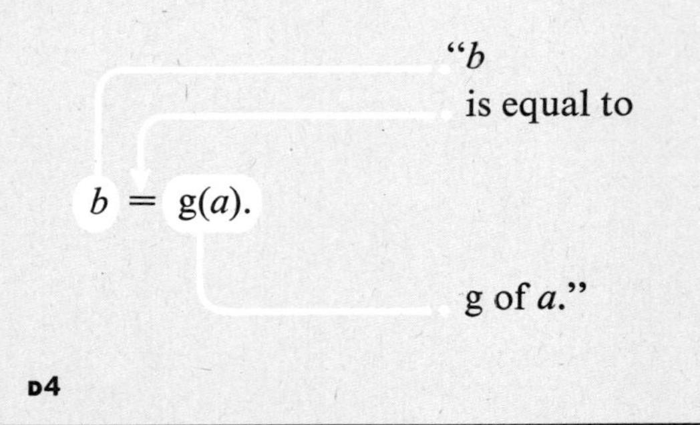

D4

S = {2, 3, 4}. T = {4, 6, 8, 10}.

B $g(a) = 2a$.

$g = \{(a, g(a)) \mid g(a) = 2a\}$.

D5

C $f(x) = 4x + 3$.

x	-4	-2	0	$\frac{1}{2}$	$7\frac{1}{2}$
$f(x)$					

D6

words, you can use this symbol to express the image of a. D4 shows how to write and read a sentence that contains this new symbol.

I Sets S and T are tabulated again in D5. How ? do you know that sentence B in D5 expresses the same condition as sentence A in D3?

J The universe for a in condition B is S. If you replace a by 2 in $g(a) = 2a$, you obtain $g(2) = 2 \cdot 2$. Which element of T is $g(2)$?

K How do you know that (2, 4) is an element of the solution set of condition B?

L What member of T is $g(3)$? What member of T is the image of 4?

M A standard description of the solution set of condition B is given in D5. Tabulate this set.

Functional notation is helpful when you need to find the elements of the range of a function. In the rest of this lesson, you will be given a condition and some of the domain elements for a function. Then you will find the corresponding range elements. In each case, you will use x as a variable for an element of the domain of a function.

A Look at D6. How do you know that the set ? of real numbers is the domain of the function determined by condition C?

B Some of the members of the domain are named in the chart in D6. Replace x by -4 in condition C. What is $f(-4)$? Copy and complete the chart in D6. To do this, you must find $f(-2)$, $f(0)$, $f(\frac{1}{2})$, and $f(7\frac{1}{2})$.

C Is each number given in the second row of your chart an element in the range of the function determined by $f(x) = 4x + 3$? Are there any other elements in the range of the function? Explain your answers.

D What set is the range of the function determined by $f(x) = 4x + 3$?

E What members of function f can you obtain from your chart?

F Now look at D7. What is the domain of the function determined by condition D?

G Is each number given in the top row of the chart in D7 an element of the domain of the function determined by condition D?

H Replace x by -5 in condition D. What is $g(-5)$? Copy and complete the chart in D7.

I Tabulate the set of range elements that you can obtain from your chart.

J Does the set that you tabulated for exercise I contain every element of the range of the function determined by condition D? Explain your answer.

D $g(x) = x^2 + 7x + 3.$

x	-5	-3	$\frac{1}{4}$	1	$1\frac{1}{2}$
$g(x)$					

D7

E $h(x) = \dfrac{x+2}{x-2}.$

D8

F $y = x^2 + 5x + 6.$

x	-3	$-\frac{2}{5}$	0	15	100
y					

D9

K Tabulate the set of elements of function g that you can obtain from your chart. How do you know that the set you just tabulated does not contain every element of the function determined by $g(x) = x^2 + 7x + 3$?

L Look at D8. What real number is not a meaningful replacement for x in $\dfrac{x+2}{x-2}$? Describe the domain of the function determined by condition E.

M Make and complete a chart for condition E. As replacements for x, use only the integers $-4, -3, -2, 0$, and 1.

N Tabulate the set of range elements that you can obtain from the chart you just made.

O Tabulate the set of elements of function h that you can obtain from your chart.

P Look at D9. What is the set of meaningful replacements for x in $x^2 + 5x + 6$? What is the domain of the function determined by condition F?

Q Suppose that function f is the name of the function determined by $y = x^2 + 5x + 6$. Use functional notation to express the condition that determines function f.

R Copy and complete the chart in D9. Notice that the second row of the chart is labeled with the letter y. Could you also label this row with the symbol $f(x)$?

In this lesson you learned how to use functional notation to express elements of a function. You also learned how to use functional notation to express a condition that determines a function.

On your own

A condition that determines a function is expressed in each of exercises 1 through 9. In each case, a finite domain is also given. First tabulate the range of each function. Then tabulate the function.

1 $f(a) = 3a^2$. Domain $= \{-\frac{1}{2}, -\frac{1}{3}, 1\frac{1}{2}, 3\}$.

2 $h(x) = 4x^2 - 3$. Domain $= \{-2, 0, \frac{1}{2}\}$.

3 $g(a) = a^2 - 2$. Domain $= \{-2, 1, 1\frac{1}{4}, 3\}$.

4 $h(x) = x^2 - x - 12$. Domain $= \{-1, 3\}$.

5 $f(y) = y^2 + 5y + 6$. Domain $= \{-4, 6\}$.

6 $g(x) = \dfrac{x^2 - 4}{x + 3}$. Domain $= \{-2, 0, 1\}$.

7 $f(x) = \dfrac{6x^2 - x - 3}{x}$. Domain $= \{-\frac{1}{2}, \frac{1}{2}\}$.

8 $g(y) = y^2 + 3y - 4$. Domain $= \{-\frac{1}{4}, 2\}$.

9 $h(x) = 3x + 4$. Domain $= \{-2\frac{1}{3}, 0, \frac{5}{6}\}$.

A condition that determines a function is expressed in each of exercises 10 through 15. The domain of each function is the set of real numbers that are meaningful replacements for x. Describe the domain. Then find four elements of the function.

10 $y = 2x^2 + 8x + 3$.

11 $f(x) = \dfrac{x+2}{x-5}$.

12 $g(x) = \dfrac{x^2 + 2x + 1}{x + 3}$.

13 $h(x) = \dfrac{4x - 3}{x}$.

14 $y = \dfrac{x+2}{x^2 - 1}$.

15 $y = \dfrac{x+1}{x^2}$.

SPECIAL CHALLENGE

If a, b, and c are integers such that $a = bc$, then b divides a and c divides a. The statement "b divides a" can be expressed by the symbol at the right. To illustrate, you know that $35 = 5 \times 7$. Hence, you know that $5 \mid 35$ and $7 \mid 35$. Likewise, $8 \mid 72$ means that there is an integer a such that $72 = 8a$. In this case, a is 9 because $72 = 8 \times 9$.

$$b \mid a.$$

For any two positive integers a and b where $b < a$, you can always find a positive integer n and a non-negative integer c such that $c < b$ and $a - nb = c$. Suppose that you replace b by 16 and a by 53. Then $53 - 3(16) = 5$. In this case, $n = 3$ and $c = 5$. Notice that $16 < 53$ and $5 < 16$.

A Show that, if $a - nb = c$, any common divisor of a and b is also a common divisor of b and c.

B How can you obtain $a = c + nb$ from $a - nb = c$?

C Show that, if $a - nb = c$, any common divisor of b and c is also a common divisor of a and b.

Exercises A, B, and C illustrate the theorem expressed below.

The universe for a, b, c, *and* n *is I. For each* a, b, c, *and* n, *if* a − nb = c, *then the greatest common divisor of* a *and* b *is the greatest common divisor of* b *and* c.

D Suppose that you want to find the greatest common divisor of 4991 and 899. Look at D1. According to statement A, what two integers have the same greatest common divisor as 4991 and 899?

The problem is simplified to one of finding the greatest common divisor of 899 and 496.

E According to statement B, what two integers have the same greatest common divisor as 899 and 496? How does statement B simplify the problem?

From statements A and B, you know that the greatest common divisor of 4991 and 899 is the same as the greatest common divisor of 496 and 403.

F How do statements C and D simplify the problem?

G Now study statement E. What is the greatest common divisor of 93 and 31? Of 4991 and 899?

The method of finding the greatest common divisor that is illustrated in D1 is based on a method credited to the Greek mathematician Euclid, who lived in the fourth century B.C.

H Study D2. What conclusion can you draw concerning the integers 473 and 149? Explain your answer.

Find the greatest common divisor of each pair of integers expressed below.

I 63, 91

J 152, 429

K 6006, 561

L 94829, 283679

M 8833404, 310503

N 173173, 91091

A $4991 - 5(899) = 496.$
B $899 - 1(496) = 403.$
C $496 - 1(403) = 93.$
D $403 - 4(93) = 31.$
E $93 - 3(31) = 0.$

D1

F $473 - 3(149) = 26.$
G $149 - 5(26) = 19.$
H $26 - 1(19) = 7.$
I $19 - 2(7) = 5.$
J $7 - 1(5) = 2.$
K $5 - 2(2) = 1.$

D2

APPLYING MATHEMATICS

For each problem, first write a sentence that expresses a condition involving one variable. Then give the answer to the problem.

1 When Mrs. Wilson moved, she sold her sofa for \$162, or $\frac{1}{3}$ less than she had paid for it. How much had she paid for the sofa?

2 Mr. Jamison invested \$1280 in two companies. One investment paid $3\frac{1}{2}\%$ interest; the other investment paid 4% interest. After three years, the total interest that he received was \$145.80. How much did Mr. Jamison invest at each rate?

3 Mrs. Taylor is 4 times as old as her daughter. In 20 years, Mrs. Taylor will be only twice as old as her daughter. How old are Mrs. Taylor and her daughter at the present time?

4 A confectioner wishes to make up 2-pound boxes of candy to sell for \$1.40 per box. He is going to mix candy that sells for \$.80 per pound with candy that sells for \$.40 per pound. How many pounds of each kind of candy must he use for 100 boxes of the mixture?

5 $\triangle JKL$ is isosceles. The length of each of the two congruent sides is 5 in. greater than 2 times the length of the third side. The perimeter of $\triangle JKL$ is 40 in. What is the length of each side of $\triangle JKL$ in inches?

6 In $\triangle ABC$, $\angle A^\circ$ is 6 greater than $\frac{1}{2}$ of $\angle B^\circ$. The measure of $\angle C$ is 15 less than twice $\angle B^\circ$. What is the measure of each angle of $\triangle ABC$ in degrees?

7 A freight train, traveling 35 mi. per hour, left Kansas City at 2:30 P.M. A passenger train left the same station 2 hr. later, traveling 50 mi. per hour in the same direction as the freight train. In how many hours should the passenger train have overtaken the freight train?

8 Mr. Stein invested part of \$1600 at 4% and the remainder at 8%. His income from the investments for the first year was exactly as much as he would have received if he had invested the entire amount at 7%. How much did he invest at 4%?

9 John has \$4.15 in nickels, dimes, and quarters. The number of quarters is 3 greater than $\frac{1}{3}$ the number of dimes. The value of the nickels is the same as the value of the dimes. How many of each kind of coin does John have?

10 Miss Green received a 15% cash discount on a television set. If she paid less than \$150 for the set, what was the selling price of the television set?

11 A chemist has 20 liters of a solution that is 30% alcohol. How many liters of pure alcohol must he add to the solution to obtain a solution that is 50% alcohol?

12 A goldsmith has one alloy that is 84% pure gold and another alloy that is 60% pure gold. How many grains of each alloy must he use to make 180 grains of an alloy that is 68% pure gold?

13 One morning Bob set out for a beach that is 12 mi. from his home and arrived $1\frac{3}{5}$ hr. later. He walked part of the way and got a ride for the rest of the way. If he walked at a rate of 3 mi. per hour and rode at a rate of 30 mi. per hour, how many miles did he walk?

14 A rectangle whose length is 6 ft. greater than its width has a perimeter of $38\frac{1}{2}$ ft. What are the length and the width of the rectangle in feet?

15 If 3 is subtracted from 5 times the absolute value of a number, the result is greater than 43. What is the number?

16 If 29 is added to $\frac{1}{5}$ of a given number, the sum is less than the difference of the additive inverse of the given number and 15. What is the given number?

CHECKING UP

If you have trouble with this test, you can find help in lessons 265 through 268.

Test 249

1 C = {1, 3, 5} and D = {4, 6}. Tabulate D × C.

2 Set K has 23 members. Set L has 15 members. How many members are in the Cartesian set K × L?

3 The relation M is a subset of G × H. Of which set is the domain of M a subset?

4 What components of the members of a relation make up the range of the relation?

5 How many members of $\{(x, y) \mid y = 3x^2\}$ have 2750 as a first component?

6 F = {7, 13, 19}. Tabulate $\{(x, y) \mid x \neq y\}$ when the universe for (x, y) is F × F.

7 Tabulate the domain of the following relation: {(1, 5), (4, 3), (1, 3), (2, 5)}.

8 $f(x) = 2x^2 + 3x - 5$. What is $f(-3)$?

9 Function f has 25 members. How many members are in the domain of function f?

10 $g(x) = 7x + 4$. What member of function g has a first component of 2?

11 What geometric figure is the locus of $\{(x, y) \mid x = 5\}$?

12 Make a graph of $\{(x, y) \mid 8 - y < 2x\}$.

13 M = {3, 7, 9}. Tabulate $\{(x, y) \mid x < y\}$ when the universe for (x, y) is M × M.

14 Q = {1, 2, 3, . . ., 10}. Tabulate the range of the relation determined by $2y < x + 5$ when the universe for (x, y) is Q × Q.

15 Give a standard description of the domain of $\{(x, y) \mid x^2 + y^2 = 9\}$.

16 Describe the domain of $\left\{(x, y) \mid y = \frac{7}{x}\right\}$.

17 Function g has 10 members. How many members are in the range of function g?

18 Function h is determined by $h(x) = x$. What is the image of 7 in function h?

22 | 269 Exploring ideas

Functions involving direct variation

In *Book 2* you studied the relations determined by $y = kx$ and $y = kx^2$. In this lesson you will learn that these relations are functions.

A Look at D1. What is the domain of the set of (x, y) that is determined by condition A? What is the range? How do you know that this set of (x, y) is a function?

B Does condition B determine a function? Does condition C determine a function?

C By what number can you replace k in $y = kx$ to obtain each of conditions A, B, and C?

D ? How do you know that, if you replace k by 0 in $y = kx$, you obtain a condition that determines a function? What are the domain and the range of this function?

E ? How do you know that, for each non-zero k, $y = kx$ determines a function? What are the domain and the range of this function?

Notice that the rôle played by the variable k in $y = kx$ is somewhat different from the rôle played by x and y. As you know, x and y are variables for the members of the domain and the range of the function determined by $y = kx$. Each (x, y) that satisfies $y = kx$ is a member of the function. We make replacements for k, however, to obtain specific conditions, each of which determines a specific function. Thus, from a given universe for k, we make replacements for k in $y = kx$ *before* we make replacements for x and y. We can then find the ordered pairs that satisfy the resulting condition.

A $y = 3x$. **D** $f(x) = 3x$.
B $y = \frac{1}{2}x$. **E** $f(x) = \frac{1}{2}x$.
C $y = -7x$. **F** $f(x) = -7x$.

D1

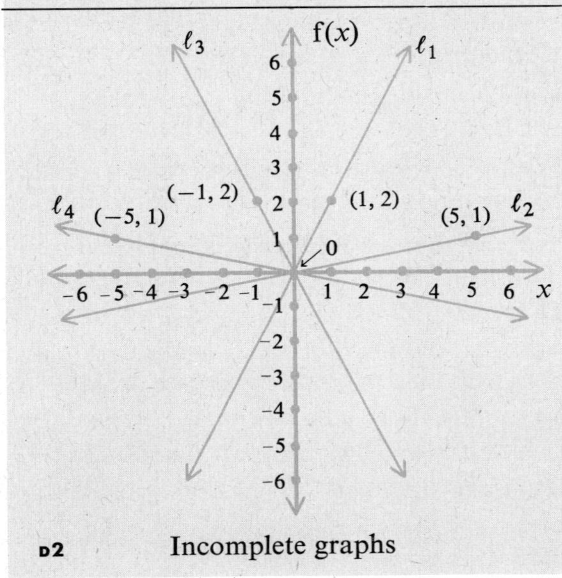

D2 Incomplete graphs

A variable like k in $y = kx$ is called a *parameter* (pə ram′ə tər). Replacements for parameters are made first. Each such replacement enables us to obtain one member of a *family of conditions*.

F Look again at D1. Which condition that is expressed in functional notation determines the same function as condition A? As condition B? As condition C?

G In $f(x) = kx$, the parameter is k. By what number can you replace the parameter to obtain each of conditions D, E, and F?

H In $\{(x, f(x)) \mid f(x) = 3x\}$, the second component of each member is the product of what number and the first component? How are the components of each member of the solution set of $f(x) = \frac{1}{2}x$ related? How are the components of each member of the solution set of $f(x) = -7x$ related?

I How are the components of each member of $\{(x, f(x)) \mid f(x) = kx\}$ related?

In each solution of a condition of the form $f(x) = kx$, $f(x)$ is equal to the product of k and x. We therefore say that $f(x)$ varies directly as x varies. The parameter in $f(x) = kx$ is the variable for the constant of variation. A condition of the form $f(x) = kx$ is a condition for direct variation.

J Can you use (x, kx), as well as $(x, f(x))$, to represent each member of the function determined by $f(x) = kx$? Explain your answer.

K What condition for direct variation determines a function each of whose members can be represented by $(x, 25x)$? By $(x, -\sqrt{6}x)$? Use functional notation in your answers.

In *Book 2* you learned that the locus of the set of (x, y) that satisfy $y = kx$ is a line that contains the origin. Since $f(x) = kx$ is essentially the same condition as $y = kx$, the locus of a set of $(x, f(x))$ likewise is a line that contains the origin. Now you will see how changing the replacement for the parameter affects the locus of $f(x) = kx$. By the "locus of $f(x) = kx$," we mean the locus of the function determined by the condition.

A What condition do you obtain when you replace the parameter in $f(x) = kx$ by 2?

B How do you know that point (0, 0) is in the locus of $f(x) = 2x$? What point in the locus has 1 as a first coördinate?

You know that the function determined by a condition of the form $f(x) = kx$ is a set of $(x, f(x))$. It is convenient, therefore, to consider the y-axis as the $f(x)$-axis when you locate the points in the locus of such a function. Notice that the axes represented in D2 are named x and $f(x)$.

C How do you know that ℓ_1, represented in D2, is the locus of $f(x) = 2x$?

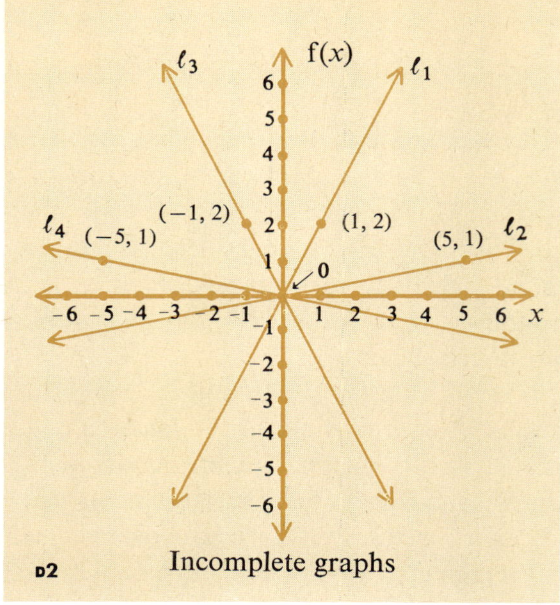

Incomplete graphs

D What condition do you obtain when you replace the parameter in $f(x) = kx$ by $\frac{1}{5}$? Explain why ℓ_2 is the locus of this condition.

E What is the intersection of the locus of $f(x) = 2x$ and the locus of $f(x) = \frac{1}{5}x$?

F Which quadrants contain points in ℓ_1? Which quadrants contain points in ℓ_2?

G ? How do you know that, if $k > 0$, only the first and third quadrants contain points in the locus of $f(x) = kx$?

H In ℓ_1, what are the second coördinates of points whose first coördinates are 2, 3, and 5, respectively?

I In ℓ_2, what are the second coördinates of points whose first coördinates are 2, 3, and 5?

J In both ℓ_1 and ℓ_2, as x increases, does $f(x)$ increase?

K Which line, ℓ_1 or ℓ_2, slants up more "steeply" from left to right?

L Suppose that k in $f(x) = kx$ is replaced by a number greater than $\frac{1}{5}$, but less than 2. Compare the locus of this condition with ℓ_1 and ℓ_2.

M Now suppose that you replace the parameter in $f(x) = kx$ by -2. Which line represented in D2 is the locus of $f(x) = -2x$?

N How do you know that ℓ_4 is the locus of $f(x) = -\frac{1}{5}x$? By what number was the parameter replaced to obtain $f(x) = -\frac{1}{5}x$?

O Which quadrants contain points in ℓ_3 and ℓ_4?

P ? How do you know that, if $k < 0$, only the second and fourth quadrants contain points in the locus of $f(x) = kx$?

Q In ℓ_3, what are the second coördinates of the points whose first coördinates are -3, -2, and -1?

R In ℓ_4, what are the second coördinates of the points whose first coördinates are -3, -2, and -1?

S Both ℓ_3 and ℓ_4 slant down from left to right. Which line slants down more steeply?

T ? Suppose that k in $f(x) = kx$ is replaced by a number greater than -2, but less than $-\frac{1}{5}$. Compare the locus of this condition with ℓ_3 and ℓ_4.

Next you will consider relations that are determined by conditions of the form $y = kx^2$.

A ? Look at D3. What are the domain and the range of the set of (x, y) determined by condition G? How do you know that this set of (x, y) is a function?

B How do you know that condition H determines a function? That condition I determines a function? What are the domain and the range of each of these functions?

C By what number can you replace k in $y = kx^2$ to obtain each of conditions G, H, and I?

D Look again at D3. Notice that conditions J, K, and L are each of the form $g(x) = kx^2$. Which of these conditions determines the same function as condition G? As condition H? As condition I?

In $g(x) = kx^2$, the variable k is the parameter. In the remaining exercises, we will not

G $y = 2x^2$.

H $y = \frac{1}{4}x^2$.

I $y = -3x^2$.

J $g(x) = 2x^2$.

K $g(x) = \frac{1}{4}x^2$.

L $g(x) = -3x^2$.

D3

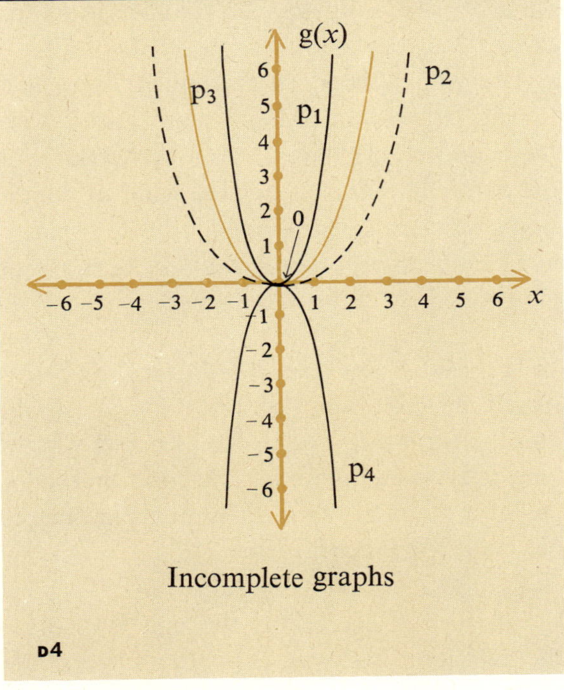

Incomplete graphs

D4

consider the function determined by $g(x) = kx^2$ when $k = 0$. The set of non-zero real numbers is the universe for the parameter.

E How do you know that $(-2, 8)$, $(1, 2)$, $(3, 18)$, and $(4, 32)$ are solutions of condition J? For each of these ordered pairs, by what number can you multiply the first component to obtain the second component?

F How do you know that $g(x)$ in $g(x) = 2x^2$ does not vary directly as x varies?

G For each ordered pair that satisfies $g(x) = kx^2$, how is the second component related to the square of the first component?

In each solution of a condition of the form $g(x) = kx^2$, $g(x)$ is equal to the product of k and x^2. We say, therefore, that $g(x)$ varies directly as x^2 varies. The parameter is the variable for the constant of variation.

H Why can you use (x, kx^2) to represent each member of the function determined by the condition $g(x) = kx^2$? What condition determines a function whose members can be represented by $(x, \frac{3}{4}x^2)$? By $(x, -.8x^2)$? By $(x, \pi x^2)$?

I If k is positive, what are the domain and the range of the function determined by $g(x) = kx^2$? If k is negative, what are the domain and the range of the function?

Earlier in this lesson you learned that $f(x) = kx$ produces a family of conditions, each of which has as its locus a line containing the origin. Now you will study the *loci* (lō′sī) of the conditions in the family produced by $g(x) = kx^2$.

In *Book 2* you learned that the locus of a condition of the form $y = kx^2$ is a parabola that contains the origin. A condition of the form $g(x) = kx^2$ has the same locus. For example, parabola p_1, represented in D4, is the locus of $g(x) = 2x^2$. Parabola p_2 is the locus of $g(x) = \frac{1}{4}x^2$.

A What is the intersection of the loci represented in D4? How do you know that the intersection of two or more different loci of conditions of the form $g(x) = kx^2$ is the set containing point $(0, 0)$?

B Remember that p_1 is the locus of $g(x) = 2x^2$. In p_1, what are the second coördinates of the points whose first coördinates are 1, 2, and 3? If the first coördinate is positive and increases, does the second coördinate increase?

C For each $x > 0$, the points in the locus of $g(x) = 2x^2$ are contained in which quadrant? For each $x < 0$, the points in the locus of $g(x) = 2x^2$ are contained in which quadrant?

D For each point in the locus of $g(x) = 2x^2$, if the first coördinate is positive, what do you

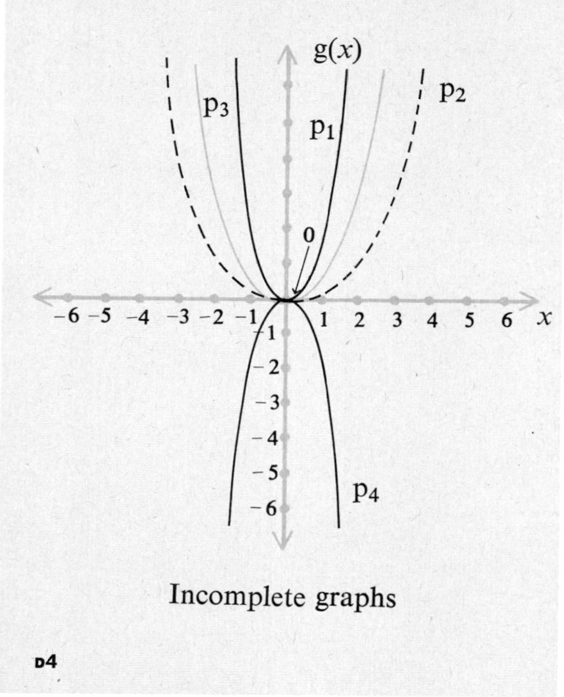

Incomplete graphs

know about the second coördinate? If the first coördinate is negative, what do you know about the second coördinate?

E How do you know that, if $k > 0$, only the first and second quadrants can contain points in the locus of $g(x) = kx^2$?

F If a point in p_1 and a point in p_2 have the same first coördinate, which point has the greater second coördinate?

G Look again at D4. Which parabola "opens wider," the one associated with $g(x) = 2x^2$ or the one associated with $g(x) = \frac{1}{4}x^2$?

H Parabola p_3 is also the locus of a condition of the form $g(x) = kx^2$. How does the constant of variation in the condition for p_3 compare with the constants of variation in $g(x) = \frac{1}{4}x^2$ and $g(x) = 2x^2$?

I Parabola p_4 is the locus of $g(x) = -2x^2$. For each point whose x-coördinate is positive, what do you know about the $g(x)$-coördinate? For each point whose x-coördinate is negative, describe the $g(x)$-coördinate.

J How do you know that, if $k < 0$, only the third and fourth quadrants can contain points in the locus of $g(x) = kx^2$?

K For each replacement of x, is $-2x^2$ the additive inverse of $2x^2$? How does the absolute value of $-2x^2$ compare with the absolute value of $2x^2$?

L Use your answers to exercise K to explain why the parabola that is associated with the condition $g(x) = -2x^2$ is a "reflection" of the parabola that is associated with the condition $g(x) = 2x^2$.

M Describe the parabola that is the locus of $g(x) = -\frac{1}{4}x^2$.

In this lesson you considered functions determined by conditions of the form $f(x) = kx$ and the form $g(x) = kx^2$. You learned what a parameter is and observed the effect on the locus of a function when different replacements are made for the parameter.

On your own

For each of exercises 1 through 5, tabulate the relation that you can obtain from the chart. Use the numbers given in the first row as first components. Then decide which kind of condition determines the relation, $f(x) = kx$ or $f(x) = kx^2$.

1

Measure of side of square	1	17	23	49
Area	1	289	529	2401

2

Number of tickets	2	3	6	10
Cost of tickets	4.50	6.75	13.50	22.50

3

Measure of side of square	$1\frac{1}{2}$	$2\frac{1}{4}$	3	$5\frac{1}{3}$
Perimeter	6	9	12	$21\frac{1}{3}$

4

Time an object falls, in seconds	1	$3\frac{1}{2}$	7	10
Distance traveled, in feet	16	196	784	1600

5

Distance a spring is stretched	$\frac{1}{2}$	$\frac{3}{4}$	1	$1\frac{1}{2}$
Force on spring	$\frac{1}{4}$	$\frac{9}{16}$	1	$2\frac{1}{4}$

For each of exercises 6 through 13, the ordered pairs given satisfy either a condition of the form $f(x) = kx$ or of the form $f(x) = kx^2$. Write a sentence that expresses the appropriate condition.

6 $(0, 0), (-4, -6), (8, 12), (5, 7\frac{1}{2})$
7 $(-3, 36), (0, 0), (10, 400), (6, 144)$
8 $(2, -32), (1, -8), (5, -200), (8, -512), (-10, -800)$
9 $(0, 0), (-13, 169), (20, -260), (5, -65)$
10 $(-5, -125), (4, -80), (-11, -605), (-3, -45)$
11 $(-6, -126), (20, 420), (-3, -63), (12, 252)$
12 $(3, -3), (-1, -\frac{1}{3}), (-9, -27), (5, -8\frac{1}{3})$
13 $(\sqrt{5}, -\sqrt{5}), (0, 0), (-.7, .7), (-2.6, 2.6)$

For each of exercises 14 through 17, copy and complete the chart. Then make a graph of the locus of the condition.

14

$f(x) = 10x.$					
x	-3	-1	0	1	3
$f(x)$					

15

$f(x) = -4x.$					
x	-4	-2	0	2	4
$f(x)$					

16

$g(x) = 7x^2.$					
x	-2	-1	0	1	2
$g(x)$					

17

$f(x) = -3x^2.$					
x	-2	-1	0	1	2
$f(x)$					

KEEPING SKILLFUL

For each of exercises 1 through 12, find the sum of the numbers named.

1 $69.72, -85.8$
2 $12\frac{1}{2}, 16\frac{7}{20}$
3 $750, -400, 321$
4 $-25\frac{3}{4}, -17\frac{8}{9}$
5 $800.65, 70.5$
6 $-72\frac{7}{10}, 84\frac{8}{15}$
7 $-.16, -.795, 12.2$
8 $34\frac{3}{4}, 17\frac{1}{2}, 8\frac{9}{10}$
9 $172, 250.5, -17.6$
10 $-725, -810, -16$
11 $25\frac{1}{4}, -125\frac{1}{3}, 16\frac{7}{8}$
12 $-13.4, 19.75, -65.8$

Find the difference of the numbers named in each of exercises 13 through 24. The first number named is the minuend.

13 $820.1, 65.7$
14 $-620, 75\frac{1}{2}$
15 $16\frac{1}{2}, -4\frac{3}{4}$
16 $-85.75, -16.7$
17 $8000, 9200$
18 $-\frac{3}{10}, \frac{7}{50}$
19 $-500.7, -250.1$
20 $65\frac{7}{8}, -12\frac{3}{25}$
21 $780.1, 62.7$
22 $-69\frac{1}{3}, -72$
23 $24.72, -85.6$
24 $-600\frac{1}{2}, 72\frac{9}{10}$

Find the product of the numbers named in each of exercises 25 through 36.

25 $-15\frac{5}{8}, -2\frac{3}{50}$
26 $-780, .875$
27 $18\frac{3}{4}, 3\frac{3}{5}$
28 $12.2, -79.8$
29 $-24\frac{7}{8}, 5\frac{1}{3}$
30 $-124.5, -.63$
31 $25\frac{3}{4}, -3\frac{1}{5}$
32 $69.42, 50.5$
33 $-700, 8\frac{3}{4}$
34 $12.7, -6.5, -.7$
35 $\frac{3}{4}, -1\frac{1}{2}, 6\frac{2}{3}$
36 $-.85, -.6, -1.7$

Find the quotient of the numbers named in each of exercises 37 through 48. The first number named is the dividend.

37 $-95, 4\frac{3}{4}$
38 $67\frac{1}{3}, -18\frac{2}{3}$
39 $-24, -600$
40 $\frac{1}{6}, 10\frac{3}{4}$
41 $3302, -254$
42 $-14\frac{2}{3}, 6\frac{3}{5}$
43 $-15\frac{7}{8}, -2\frac{1}{4}$
44 $.1515, 1.5$
45 $.7553, .91$
46 $785.3, 72$ (Tenths)
47 $-2575, 35$ (Ones)
48 $-250.4, -.65$ (Tenths)

A $f(x) = \frac{k}{x}$.

B $f(x) = \frac{30}{x}$.

C $f(x) = 30\left(\frac{1}{x}\right)$.

D1

22 **270** Exploring ideas

Functions involving inverse variation

In the preceding lesson you discovered that the relations determined by $y = kx$ and $y = kx^2$ are functions. In this lesson you will see that $y = \frac{k}{x}$ and $y = \frac{k}{x^2}$ also determine functions. We will not consider the cases in which $k = 0$.

A Suppose that we replace k in $y = \frac{k}{x}$ by 3. What is the domain of $\left\{(x, y) \mid y = \frac{3}{x}\right\}$? What is the range of this relation? How do you know that this relation is a function?

B How can you obtain $y = \frac{-7}{x}$ from $y = \frac{k}{x}$? Explain why $y = \frac{-7}{x}$ determines a set of (x, y) that is a function.

C For each non-zero k, $\left\{(x, y) \mid y = \frac{k}{x}\right\}$ is a function. Suppose that we use the letter "f" to name the function determined by $y = \frac{k}{x}$. Use functional notation in a standard description of function f.

D Now look at D1. In condition A, which variable is the parameter? How was condition B obtained from A? Now replace x in condition B by -6, -5, 2, 3, and 10. Determine $f(x)$ for each of these replacements.

E Tabulate the subset of function f whose members have first components of -6, -5, 2, 3, and 10.

F Why can condition B also be expressed by sentence C in D1?

G Think about the set that you tabulated for exercise E. By what number can you multiply the reciprocal of each first component to obtain the second component?

H Think about the set of $(x, f(x))$ that satisfy condition B. By what number can you multiply the reciprocal of each first component to obtain the second component?

I For each member of $\left\{(x, f(x)) \mid f(x) = \frac{k}{x}\right\}$, how is the second component related to the reciprocal of the first component?

For each $(x, f(x))$ that satisfies $f(x) = \frac{k}{x}$, $f(x)$ is equal to the product of k and $\frac{1}{x}$. For this reason, we say that $f(x)$ varies directly as $\frac{1}{x}$ varies and the parameter k is a variable for the constant of variation.

Since $\frac{1}{x}$ is the reciprocal, or multiplicative inverse, of x, we can also say that $f(x)$ varies inversely as x. If, for each $(x, f(x))$ that satisfies a condition, $f(x)$ is the product of the constant of variation and $\frac{1}{x}$, then $f(x)$ varies inversely as x.

J ? Describe the domain and the range of a function determined by $f(x) = \frac{k}{x}$. Remember that the universe for the parameter is the set of non-zero real numbers.

K Look again at D1. If you replace x in condition B by successively greater positive numbers, does f(x) increase, or does it decrease?

L Now replace k in condition A by -16. What condition do you obtain? Think about the set of $(x, f(x))$ that satisfy $f(x) = \frac{-16}{x}$. By what number can you multiply the reciprocal of each first component to obtain the second component? Tabulate the set of members of $\left\{(x, f(x)) \mid f(x) = \frac{-16}{x}\right\}$ whose first components are -8, -4, 1, and 2.

From your work in *Book 2*, you will recall that the locus of $y = \frac{k}{x}$ is called a hyperbola. Hence, the locus of $f(x) = \frac{k}{x}$ is a hyperbola.

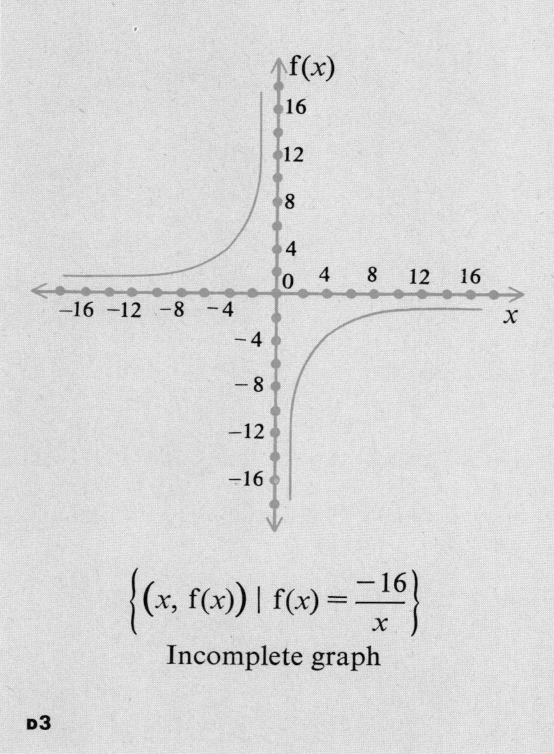

$\left\{(x, f(x)) \mid f(x) = \frac{-16}{x}\right\}$

Incomplete graph

D3

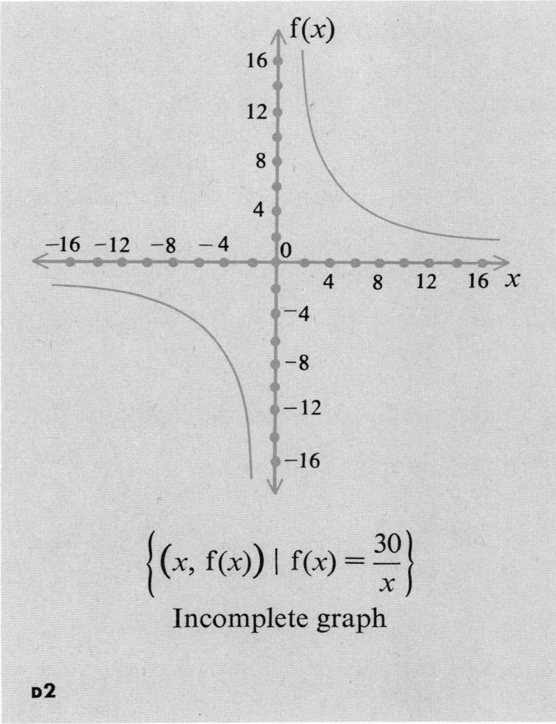

$\left\{(x, f(x)) \mid f(x) = \frac{30}{x}\right\}$

Incomplete graph

D2

M The locus of $f(x) = \frac{30}{x}$ is represented in D2. Which quadrant includes the part of the hyperbola that is associated with solutions whose components are both positive? Whose components are both negative?

N ? Why is the locus of $f(x) = \frac{k}{x}$, where $k > 0$, included in the first and third quadrants?

O How does the locus of $f(x) = \frac{30}{x}$ indicate what happens to f(x) as x is replaced by successively greater positive numbers?

P The graph in D3 represents the locus of $f(x) = \frac{-16}{x}$. For each positive replacement of x, is the corresponding f(x) a positive number, or is it a negative number? For each negative replacement of x, what can you say about the corresponding f(x)?

D $h(x) = \frac{k}{x^2}$.

E $h(x) = \frac{64}{x^2}$.

F $h(x) = \frac{-36}{x^2}$.

D4

Q Why is the locus of $f(x) = \frac{k}{x}$, where $k < 0$, included in the second and fourth quadrants?

R Does any point in the locus of $f(x) = \frac{k}{x}$ have zero as one of its coördinates? Explain your answer.

Next we will consider the set of (x, y) that is determined by $y = \frac{k}{x^2}$.

A How can you obtain $y = \frac{4}{x^2}$ from $y = \frac{k}{x^2}$? What is the domain of $\left\{(x, y) \mid y = \frac{4}{x^2}\right\}$? What is the range? Is the set a function?

B How can you obtain $y = \frac{-5}{x^2}$ from $y = \frac{k}{x^2}$? What is the domain of $\left\{(x, y) \mid y = \frac{-5}{x^2}\right\}$? What is the range? Is the set a function?

C For each non-zero k, $\left\{(x, y) \mid y = \frac{k}{x^2}\right\}$ is a function. If you use the letter "h" to name this function, how can you use functional notation in a standard description of the function?

D Now look at D4. How was condition E obtained from condition D? Replace x in condition E by -4, -2, 1, and 8. For each of these replacements, determine $h(x)$.

E Which members of $\left\{(x, h(x)) \mid h(x) = \frac{64}{x^2}\right\}$ have -4, -2, 1, and 8 as first components?

F Why can condition E also be expressed by the sentence $h(x) = 64\left(\frac{1}{x^2}\right)$?

G Think about the ordered pairs you named for exercise E. By what number can you multiply the reciprocal of the square of -4 to obtain 4? By what number can you multiply the reciprocal of the square of 8 to obtain 1?

H For each member of $\left\{(x, h(x)) \mid h(x) = \frac{64}{x^2}\right\}$, is the second component equal to the product of 64 and the reciprocal of the square of the first component?

I For each member of $\left\{(x, h(x)) \mid h(x) = \frac{k}{x^2}\right\}$, how is the second component related to the reciprocal of the square of the first component?

For each $(x, h(x))$ that satisfies $h(x) = \frac{k}{x^2}$, $h(x)$ is equal to the product of k and $\frac{1}{x^2}$. This means that $h(x)$ varies directly as $\frac{1}{x^2}$ varies. Since $\frac{1}{x^2}$ is the multiplicative inverse of x^2, we also say that $h(x)$ varies inversely as x^2. The parameter k is a variable for the constant of variation.

J How do you know that the domain of a function determined by $h(x) = \frac{k}{x^2}$ is the set of non-zero real numbers?

K What is the range of the function determined by $h(x) = \frac{k}{x^2}$ when $k > 0$? What is the range of the function when $k < 0$?

L The locus of $h(x) = \frac{64}{x^2}$ is represented in D5. How do you know that the two-part curve does not contain any points in the x-axis or the $h(x)$-axis?

M Which quadrants include the locus of $h(x) = \frac{64}{x^2}$? When $k > 0$, why is the locus of $h(x) = \frac{k}{x^2}$ included in the first and second quadrants?

N Study the locus represented in D5. As x is replaced by successively greater positive numbers, what happens to $h(x)$?

O Look again at D4. In condition F, does $h(x)$ vary inversely as x^2? Describe the domain and the range of the function determined by F.

P The graph in D6 represents the locus of condition F. Which quadrants include the locus of this condition?

Q Explain why the locus of $h(x) = \frac{k}{x^2}$, when $k < 0$, is included in the third and fourth quadrants.

R Does any point in the locus of condition F have zero as its x-coördinate? As its $h(x)$-coördinate?

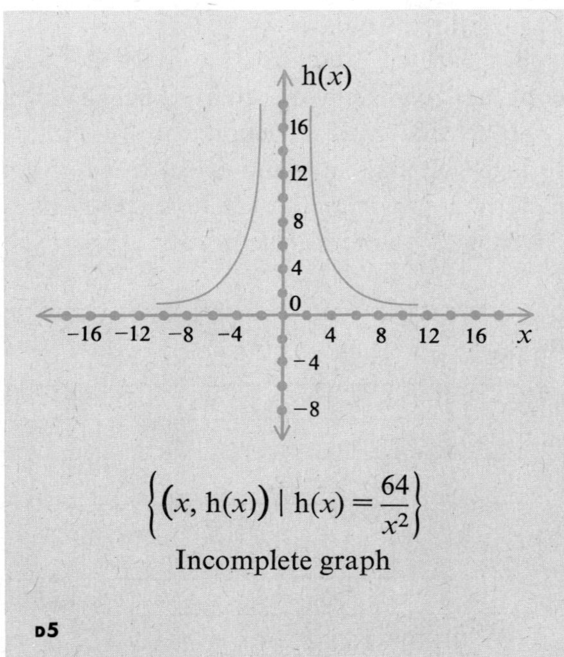

$\left\{(x, h(x)) \mid h(x) = \frac{64}{x^2}\right\}$

Incomplete graph

D5

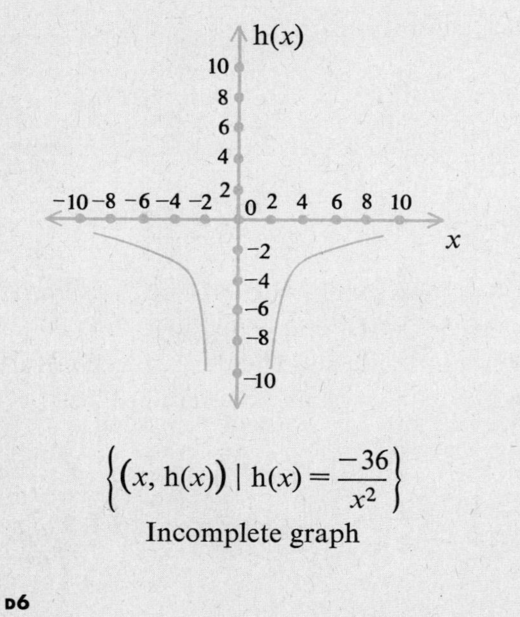

$\left\{(x, h(x)) \mid h(x) = \frac{-36}{x^2}\right\}$

Incomplete graph

D6

Actually, each function that we have considered in this lesson and in lesson 269 is determined by a condition of the form $f(x) = kx^n$.

S If $n = 1$, what is $f(x) = kx^n$? What geometric figure is the locus of $f(x) = kx$?

T If $n = 2$, what is $f(x) = kx^n$? What geometric figure is the locus of $f(x) = kx^2$?

U What geometric figure is the locus of $f(x) = kx^n$ when $n = -1$? If $n = -2$, how do you know that the locus of $f(x) = kx^n$ is a two-part curve?

In this lesson you considered functions determined by $f(x) = \frac{k}{x}$ and $f(x) = \frac{k}{x^2}$ and you studied the loci of these functions.

On your own

1 Which conditions expressed below are of the form $f(x) = \frac{k}{x}$?

$f(x) = -3x.$	$f(x) = x^{-1}.$
$f(x) = \frac{x}{4}.$	$f(x) = \frac{-2}{5x}.$

2 Which conditions expressed below are of the form $f(x) = \frac{k}{x^2}$?

$f(x) = -8\left(\frac{1}{x^2}\right)$. $\quad f(x) = \frac{1}{x^2}$.

$f(x) = x^2$. $\quad f(x) = \frac{2}{x}$.

For each condition expressed in exercises 3 through 10, first tell which quadrants contain points in the locus. Then tell how f(x) varies and give the constant of variation.

3 $f(x) = \frac{10}{x^2}$.

4 $f(x) = \frac{-4}{x}$.

5 $f(x) = -\frac{2}{7}x$.

6 $f(x) = \frac{3}{x}$.

7 $f(x) = \frac{-9}{x^2}$.

8 $f(x) = 14\left(\frac{1}{x^2}\right)$.

9 $f(x) = x^2$.

10 $f(x) = 6\left(\frac{1}{x}\right)$.

For each condition expressed in exercises 11 through 14, tell what geometric figure is its locus.

11 $g(x) = 2x^2$.

12 $f(x) = \frac{8}{x}$.

13 $h(x) = -5x$.

14 $g(x) = \frac{-7}{x}$.

For each of exercises 15 through 18, first tabulate the relation that you can obtain from the chart. Use the numbers expressed in the first row as first components. Then tell whether the relation is determined by a condition of the form $f(x) = \frac{k}{x}$ or a condition of the form $f(x) = \frac{k}{x^2}$.

15

Number of workers	1	2	3	4
Time required to complete a task	8	4	$2\frac{2}{3}$	2

16

Distance of screen from source of light	7.5	15	30	60
Measure of intensity of light on screen	80	20	5	1.25

17

Number of contributors to collection	4	6	8	10
Amount contributed per person	60	40	30	24

18

Pressure exerted on a gas	3	6	10	20
Volume of gas	40	20	12	6

For each of exercises 19 through 22, the given ordered pairs satisfy a condition of one of these forms: $f(x) = \frac{k}{x}$ or $f(x) = \frac{k}{x^2}$. Write a sentence that expresses the condition.

19 $(-10, 4), (8, -5), (2, -20), (-4, 10)$

20 $(12, 1), (6, 4), (3, 16), (9, 1\frac{7}{9})$

21 $(225, 4), (2, 450), (30, 30), (100, 9)$

22 $(4, 62), (124, 2), (10, 24.8), (-8, -31)$

For each of exercises 23 through 26, first copy and complete the chart. Then use the $(x, f(x))$ that you can obtain from your chart to help you make a graph of the locus of the condition. Use letters to label the points associated with the pairs given in your chart.

23 $f(x) = \frac{225}{x^2}$.

x	-15	-10	-5	-3	3	5	10	15
f(x)								

24

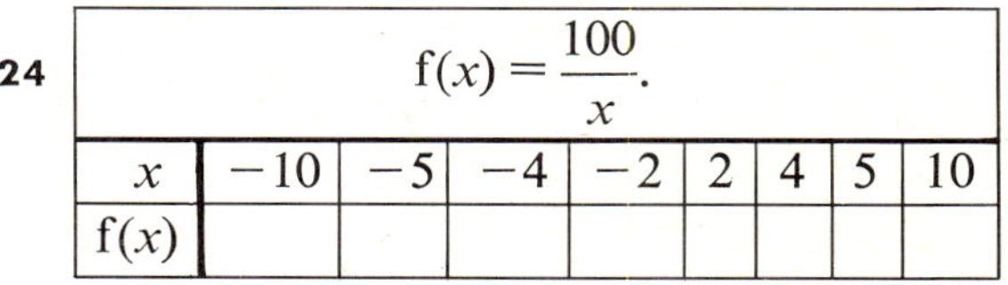

$f(x) = \frac{100}{x}$.

x	-10	-5	-4	-2	2	4	5	10
f(x)								

25

$f(x) = \frac{-144}{x^2}$.								
x	-6	-4	-3	-2	2	3	4	6
$f(x)$								

26

$f(x) = \frac{-132}{x}$.								
(x)	-6	-4	-3	-2	2	3	4	6
$f(x)$								

KEEPING SKILLFUL

For each condition expressed below, tabulate the solution set, if possible. Otherwise, give a standard description of the solution set.

1 $\frac{1}{4}(x - 5) + \frac{1}{2} = \frac{5}{8}x$.
2 $5y + 3 > 30$.
3 $\frac{2}{3}y + \frac{3}{4}y = 12$.
4 $10 - 2y > 4 \vee y + 5 = 2y + 3$.
5 $|x - 60| = 18$.
6 $6x - 4\frac{1}{2}x = 2x - 15$.
7 $6(y - 25) = 126$.
8 $6x + 3.5 < 4x - 2.5$.
9 $1\frac{1}{3}y < 20 \wedge 5\frac{1}{4}(x - 6) > 2$.
10 $21.5 - 3x = 4x + 3.3$.
11 $10(x - 3) + 8 = 20x$.
12 $12 - 10(x + 2) > 15x$.
13 $\frac{1}{4}y > \frac{1}{6}y + \frac{1}{2}$.
14 $(x + 1)^2 - (x + 5)^2 = 20 \wedge x + .5 < -4.5$.
15 $\frac{1}{2}|x| + 45 = 70$.
16 $3(x - .2) - 2(x + 1) < 2.5$.
17 $3 - (.8 + 4x) = 2x + (.5 - x)$.
18 $(y + 3)(y + 5) = (y - 4)(y + 10)$.
19 $2|x| + 15\frac{1}{2} = 30$.
20 $3(x - 4) > 2(x - 1) \wedge 5(x - 6) < 2(x + 1)$.
21 $|x + .5| = 6 \wedge x > 0$.
22 $6 - \frac{y + 6}{8} = 14$.
23 $\frac{y + 5}{4} = 2(y + 3) \vee \frac{y + 3}{5} = y + 7$.

22 271 **Exploring problems**

Problems involving variation

Most of the problems in this lesson are of a kind that by now should be familiar to you. All these problems concern the idea of variation. You will be able to solve each of them by using one of the conditions for variation that you have just studied: $y = kx$, $y = kx^2$, $y = \frac{k}{x}$, and $y = \frac{k}{x^2}$.

Read the problem in D1. For this problem, you can use a condition of the form expressed at the right. Use x as a variable for the width of the photograph in inches. Use y as a variable for the height in inches.

$$y = kx.$$

A You know that the width of the original photograph is 22 in. and the height is $16\frac{1}{2}$ in. Therefore, $(22, 16\frac{1}{2})$ is one (x, y) that satisfies $y = kx$. This information will help you find the value of k for $y = kx$. For what is k a variable?

B If you replace x by 22 and y by $16\frac{1}{2}$ in $y = kx$, what condition do you obtain?

A photograph of the Emerson High School football team is 22 in. wide and $16\frac{1}{2}$ in. high. If the photograph is used in the yearbook, it must be reduced so that it is 10 in. wide. What will be the height of the reduced photograph in inches?

D1

C What k satisfies $16\frac{1}{2} = k(22)$?

D If you replace k by $\frac{3}{4}$ in $y = kx$, what condition do you obtain?

E Remember that the problem in D1 asks you to find the height of the reduced photograph if the width is 10 in. If you replace x by 10 in $y = \frac{3}{4}x$, do you obtain the condition expressed at the right?

$y = \frac{3}{4}(10).$

F What number satisfies $y = \frac{3}{4}(10)$?

You can use the number that you obtained to get the answer to the problem. The height of the reduced photograph will be $7\frac{1}{2}$ in.

Read the problem in D2.

G From the problem in D2, you know that the maximum range of a projectile varies directly as the square of the initial velocity. Use x as a variable for the initial velocity in feet per second. Use y as a variable for the maximum range of the projectile in feet. How do you know that you can use a condition of the form expressed at the right?

$y = kx^2.$

H You know that one projectile has an initial velocity of 120 ft. per second and a maximum range of 2448 ft. What numbers should you use as replacements for x and y to determine the value of k in $y = kx^2$? What condition do you obtain?

I What is a standard name of $(120)^2$?

J To find the k that satisfies the condition $2448 = k(14400)$, you must find the quotient of what numbers? What decimal expresses this quotient?

K If you replace k by .17 in $y = kx^2$, what condition do you obtain?

L The problem in D2 asks you to find the maximum range of a projectile that has an initial velocity of 210 ft. per second. Why do you replace x by 210 in $y = .17x^2$? What condition do you obtain?

A photograph of the Emerson High School football team is 22 in. wide and $16\frac{1}{2}$ in. high. If the photograph is used in the yearbook, it must be reduced so that it is 10 in. wide. What will be the height of the reduced photograph in inches?

D1

The maximum range of a projectile varies directly as the square of the initial velocity. One projectile that has a maximum range of 2448 ft. has an initial velocity of 120 ft. per second. The initial velocity of another projectile is 210 ft. per second. What is the maximum range of the second projectile in feet?

D2

A train, traveling at a rate of 45 mi. per hour, went from Crawford to Spencer in 4 hr. The return trip from Spencer to Crawford took 6 hr. because of a sleet storm. How many miles per hour did the train travel on the return trip?

D3

M Explain how to obtain $y = .17(44100)$ from $y = .17(210)^2$. What number satisfies $y = .17(44100)$?

N Give the answer to the problem in D2.

Now you will solve problems that involve conditions for inverse variation.

Read the problem in D3. Use x as a variable for the rate that the train travels. Use y as a variable for the time required for the trip.

A We assume, of course, that the distance from Crawford to Spencer is the same as the distance from Spencer to Crawford. Suppose that the train traveled twice as fast on the return trip. How would the time required to travel between the two towns be affected? Suppose that the train traveled $\frac{1}{3}$ as fast. How would the time required for the trip be affected?

B Does the time vary directly as the rate varies? Does the time vary inversely as the rate?

In this case, the time varies inversely as the rate. Therefore, you know that a condition of the form expressed at the right is appropriate for the problem.

$$y = \frac{k}{x}.$$

C You know that the train, traveling at 45 mi. per hour, went from Crawford to Spencer in 4 hr. By what numbers do you replace x and y to determine the value of k in $y = \frac{k}{x}$? What condition do you obtain?

D What number satisfies the condition that you obtained for exercise C? What number do you use as a replacement for k in $y = \frac{k}{x}$?

E The problem in D3 asks you to find how many miles per hour the train traveled on the return trip, which took 6 hr. What number satisfies the condition expressed at the right?

$$6 = \frac{180}{x}.$$

F Give the answer to the problem in D3.

Read the problem in D4. Use x as a variable for the distance of the rocket from the center of the earth in miles. Use y as a variable for the weight of the rocket in pounds.

The weight of an object varies inversely as the square of its distance from the center of the earth. A rocket that is 5000 mi. from the center of the earth weighs 384 lb. What is its weight in pounds when it is 8000 mi. from the center of the earth?

D4

From the problem, you know that the weight of the rocket varies inversely as the square of its distance from the center of the earth. This means that a condition of the form expressed at the right is appropriate.

$$y = \frac{k}{x^2}.$$

G What replacements do you make for x and y to determine the value of k in $y = \frac{k}{x^2}$? What condition do you obtain?

H What is a standard name of $(5000)^2$? Why are $384(25{,}000{,}000) = k$ and $384 = \frac{k}{25{,}000{,}000}$ equivalent conditions?

I What number satisfies $384(25{,}000{,}000) = k$? Is the scientific notation for this number the numeral 9.6×10^9?

REMINDER

In scientific notation, a number is expressed as the product of a number from 1 to 10 and a power of 10.

See lesson 143, page 168, Book 2.

J 9.6×10^9 is the constant of variation for the problem in D4. If you replace k in $y = \frac{k}{x^2}$ by 9.6×10^9, what condition do you obtain?

K You are asked to find the weight of the rocket when it is 8000 mi. from the center of the earth. When you replace x by 8000 in $y = \frac{9.6 \times 10^9}{x^2}$, what condition do you obtain?

The weight of an object varies inversely as the square of its distance from the center of the earth. A rocket that is 5000 mi. from the center of the earth weighs 384 lb. What is its weight in pounds when it is 8000 mi. from the center of the earth?

D4

L Is $(8000)^2 = 6.4 \times 10^7$? How do you know?

M To find the y that satisfies the condition that you obtained for exercise K, you must find the quotient of 9.6×10^9 and 6.4×10^7. What is the quotient of 9.6 and 6.4? What is the quotient of 10^9 and 10^7? What y satisfies the condition?

N What is a standard name of 1.5×10^2?

O Give the answer to the problem in D4.

In this lesson you used conditions for variation to solve problems.

On your own

For each problem, first choose a condition for variation and determine the constant of variation. Next write a sentence that expresses a condition that will help you obtain the answer to the problem. Then give the answer.

1 If 63 students share the expenses of a class party, each student's share will be \$.70. If 45 students share the same expenses equally, how much will each student's share be?

2 A cook has a recipe for chili that requires $2\frac{2}{3}$ cups of tomatoes. This recipe makes enough chili to serve 12 persons. If the cook wants to make chili for 75 persons, how many cups of tomatoes should he use?

3 The area of square ABCD is 196 sq. in. The measure of a side of square ABCD is 14 in. The area of square JKLM is 361 sq. in. What is the measure of a side of JKLM in inches?

4 The volume of a gas varies inversely as the pressure. If the volume of a gas is 39 cu. ft. when the pressure is 5 lb., what is its volume in cubic feet when the pressure is 15 lb.?

5 On a road map, $1\frac{1}{2}$ in. represents a distance of 30 mi. The actual distance between Niles and Raleigh is 45 mi. On the map, Niles and Raleigh are how many inches apart?

6 The maximum safe load for a certain type of beam varies directly as the square of its vertical dimension. For a beam that has a vertical dimension of 8 in., the maximum safe load is 6000 lb. What is the maximum safe load in pounds of a beam that is made of the same material and has a vertical dimension of 12 in.?

7 Three machines can print the addresses from a mailing list in 20 min. In how many minutes can four machines print the same addresses?

8 The energy of a moving object varies directly as the square of its velocity. A certain object moving with a velocity of 24 ft. per second has an energy of 90 foot-pounds. What is the energy in foot-pounds of the same object if it is moving at 40 ft. per second?

KEEPING SKILLFUL

In each exercise below, a condition that determines a relation and the domain of the relation are given. In each case, the relation is a set of (x, y). Tabulate the relation.

1 $y = x + 5$. Domain $= \{-1, 0, 2, 4\}$.

2 $2y = x$. Domain $= \{-2, 0, 2, 5\}$.

3 $y = -2x$. Domain $= \{-6\frac{1}{2}, -4, -2\frac{1}{3}, 0\}$.

4 $3x + 2 = y$. Domain $= \{0, 1, 9, 10\frac{1}{2}\}$.

5 $\frac{x}{y} = 4$. Domain $= \{-2, -1.8, 6, 9.5\}$.

6 $y = \frac{3}{x}$. Domain $= \{-3, -\frac{1}{3}, 1\frac{1}{2}, 6\}$.

22 **272** **Exploring ideas**

Some special functions

Most of your work with functions will concern a few common and useful functions. Functions determined by conditions of the form $y = kx^n$ are examples of what we mean. There are functions less well known, however, that can give you a broader knowledge of the concept of a function. This lesson will acquaint you with some of these special functions.

Suppose that a vending machine dispenses candy at 1¢ per piece. The machine is broken, with the result that each time a penny is inserted, the candy fails to come out and the coin is not returned. The chart in D1 is a record of various numbers of pennies spent in the machine and the number of pieces of candy received in each case.

A Let x represent a number of pennies; let $f(x)$ represent the corresponding number of pieces of candy received. Tabulate the set of $(x, f(x))$ that you can obtain from the chart.

B In the set that you just tabulated, what is $f(1)$? What is $f(3)$? What is $f(5)$?

C ? What condition is satisfied by each member of the set you tabulated for exercise A?

D Think about the function in D × D that is determined by $f(x) = 0$ when the domain of function f is D. What is the range of function f?

E ? Is the set that you tabulated for exercise A a subset of function f? Does the set you tabulated contain every member of function f? How do you know that function f is an infinite set?

Pennies spent	1	2	3	4	5
Pieces of candy received	0	0	0	0	0

D1

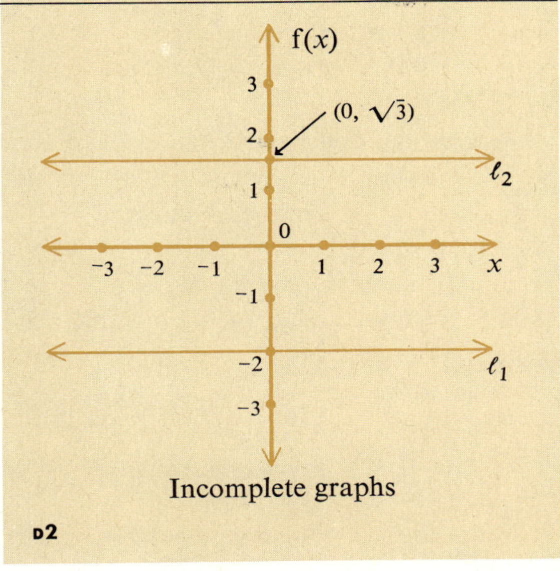

Incomplete graphs

D2

F Look at D2. How do you know that the x-axis is the locus of the function that is determined by $f(x) = 0$?

G The condition $f(x) = -2$ determines a function in D × D that is somewhat like the function determined by $f(x) = 0$. The domain of the function determined by $f(x) = -2$ is D. Tabulate the range. Is the function infinite? Which line represented in D2 is the locus of $f(x) = -2$?

H The condition $f(x) = \sqrt{3}$ also determines a function in D × D. The domain is D. Tabulate the range. In this case, is the function infinite? Which line represented in D2 is the locus of $f(x) = \sqrt{3}$?

I By what can you replace the parameter k in $f(x) = k$ to obtain $f(x) = 0$? To obtain $f(x) = -2$? To obtain $f(x) = \sqrt{3}$?

Actual age	$8\frac{1}{3}$	9	$10\frac{51}{52}$	11	$12\frac{1}{3}$
Recorded age	8	9	10	11	12

D3

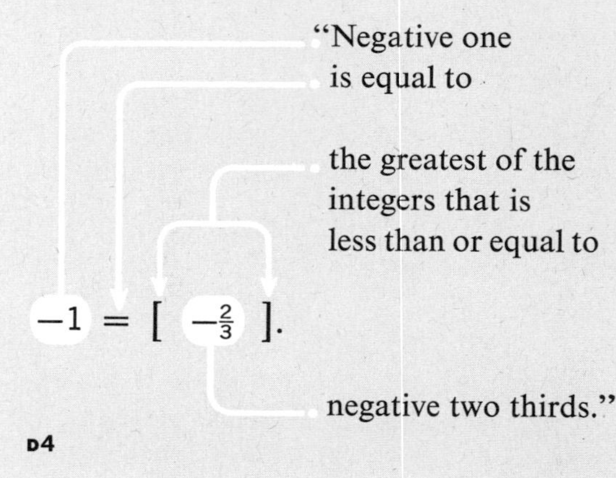

"Negative one
is equal to
the greatest of the
integers that is
less than or equal to
−1 = [−2/3].
negative two thirds."

D4

constant function. A function determined by a condition of the form $f(x) = k$. The domain of the function is D.

greatest-integer function. The function that is determined by $g(x) = [x]$. The domain is D.

Functions that are determined by conditions like $f(x) = 0$, $f(x) = -2$, and $f(x) = \sqrt{3}$ are *constant functions.* A constant function is a function that is determined by a condition of the form $f(x) = k$. The domain is D.

J How many elements are in the domain of any constant function? How many elements are in the range?

K Describe the locus of any constant function.

The constant function is one special function. Next you will study another special function whose range is the set of integers.

A If a person records his age as 14 years, it is usually understood that his actual age is greater than or equal to 14, but less than 15. If a person records his age as 28 years, what could his actual age be?

B If a person's actual age in years is in the interval $\{x \mid 21 \leqq x < 22\}$, how would he probably record his age, as 21 or as 22?

In the chart in D3, each numeral in the first row represents an actual age in years. Each numeral in the second row represents a recorded age. The first column in the chart, for example, indicates that a person who is actually $8\frac{1}{3}$ years old would record his age as 8 years.

C Which column of the chart indicates that a person who is actually 11 years old would record his age as 11 years?

D Let x represent an actual age and let $g(x)$ represent the corresponding recorded age. Tabulate the set of $(x, g(x))$ that you can obtain from the chart in D3.

E Is each $g(x)$ that you can obtain from the chart an integer?

F For which ordered pairs is $g(x)$ equal to x? For which ordered pairs is $g(x)$ less than x? Is $g(x)$ greater than x for any ordered pairs?

G Notice how each x is related to the corresponding $g(x)$. Think of the set of integers that are less than or equal to $8\frac{1}{3}$. Is $g(8\frac{1}{3})$ the greatest of these integers? Think of the set of integers that are less than or equal to 9. Is $g(9)$ the greatest of these integers? Think of the set of integers that are less than or equal to $10\frac{51}{52}$. Is $g(10\frac{51}{52})$ the greatest of these?

H Use your answers to exercise G to explain how $g(11)$ is related to 11 and how $g(12\frac{1}{3})$ is related to $12\frac{1}{3}$.

I For each $(x, g(x))$ how is $g(x)$ related to x?

Mathematicians use a special symbol for the greatest of the integers that is less than or equal to a given number. The symbol at the right names the greatest of the integers that is less than or

$$[x]$$

equal to x. D4 shows how to write and read a sentence that contains the new symbol.

J How do you know that $-1 = [-1]$? How do you know that $0 = [0]$? What integer is $[\frac{1}{3}]$? What integer is $[2]$?

K ? Suppose that a function is determined by $g(x) = [x]$ and the domain of the function is D. How is the set of $(x, g(x))$ that you tabulated for exercise D related to function g?

The function g is known as the *greatest-integer function*. It is the function that is determined by $g(x) = [x]$. The domain is D.

L If function g is the greatest-integer function, what is $g(-7)$? What number is the image of $\sqrt{2}$? What number is the image of $\frac{15}{4}$?

M ? Describe the range of the greatest-integer function.

N What is $g(-2)$? What is $g(-1\frac{1}{2})$? What is $g(-1\frac{8}{9})$? What is $g(-1)$? Explain why $g(x) = -2$ for each x such that $-2 \leqq x < -1$.

O ? Describe the first coördinates of the points in the locus of function g that have -2 as a second coördinate. Are these points the locus of $\{(x, g(x)) \mid g(x) = -2\}$? Notice how these points are represented in the graph in D5. Is point $(-1, -2)$ in the locus of function g?

P ? For function g, explain why the image of x is -1 for each x such that $-1 \leqq x < 0$.

Q In the locus of function g, which points have a second coördinate of -1? Are all these points represented in D5? Is point $(0, -1)$ in the locus of function g?

R Which points in the locus of function g have a second coördinate of 0? Of 1? Are all these points represented in D5?

S ? Is the origin in the locus of function g? Is point (2, 2) in the locus?

Of course, D5 shows an incomplete graph of the greatest-integer function. A function whose graph is like the graph in D5 is sometimes called a *step function*.

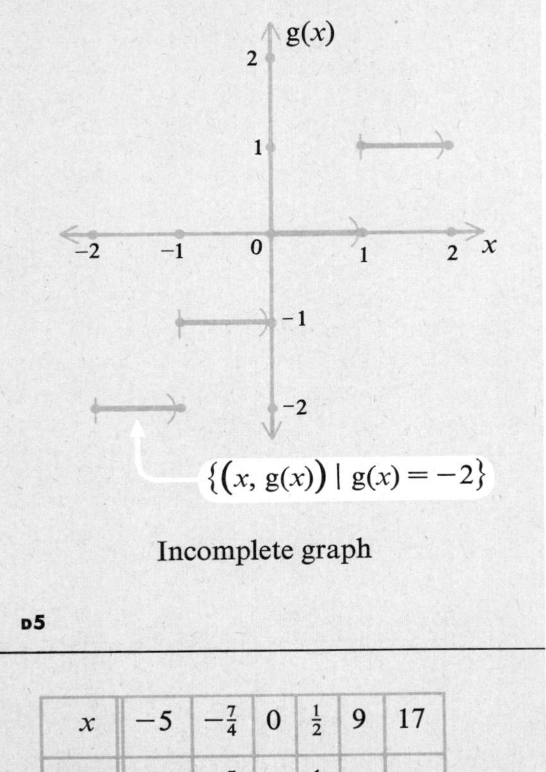

Incomplete graph

D5

x	-5	$-\frac{7}{4}$	0	$\frac{1}{2}$	9	17
h(x)	5	$\frac{7}{4}$	0	$\frac{1}{2}$	9	17

D6

In the exercises that follow, you will study a function that involves absolute value.

A Tabulate the set of $(x, h(x))$ that you can obtain from the chart in D6.

B What is the absolute value of -5? What is $h(-5)$? What is the absolute value of $-\frac{7}{4}$?

REMINDER

If $x \geqq 0$, then the absolute value of x is x. If $x < 0$, then the absolute value of x is $-x$.

See lesson 262, page 273.

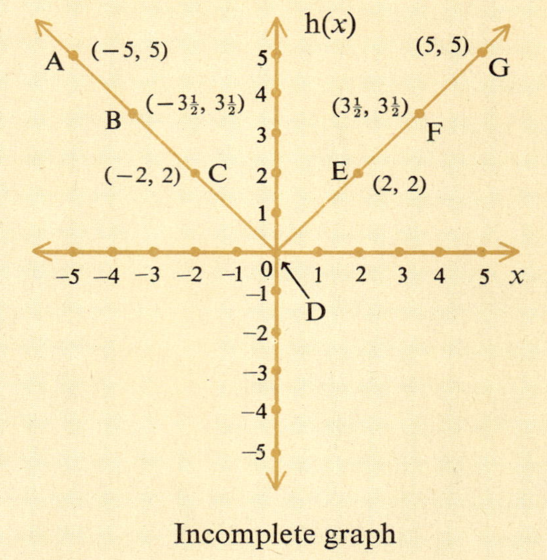

D7

absolute-value function. The function that is determined by $h(x) = |x|$. The domain is D.

What is $h(-\frac{7}{4})$? For each member of the set that you tabulated, how is $h(x)$ related to x?

C Think about the function that is determined by $h(x) = |x|$. The domain is D. Is each ordered pair that you tabulated for exercise A a member of this function? Is function h an infinite set?

The function h is the *absolute-value function.* It is the function that is determined by $h(x) = |x|$. The domain is D.

D If function h is the absolute-value function, what is $h(-100)$? What is $h(-50)$? What is $h(-10)$? What is $h(-\frac{3}{8})$? What can you say about the image of x if $x < 0$?

E What is $h(0)$? What is $h(x)$ if $x > 0$?

F ? Describe the range of the absolute-value function.

G Look at D7. Name the coördinates of points A, B, and C. How do you know that each pair of coördinates satisfies $h(x) = |x|$?

H ? For all negative replacements of x, is the locus of $h(x) = |x|$ the same as the locus of $h(x) = -x$? Explain your answer.

I Which ray represented in D7 is included in the locus of $h(x) = -x$?

J Notice that point D is the origin. Why is point D in the locus of $h(x) = |x|$?

K Does each of points E, F, and G have coördinates that satisfy $h(x) = |x|$?

L For all positive replacements of x, is the locus of $h(x) = |x|$ the same as the locus of $h(x) = x$? Explain your answer.

M Which ray represented in D7 is included in the locus of $h(x) = x$?

From exercises G through M, you can see that the graph in D7 is a graph of the absolute-value function.

N ? Explain why the locus of the absolute-value function contains no points in the third and fourth quadrants.

In this lesson you were introduced to constant functions, the greatest-integer function, and the absolute-value function.

On your own

The conditions expressed in exercises 1 through 8 determine functions. For each function, find $f(-6)$, $f(0)$, and $f(6)$.

1 $f(x) = -1$.
2 $f(x) = |x|$.
3 $f(x) = |x| + 7$.
4 $f(x) = [x]$.
5 $f(x) = -2|x|$.
6 $f(x) = |x - 5|$.
7 $f(x) = [x] + 4|x|$.
8 $f(x) = 3|x - 1|$.

The conditions expressed in exercises 9 through 16 determine functions. In each case, the domain is D. For each exercise, complete the chart. Then make a graph of the function.

9

$f(x) = 2\|x\|$.							
x	−3	−2	−1	0	1	2	3
$f(x)$							

10

$f(x) = \mid x \mid + 3.$							
x	-2	-1	$-\frac{1}{2}$	0	$\frac{1}{2}$	1	2
$f(x)$							

11

$f(x) = [x] + 2.$							
x	-2	$-\frac{3}{2}$	-1	$-\frac{1}{2}$	0	$\frac{1}{2}$	1
$f(x)$							

12

$f(x) = 3[x].$							
x	-2	$-\frac{4}{3}$	-1	$-\frac{2}{3}$	0	$\frac{1}{3}$	1
$f(x)$							

13

$f(x) = \mid x - 3 \mid.$							
x	-1	0	2	3	4	6	7
$f(x)$							

14

$f(x) = 2 \mid x - 3 \mid.$							
x	-1	0	2	3	4	6	7
$f(x)$							

15

$f(x) = \mid x - 3 \mid + 1.$							
x	-1	0	2	3	4	6	7
$f(x)$							

16

$f(x) = 2 \mid x - 3 \mid + 1.$							
x	-1	0	2	3	4	6	7
$f(x)$							

17 Suppose that the postage for first-class mail is 5 cents per ounce. This means that, if the weight of a piece of mail is less than or equal to 1 ounce, the postage is 5 cents; if the weight is greater than 1 ounce but less than or equal to 2 ounces, the postage is 10 cents; and so on. Use $g(x)$ to represent the postage and make a graph of the locus of function g. The domain is the set of positive real numbers.

APPLYING MATHEMATICS

For each problem, first choose a condition for variation and determine the constant of variation. Then express a condition for the problem and give the answer.

1 The price of a diamond varies directly as the square of its weight. If the price of a diamond that weighs $\frac{2}{3}$ of a carat is $840, what is the price of a diamond of the same quality that weighs $2\frac{1}{4}$ carats?

2 The volume of a confined gas varies inversely as the pressure. The volume of a gas is $45\frac{3}{4}$ cu. ft. under 4 lb. of pressure. What is the volume in cubic feet of the gas when the pressure is 6 lb.?

3 When 8 cu. in. of water freezes, 8.8 cu. in. of ice is formed. How many cubic inches of water must freeze to form 132 cu. in. of ice?

4 The distance traveled by a free-falling object varies directly as the square of the time that the object falls. A free-falling object falls 16 ft. in 1 sec. How many feet will the object fall in $6\frac{1}{2}$ sec.?

5 The amount of light that falls on an object varies inversely as the square of the distance between the object and the source of light. If 10 foot-candles of light fall on a book that is 2 ft. away from a lamp, how much light falls on the book when it is 3 ft. from the lamp?

6 The area of ⊙A is 12.56 sq. in. The measure of a radius of ⊙A is 2 in. The area of ⊙B is 17.27 sq. in. What is the measure in inches of a radius of ⊙B?

7 Six pipes of the same diameter can fill a swimming pool in 7 hr. In how many hours will five of these pipes fill the pool?

8 The force needed to push an object up an inclined plane varies directly as the weight of the object. A force of 45 lb. is needed to push a 70-lb. object up a certain ramp. How many pounds of force are needed to push a 91-lb. object up the same ramp?

9 The distance that a ball rolls down an inclined plane varies directly as the square of the time that the ball is rolling. If a ball rolls 5 ft. in the first second, how many feet will it roll in 8 sec.?

10 The weight of an object on Neptune varies directly as its weight on earth. Mr. Carson weighs 185 lb. on earth; if he were on Neptune, he would weigh 259 lb. Mrs. Carson weighs 125 lb. on earth. How many pounds would she weigh on Neptune?

11 The living room in the Cranes' house is $12\frac{1}{2}$ ft. wide. On a floor plan of the house, 2 in. represents 9 ft. of actual distance. How many inches on the floor plan represent the width of the Cranes' living room?

12 The electrical resistance of a wire varies inversely as the square of a diameter of the wire. The resistance of a certain wire whose diameter is $\frac{1}{4}$ in. is $\frac{1}{4}$ ohm. What is the resistance in ohms of a wire of the same kind and length whose diameter is $\frac{1}{8}$ in.?

13 The distance a spiral spring is stretched varies directly as the weight of an object that is hung on the spring. A certain spring is stretched .4 cm. by an object that weighs 20 g. How many centimeters would the spring be stretched by an object that weighs 50 g.?

14 The weight of an object varies inversely as the square of its distance from the center of the earth. An object that is 6000 mi. from the center of the earth weighs 400 lb. How many pounds would the object weigh if it were 8000 mi. from the center of the earth?

15 A wheel that has a circumference of 90 in. must revolve 704 times to cover a certain distance. How many times must a wheel that has a circumference of 40 in. revolve to cover the same distance?

CHECKING UP

The small numerals within parentheses tell what pages to turn to for help if you need it.

Test 250

Tell what words or symbols best complete exercises 1 through 11.

1 A relation is a set of ~~~. (291)

2 In $y = kx$, ~~~ is the parameter. (311)

3 If A has 6 members and B has 9 members, then $A \times B$ has ~~~ members. (291)

4 A condition of the form $f(x) = kx$ is a condition for ~~~ variation. (311)

5 A relation in $R \times S$ is a ~~~ of $R \times S$. (292)

6 If you replace n in $y = 5x^n$ by ~~~, you obtain $y = \frac{5}{x^2}$. (319)

7 The ~~~ of a relation in $R \times S$ is the subset of R that consists of all the first components of the elements of the relation. (297)

8 In the function determined by $y = [x]$, ~~~ is the image of $5\frac{2}{3}$. (326)

9 $U = \{3, 6, 9\}$ and $T = \{5, 10, 15, 20, 25\}$. In the Cartesian set $U \times T$, each member of set U is paired with exactly ~~~ members of set T. (291)

10 The real number ~~~ is not a member of the domain of the function that is determined by $f(x) = \frac{x-5}{x+3}$. (307)

11 A ~~~ is a relation in which each element of the domain is paired with exactly one element of the range. (300)

Test 251

From the list below each exercise, choose the correct answer for the exercise.

12 $A = \{1, 2\}$ and $B = \{2, 3\}$. An example of a relation in $A \times B$ is ~~~. (292)

a $\{(1, 2), (2, 3)\}$ **c** $\{(1, 3), (3, 2)\}$

b $\{(1, 1), (2, 2)\}$ **d** $\{(3, 3), (2, 3)\}$

13 The range of a relation is the set of all ~~~ of the elements of the relation. (297)

a ordered pairs c second components
b coördinates d constant factors

14 The domain of $\{(7, 9), (8, 10), (8, 7)\}$ is ~~~. (297)

a $\{7, 8, 9, 10\}$ c $\{7, 8, 9\}$
b $\{7, 9, 10\}$ d $\{7, 8\}$

15 If $f(x) = [x]$, then ~~~ is not equal to -3. (326)

a $f(-2.5)$ c $f(-3.5)$
b $f(-3.0)$ d $f(-2.75)$

16 A constant function is a function in $D \times D$ that is determined by a condition of the form ~~~. (326)

a $f(x) = ax + b$ c $h(x) = |x|$
b $g(x) = k$ d $f(x) = mx + ny$

17 x varies inversely as y. When $x = 100$, $y = 2$. When $y = 8$, x is equal to ~~~. (316)

a $12\frac{1}{2}$ b 25 c 200 d 400

18 If $f(x) = x^2 - 3x + 5$, then ~~~ is equal to 5. (306)

a $f(1)$ b $f(2)$ c $f(3)$ d $f(4)$

19 $\{(1, 1), (1, 2), (1, 3), (2, 2), (3, 2)\}$ is the universe for (x, y). The relation determined by ~~~ contains exactly one member. (293)

a $x = y$ b $y > x$ c $x > y$ d $x \geqq y$

20 If $k < 0$, then the locus of $f(x) = \frac{k}{x^2}$ is included in the ~~~ quadrants. (319)

a first and second c second and third
b first and third d third and fourth

21 $S = \{1, 2, 3\}$. The universe for $(x, f(x))$ is $S \times S$. The function $\{(2, 1), (3, 3)\}$ is determined by ~~~. (294)

a $f(x) = x^2 - 2x$ c $f(x) = \frac{1}{2}x$
b $f(x) = 2x - 3$ d $f(x) = 4x^{-2}$

22 If $g(x) = 4x - 5$, then in function g, the image of 3 is ~~~. (305)

a 17 c 7
b $\frac{5}{4}$ d $\frac{4}{5}$

Test 252

For each problem, choose a condition for variation and determine the constant of variation. Then write a sentence that expresses a condition for the problem and give the answer.

23 The frequency of a radio wave varies inversely as the length of the wave. A radio wave that is 500 m. long has a frequency of 600 kilocycles. What is the frequency in kilocycles of a radio wave that has a length of 100 m.? (321)

24 The weight of an object varies inversely as the square of its distance from the center of the earth. If a man weighs 150 lb. on the earth's surface, how many pounds would he weigh 4800 mi. from the center of the earth? Use 4000 mi. as an approximation of the measure of a radius of the earth. (321)

25 The magnitude of the force that the wind exerts on a sail varies directly as the square of the speed of the wind. On a certain sail, a wind of 15 miles per hour exerts a force that has a magnitude of 50 lb. What is the magnitude in pounds of the force that a wind of 25 miles per hour exerts on the sail? (321)

26 The amount of heat that is produced in an electric wire varies directly as the square of the current. A current of 5 amperes produces 60 calories of heat in an electric wire. How many calories of heat are produced by a current of 12 amperes? (321)

27 The distance an object falls varies directly as the square of the time the object has been falling. In 2 seconds, an object falls 64 ft. In how many seconds will an object fall a distance of 256 ft.? (321)

28 Mr. Richards earned a commission of \$1360 when he sold some machines worth a total of \$17,000. How much commission would Mr. Richards earn if he sold \$30,000 worth of machines? (321)

CHECKING UP

The small numerals within parentheses tell what pages to turn to for help if you need it.

Test 253

Write "T" for each sentence below that expresses a true statement. Write "F" for each sentence that expresses a false statement.

1 For any pair of real numbers, if the first number is less than the second, then the difference of the second and first numbers is positive. (91)

2 $|-19| > 5$. (273)

3 Scale drawings are necessary for solving all problems that involve displacements. (15)

4 Two or more statements are consistent if none of the statements contradicts any of the other statements or contradicts a conclusion that is reached from any of the other statements. (92)

5 A nonrepeating infinite decimal expresses exactly one rational number. (70)

6 Zero is less than the product of -3 and 4. (85)

7 $(2^3)^2 = 2^6$. (172)

8 All integers are rational numbers. (180)

9 A true conditional can have a true antecedent and a false consequent. (123)

10 The absolute value of a positive number is negative. (273)

11 $\{x \mid |x| = 5\} = \{x \mid x = 5 \wedge x = -5\}$. (275)

12 Each rational condition is also a polynomial condition. (253)

Test 254

Tell what words or symbols best complete exercises 13 through 23.

13 The sum of any two positive real numbers is a ~~~~ real number. (90)

14 A name for the set of ~~~~ numbers is D. (9)

15 Two vectors that are directed segments and that have the same length and the same direction are ~~~~. (20)

16 The ~~~~ for a variable is the set of permissible replacements for the variable. (254)

17 A statement that involves one or more connectives is a ~~~~ statement. (118)

18 The absolute difference of 1.6 and 2.5 is the number ~~~~. (17)

19 A perfect square always has an ~~~~ number of factors in its prime factorization. (146)

20 If you multiply each side of a polynomial condition for equality by x, the condition that you obtain always has ~~~~ as a solution. (256)

21 An ~~~~ proof is one in which you show that a statement is true by establishing that its negation is false. (147)

22 The solution set of $x > 8 \wedge x < 11$ is an open ~~~~ in D. (100)

23 The transitive property of "less than" enables you to obtain ~~~~ from $0 < b$ and $b < a + b$. (86)

Test 255

From the list below each exercise, choose the correct answer for the exercise.

24 In $\triangle$EFG, $\angle E° = 90$. Side ~~~~ is opposite $\angle$F. (29)

a FE **b** GF **c** EG **d** FG

25 A complete factorization of 45 is ~~~~. (206)

a $1 \times 5 \times 9$ **c** $\{3, 9, 15, 45\}$

b $3 \times 3 \times 5$ **d** $\{1, 3, 5, 9, 15, 45\}$

26 The binomial ~~~~ is equal to the sum of $5x - 11$ and $7 + 4x$. (185)

a $12x - 7$ **c** $20x - 18$

b $9x - 4$ **d** $x - 18$

27 The solution of $4x - 20 = 15 - 3x$ is not a solution of ~~~~. (255)

a $4(x - 5) + 3x = 15$ **c** $4x + 3x = 20 + 15$

b $4 - \frac{20}{x} = \frac{15}{x} - 3$ **d** $4 = \frac{15 - 3x}{x - 5}$

28 The set of integers is not closed under ~~~. (211)

a addition **c** multiplication
b subtraction **d** division

29 The ~~~ is the property that enables you to derive the condition $\frac{1}{2}(n) < \frac{1}{2}(\sqrt{7})$ from $n < \sqrt{7}$. (86)

a positive-multiplier property of "less than"
b trichotomy property
c sum property of "less than"
d replacement property of "less than"

30 The sentence ~~~ expresses the difference property of real numbers. (82)

a $a - b = b - a$
b $a - b = a + (-b)$
c $a - (b - c) = (a - b) - c$
d $a(b - c) = ab - ac$

31 The condition $ax + b = 0$, where $a \neq 0$, has exactly one solution, and that solution is ~~~. (260)

a $\frac{-b}{a}$ **b** $\frac{-a}{b}$ **c** $-b$ **d** $-\left(\frac{-b}{a}\right)$

32 In the coördinate plane, points (0, 0), (3, −7), and (−1, 4) are three vertices of a parallelogram. Point ~~~ is the fourth vertex of the parallelogram. (47)

a (4, 11) **b** (3, 4) **c** (2, −3) **d** (3, −1)

33 In a right triangle, suppose that you know the measure of one acute angle and of the hypotenuse. You can then use ~~~ to find the measure of the side opposite the given acute angle. (29)

a $\cos t = \frac{x}{r}$ **c** $\tan t = \frac{y}{x}$
b $c^2 = a^2 + b^2$ **d** $\sin t = \frac{y}{r}$

34 ~~~ is a function in D × D. (300)

a {(1, 3), (3, 1), (2, 3)}
b {(1, 1), (2, 2), (2, 1)}
c {(1, 2), (2, 3), (1, 3)}
d {(1, 3), (2, 3), (2, 1)}

Unit 23

Linear and quadratic functions

23 | 273 | Exploring ideas

Graphic study of functions

In unit 22 you learned that a function is a special kind of relation. In this unit you will study two functions that are widely used in mathematics—the linear function and the quadratic function. Then you will see how solutions of quadratic conditions are related to quadratic functions.

First you will study graphs of various functions. The procedures involved in making such graphs will be useful when you consider linear and quadratic functions.

A A standard description of function g is given in D1. Line ℓ_1 is the locus of function g. For each point in the x-axis, is there a point in the locus that is directly above, or directly below, or identical with, the point?

B For each point in the y-axis, is there a point in the locus of function g that is to the right of, or to the left of, or identical with, the point?

C If $x < 2$, is $y < 0$? What is y if $x = 2$? Describe y if $x > 2$. Use the graph of function g to explain your answers.

D The chart in D2 gives seven replacements for x in $y = 2x - 4$. Copy and complete the chart.

Notice that if you first replace x by -6, then by -4, and then by -2 in $y = 2x - 4$, you are replacing x by successively greater negative numbers.

E If you replace x in $y = 2x - 4$ by successively greater negative numbers, does y increase or does y decrease? If you replace x by successively greater positive numbers, what happens to y?

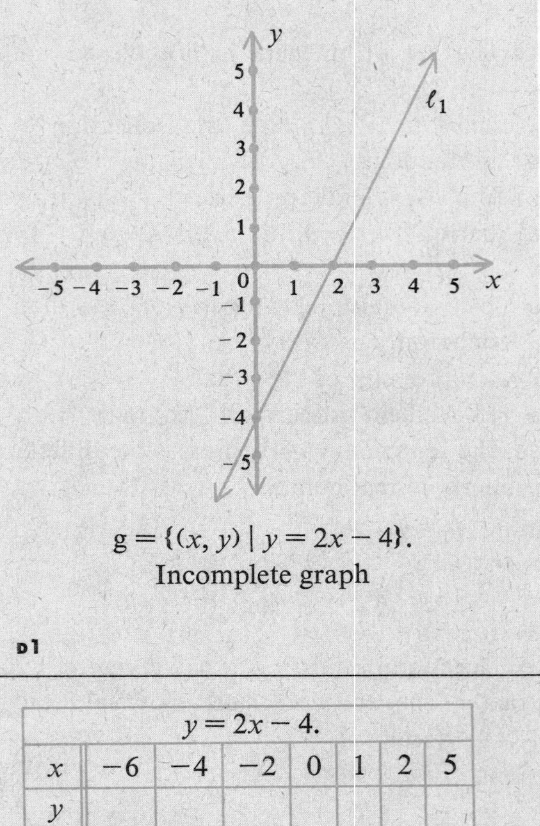

$g = \{(x, y) \mid y = 2x - 4\}$.
Incomplete graph

D1

$y = 2x - 4$.							
x	-6	-4	-2	0	1	2	5
y							

D2

F Look again at D1. Explain why the locus of function g slants upward to the right.

G Is point $(0, -4)$ the point in which the locus of function g intersects the y-axis?

Point $(0, -4)$ is known as the y-*intercept* (in′tər sept′) of the locus of $y = 2x - 4$. The point in which any given locus intersects the y-axis is a y-intercept of that locus.

H The first coördinate of a y-intercept is always what number?

I Look again at D1. In which point does the locus of function g intersect the x-axis?

Point $(2, 0)$ is the x-*intercept* of the locus of $y = 2x - 4$. The point in which any given locus intersects the x-axis is an x-intercept of that locus.

J The second coördinate of an x-intercept is always what number?

K Now look at D3. The semicircle represented in D3 is the locus of function h, which is determined by $h(x) = \sqrt{16 - x^2}$. What closed interval is the domain of function h? What closed interval is the range of function h? Use the graph to explain your answers.

L How does the graph in D3 indicate that, for each x in the domain of function h, $h(x) \geqq 0$?

Notice that, since we have used the symbol $h(x)$ instead of the symbol y in the standard description of function h, we have also used the symbol $h(x)$ to name the second axis.

M How do you know that point (0, 4) is the $h(x)$-intercept of the locus of function h?

N If $h(x) = 0$, what is x? Name the two x-intercepts of the locus of function h.

O If $x = 2$, then $h(2) = \sqrt{16 - 2^2}$, or $\sqrt{12}$. Is $(2, \sqrt{12})$ an element of function h?

P Show that each ordered pair named below is an element of function h.

$(-2, \sqrt{12})$ $(3, \sqrt{7})$ $(-3, \sqrt{7})$
$(-1, \sqrt{15})$ $(1, \sqrt{15})$

Q If x is replaced in $h(x) = \sqrt{16 - x^2}$ by successively greater negative numbers, what happens to $h(x)$? Explain why the locus of function h curves upward to the right in the second quadrant.

R If x is replaced by successively greater positive numbers, what happens to $h(x)$? Explain why the locus of function h curves downward to the right in the first quadrant.

Notice that, in the locus of function h, the set of points whose first coördinates are negative seems to be a reflection of the set of points whose first coördinates are positive. We say, therefore, that the locus of the function is symmetric with respect to the $h(x)$-axis. If you could fold the plane along the $h(x)$-axis, the curves in the two quadrants would coincide.

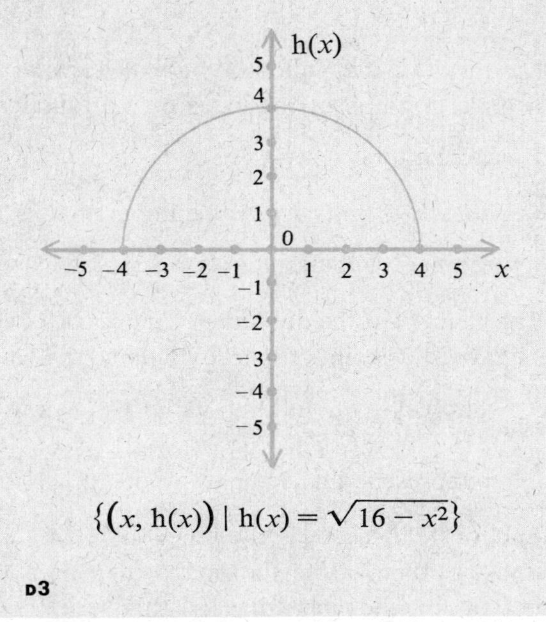

$\{(x, h(x)) \mid h(x) = \sqrt{16 - x^2}\}$

D3

S Show that, if $h(x) = \sqrt{16 - x^2}$, then $h(x)$ is equal to $h(-x)$.

T If a function f is such that $f(x) = f(-x)$, then the locus of the function is symmetric with respect to the $f(x)$-axis. How would this information be helpful if you were making a graph of the function?

U Make a graph of the locus of a function g that has the following characteristics.

1 The domain is D, and the range is the set of non-positive real numbers.

2 The x-intercept of the locus of function g is point (0, 0), and the $g(x)$-intercept of the locus is point (0, 0).

3 As x is replaced by successively greater negative numbers, $g(x)$ increases.

4 As x is replaced by successively greater positive numbers, $g(x)$ decreases.

5 $g(x) = g(-x)$.

V Is there only one locus that satisfies the requirements given in exercise U? Make a graph that is different from the one you made for exercise U to explain your answer.

In the work that follows, you will learn how to make a graph of the locus of the function determined by $f(x) = \frac{1}{x^2}$.

A You know that any real number that is a meaningful replacement for x in $f(x) = \frac{1}{x^2}$ is an element of the domain of function f. Give a standard description of the domain.

B From $f(x) = \frac{1}{x^2}$, you know that you can use $\frac{1}{x^2}$ to represent an element of the range of function f. If $x < 0$, is the image of x greater than 0? If $x > 0$, is the image of x greater than 0, or is the image of x less than 0?

C Explain why $f(x)$ cannot be equal to 0.

D Is there a negative number that is in the range of function f? Is 0 in the range? Describe the range.

E Use the information that you have obtained from exercises A through D to explain why the locus of the function determined by $f(x) = \frac{1}{x^2}$ is included in only the first and second quadrants of the plane. How do you know that the locus does not have an x-intercept? Does the locus have an $f(x)$-intercept?

F $\{\frac{1}{2}, \frac{2}{3}, 1, 2, 4, 40\}$ is a subset of the domain of function f. For each member of this subset, give the image.

G If x in $f(x) = \frac{1}{x^2}$ is replaced by successively greater positive numbers, does $f(x)$ decrease?

H $\{-40, -4, -2, -1, -\frac{2}{3}, -\frac{1}{2}\}$ is a subset of the domain of function f. For each member of this subset, give the image.

I If x is replaced by successively greater negative numbers, what happens to $f(x)$?

J Look at D4. Each of points A through J is

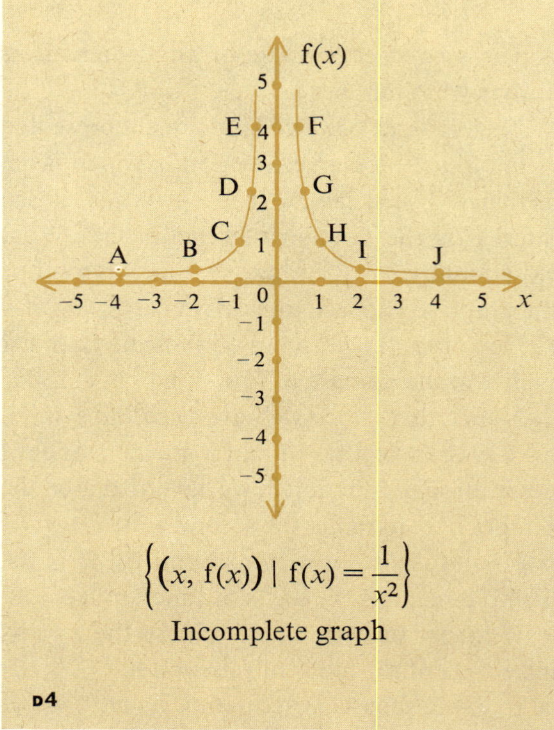

$\left\{(x, f(x)) \mid f(x) = \frac{1}{x^2}\right\}$

Incomplete graph

D4

associated with an $(x, f(x))$ that you can obtain from exercise F or exercise H. Name the coördinates of each point.

Each point in the two-part curve represented in D4 is associated with an element of function f, and each element of function f is associated with a point in the curve. Therefore, the two-part curve is the locus of function f.

K Look again at D4. Notice that the locus of the function curves upward to the right in the second quadrant. Thus, the graph shows that, as x is replaced by successively greater negative numbers, $f(x)$ increases. How does the graph show that $f(x)$ decreases if x is replaced by successively greater positive numbers?

L What happens to $f(x)$ as x approaches 0?

M What one point in the x-axis is not directly below a point in the locus of function f? What does this tell you about the domain?

N Explain why the locus of function f does not intersect either axis.

O Is the locus of function f symmetric with respect to the f(x)-axis? Explain your answer.

Now you will make a graph of the locus of the function determined by $h(x) = x^2 + 1$.

P If x is a real number, is $x^2 + 1$ a real number? Describe the domain of the function determined by $h(x) = x^2 + 1$.

Q Explain why $\{h(x) \mid h(x) \geqq 1\}$ is the range of function h. How do you know that the locus of function h has no x-intercepts?

R If $x = 0$, what is h(x)? What is the h(x)-intercept of the locus of function h?

S What quadrants of the plane contain points in the locus of function h?

T Name six members of function h.

U If x in $h(x) = x^2 + 1$ is replaced by successively greater negative numbers, what happens to h(x)? How would you show this in a graph of function h?

V If x is replaced by successively greater positive numbers, what happens to h(x)? How would you show this in a graph of function h?

W Show that the locus of function h is symmetric with respect to the h(x)-axis.

X Make a graph of the locus of the function determined by $h(x) = x^2 + 1$.

In this lesson you studied graphs of the loci of several functions.

On your own

Each graph in D5 represents the locus of a function. Answer exercises 1 through 5 for each function.

1 Describe the domain and the range.

2 What happens to f(x) if x is replaced by successively greater negative numbers? By successively greater positive numbers?

3 Name each x-intercept of the locus.

4 Name each f(x)-intercept of the locus.

5 Is the locus of function f symmetric with respect to the f(x)-axis?

A

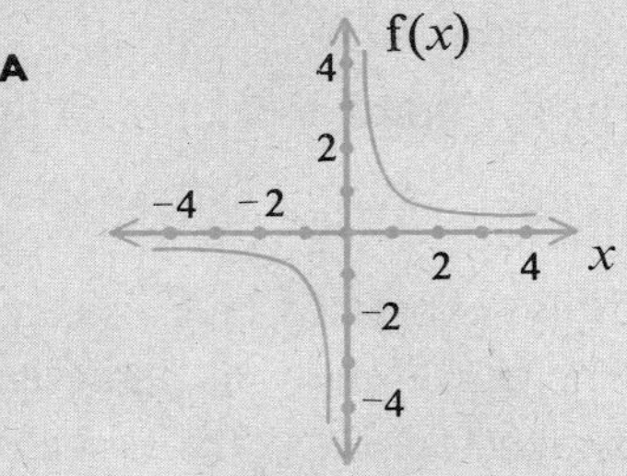

$\{(x, f(x)) \mid f(x) = \frac{1}{x}\}$

B

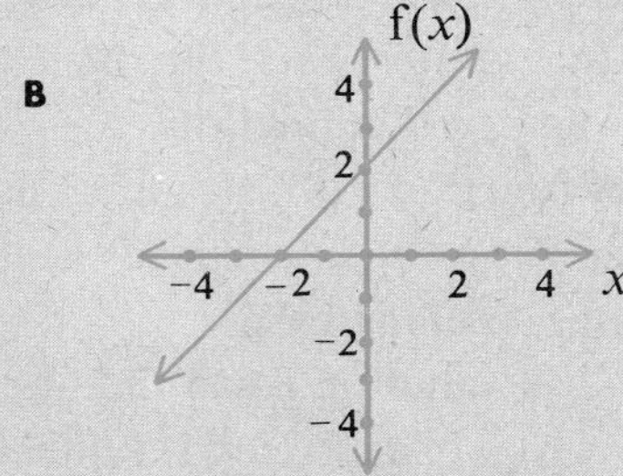

$\{(x, f(x)) \mid f(x) = x + 2\}$

C

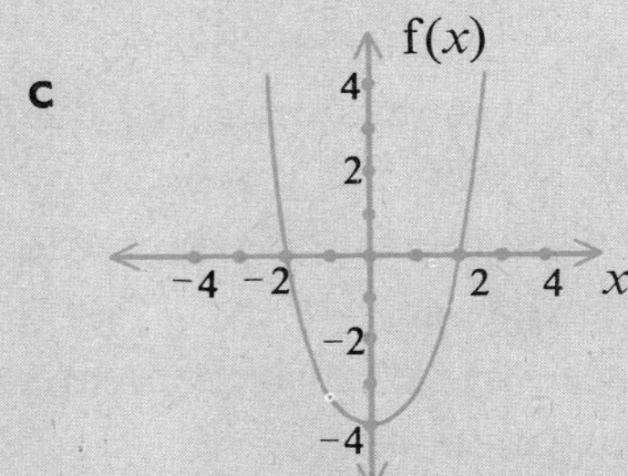

$\{(x, f(x)) \mid f(x) = x^2 - 4\}$

D

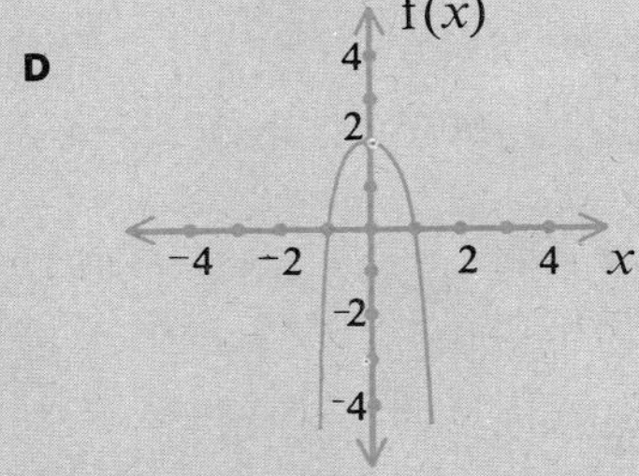

$\{(x, f(x)) \mid f(x) = -2x^2 + 2\}$

Incomplete graphs

D5

6 Explain why the domain of the function determined by $f(x) = \frac{1}{1+x}$ is $\{x \mid x \neq -1\}$.

Each condition expressed below determines a function. For each function, name each x-intercept and each $f(x)$-intercept of its locus.

7 $f(x) = -3x + 7$.

8 $f(x) = 3x$.

9 $f(x) = 4x^2$.

10 $f(x) = x^2 - 16$.

11 The characteristics of a function f are given below. Make two graphs, each of which could represent the locus of the function.

a The locus of function f is a straight line.

b Point (0, 0) is the only intercept of the locus.

c As x increases, $f(x)$ increases.

12 Suppose that a function f has the first two characteristics given in exercise 11, but as x increases, $f(x)$ decreases. Make two graphs each of which could represent the locus.

13 Make a graph that could represent the locus of function g, described below.

a $\{x \mid -3 \leqq x \leqq 3\}$ is the domain of the function, and $\{g(x) \mid 0 \leqq g(x) \leqq 3\}$ is the range.

b The locus of function g is symmetric with respect to the $g(x)$-axis.

c If x is replaced by successively greater negative numbers, $g(x)$ increases.

14 Make a graph of the locus of a function h. The domain is D and the range is $\{3\}$.

KEEPING SKILLFUL

Find the vector sum for each of the exercises below.

1 $(6, 4) \oplus (-8, 15)$

2 $(0, 0) \oplus (7, 10)$

3 $(-\frac{1}{4}, 3) \oplus (\frac{3}{4}, -\frac{1}{8})$

4 $(-8, -4) \oplus (-\frac{1}{6}, -\frac{1}{2})$

5 $(\frac{1}{2}, \frac{1}{6}) \oplus (\frac{3}{4}, -\frac{1}{3})$

6 $(-8, -9) \oplus (0, 0)$

7 $(-3, -\frac{1}{4}) \oplus (\frac{5}{8}, \frac{3}{4})$

8 $(-15, 1) \oplus (6, 14)$

9 $(1.375, -.625) \oplus (2.5, -.555)$

10 $(6 + 3, 9 - 10) \oplus (6 + 3, 15 - 12)$

11 $(8.75 - 6.5, 5 - 8.5) \oplus (10 - 12.75, 2.8 + 6)$

12 $(600 - 700, 0) \oplus (500 - 800, -\sqrt{27})$

23 **274** Exploring ideas

The linear function

From earlier lessons you know that the loci of certain functions are lines. In this lesson you will learn how to recognize conditions that determine functions of this kind.

A Notice that the conditions expressed in D1 determine functions. Why can you use the ordered pair $(x, 2x + 3)$ to represent each element of the function determined by condition A? Is $2x + 3$ a polynomial?

If the second component of each element of a function can be represented by a polynomial, then the function is a *polynomial function*. The degree of a polynomial function is the same as the degree of the polynomial involved.

B How do you know that each of conditions A through D determines a polynomial function? What is the degree of each function?

A first-degree polynomial function is called a *linear function*. The standard form of a condition that determines a linear function is $f(x) = mx + b$, where $m \neq 0$. Consider m and b as parameters.

C Which conditions expressed in D1 determine linear functions?

D What replacements were made for the parameters m and b in $f(x) = mx + b$ to obtain condition A? What replacements were made in $h(x) = mx + b$ to obtain condition C?

To make a graph of the locus of a linear function, it is convenient to find the intercepts of the locus.

E Think again about condition A. Remember that you can use $(x, 2x + 3)$ to represent each

A $f(x) = 2x + 3$.
B $g(x) = 5x^2 - 6x + 3$.
C $h(x) = -3x + 0$.
D $g(x) = 2x^3 - 1$.

D1

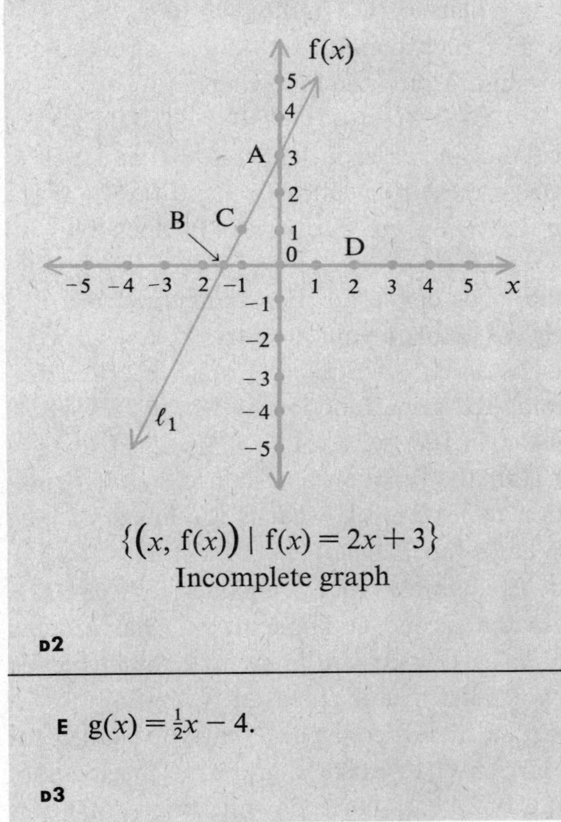

$\{(x, f(x)) \mid f(x) = 2x + 3\}$
Incomplete graph

D2

E $g(x) = \frac{1}{2}x - 4$.

D3

member of the function determined by the condition $f(x) = 2x + 3$. How do you know that point $(0, (2 \cdot 0 + 3))$, or point $(0, 3)$, is the $f(x)$-intercept of the locus of function f?

F Remember that the second coördinate of an x-intercept of a locus is 0. If $f(x) = 0$, what x satisfies $0 = 2x + 3$? What is the x-intercept of the locus of function f?

So far, you have determined two points in the locus of function f. The line determined by these two points is represented in D2.

G In the graph in D2, what letter names the x-intercept of the locus of function f? What letter names the $f(x)$-intercept?

H Point C is point $(-1, 1)$. Point D is point $(2, 0)$. Which ordered pair, $(-1, 1)$ or $(2, 0)$, is a solution of $f(x) = 2x + 3$?

I Is the ordered pair that you selected in exercise H associated with a point in ℓ_1?

Every point in the line determined by points $(-\frac{3}{2}, 0)$ and $(0, 3)$ is in the locus of the function determined by $f(x) = 2x + 3$. The points in ℓ_1 are the only points in the locus of function f. Hence, ℓ_1 is the locus of function f. It is possible to prove that the locus of any linear function is a line. However, we will accept this without proof. Because any two points determine a line, you need to locate only two points in the locus of a linear function to make a graph of the locus.

J How do you know that the condition expressed in D3 determines a linear function?

K How do you know that point $(0, -4)$ is the $g(x)$-intercept of the locus of function g?

L If $g(x) = 0$, what x satisfies $0 = \frac{1}{2}x - 4$? What element of function g has 0 as its second component?

The first component of $(8, 0)$ is the *zero of the function* determined by $g(x) = \frac{1}{2}x - 4$. For any function, the first component of any member whose second component is 0 is a zero of the function.

M ? How do you know that the zero of function g is the first coördinate of the x-intercept of the locus of function g?

N Do points $(0, -4)$ and $(8, 0)$ determine the locus of function g? Explain your answer.

O Make a graph of the locus of function g.

Next you will examine several characteristics of linear functions. To do this, you will work with the standard form of a condition that determines a linear function. That is, you will work with $f(x) = mx + b$.

A You know that x is in the domain of the function that is determined by $f(x) = mx + b$ if $mx + b$ is a real number. For each m and b, if $x \in D$, is $mx + b \in D$? Use properties of multiplication and addition of real numbers to explain your answer.

B You know that 0 is the first coördinate of the $f(x)$-intercept of the locus of a function determined by $f(x) = mx + b$. If $x = 0$, is $f(0) = b$? What is the $f(x)$-intercept of the locus of function f?

C If $f(x) = 0$, is $0 = mx + b$? How can you obtain $\frac{-b}{m} = x$ from $0 = mx + b$?

D Is $\frac{-b}{m}$ the zero of function f? What is the x-intercept of the locus of function f?

From exercises A through D, you have gained the following information about the linear function. For every real number x, $mx + b$ is also a real number. Therefore, the domain of every linear function is the set of real numbers. The locus of every linear function is a line. Point $(0, b)$ is the $f(x)$-intercept of the locus of function f, and point $\left(\frac{-b}{m}, 0\right)$ is the x-intercept of the locus. $\frac{-b}{m}$ is the zero of the function.

A condition that determines a linear function is expressed in each exercise below. For each exercise, first tell what replacements were made for m and b in $f(x) = mx + b$ to obtain the given condition. Next, give the coördinates of the intercepts of the locus of function f. Then give the zero of the function.

E $f(x) = 15x + 45$.

F $f(x) = 4x - 12$.

G $f(x) = \frac{1}{4}x$.

H $f(x) = -6x + 2$.

I $f(x) = -3x - 7$.

J $f(x) = .5x + .01$.

Next you will see how the replacements for m and b in $f(x) = mx + b$ affect a linear function.

A What condition do you obtain if you replace m by 1 and b by 0 in $f(x) = mx + b$? If you replace m by 3 and b by -10?

B For each condition that you obtained for exercise A, find the following:

$f(-100)$ $f(-10)$ $f(10)$ $f(100)$

C As x increases in $f(x) = 1x + 0$ and also in $f(x) = 3x - 10$, what happens to $f(x)$?

D ? In $f(x) = mx + b$, if $m > 0$, does $f(x)$ increase as x increases, regardless of b? Does the locus of the function slant upward to the right? Explain your answers.

E Does $f(x) = 3(2x - 3) + 2(5 - 2x)$ determine the same function as $f(x) = 2x + 1$? Is $m > 0$ in $f(x) = 2x + 1$?

F For the function determined by the condition $f(x) = 2x + 1$, what is the image of -2? What is the image of 3?

G The numbers that you named for exercise F are the second components of what ordered pairs? How do you know that these ordered pairs determine the locus of $f(x) = 2x + 1$?

H Use the ordered pairs that you named for exercise G to make a graph of the locus of $f(x) = 2x + 1$. How do you know that this graph also represents the locus of the function determined by $f(x) = 3(2x - 3) + 2(5 - 2x)$?

I How does the graph that you just made show that $f(x)$ increases as x increases?

J What condition do you obtain if you replace m by -1 and b by 0 in $f(x) = mx + b$? If you replace m by -3 and b by -10?

K For each condition that you obtained for exercise J, find the following:

$f(-100)$ $f(-10)$ $f(10)$ $f(100)$

L ? If $m < 0$ in $f(x) = mx + b$, does $f(x)$ decrease as x increases? Does the locus of the function slant downward to the right? Explain your answers.

M In $f(x) = -\frac{1}{2}x + 3$, how do you know that $f(x)$ decreases as x increases?

N Make a graph of $f(x) = -\frac{1}{2}x + 3$. How does your graph show that $f(x)$ decreases as x increases?

O As x increases in $f(x) = 2x - 1$, what happens to $f(x)$?

P You know that $\frac{-b}{m}$ is the zero of a linear function. What is the zero of the linear function determined by $f(x) = 2x - 1$?

Q In $f(x) = 2x - 1$, if $x > \frac{1}{2}$, how do you know that $f(x) > 0$? Describe $f(x)$ if $x < \frac{1}{2}$.

R ? Explain why $f(x) > 0$ in $f(x) = mx + b$ if $m > 0$ and $x > \frac{-b}{m}$. Describe x if $m > 0$ and $f(x) < 0$.

S Put $g(x) = (2x - 1)(x + 3) - 2(x^2 + 5x + 3)$ in the form $g(x) = mx + b$. How do you know that $g(x)$ decreases as x increases? What is the zero of function g?

T Explain why $g(x) < 0$ if and only if $x > -1\frac{4}{5}$. Describe $g(x)$ if $x < -1\frac{4}{5}$.

U ? Explain why $f(x) < 0$ in $f(x) = mx + b$ if $m < 0$ and $x > \frac{-b}{m}$. Describe x if $m < 0$ and $f(x) > 0$.

In this lesson you learned that a function determined by $f(x) = mx + b$ is a linear function. You also studied the rôle of the parameters m and b in $f(x) = mx + b$ and used this information to determine the loci of linear functions.

On your own

Each condition expressed in D4 determines a function. Use D4 in connection with exercises 1 through 4.

1 Which conditions determine polynomial functions?

F $f(x) = x^2 - 4.$

G $g(x) = 7x - 14.$

H $h(x) = \frac{3}{x + 1}.$

I $g(x) = -5x.$

D4

J $f(x) = 3x.$

K $f(x) = -\frac{1}{2}(x - 4).$

L $f(x) = (x - 3)(x + 2) - (x + 4)(x + 1).$

M $f(x) = (x + 2)(x + 3) - (2 + x)^2.$

D5

2 Which conditions determine linear functions?

3 Name the zero of each linear function.

4 For each linear function, name the intercepts of the locus.

Use D5 in connection with exercises 5 through 13. Each condition expressed in D5 determines a linear function.

5 Put each condition in the standard form $f(x) = mx + b$.

6 Name the intercepts of the locus of each function.

7 For which functions does $f(x)$ increase as x increases?

8 For which functions does $f(x)$ decrease as x increases?

9 Name the zero of each function.

10 For each function, describe $f(x)$ if x is greater than the zero of the function.

11 For each function, describe $f(x)$ if x is less than the zero of the function.

12 For which function does the locus contain the point of origin?

13 The loci of which two functions intersect in a point in the $f(x)$-axis?

The locus of a linear function is described in each exercise below. Make a graph of each locus.

14 Point $(-3, 1)$ and point $(2, 2)$ are in the locus.

15 Points $(1, -2)$ and $(2, 4)$ are in the locus.

16 The zero of the function is 2, and point $(-2, -4)$ is in the locus.

17 In the locus of the function, the x-intercept is the same as the $f(x)$-intercept, and point $(1, 2)$ is in the locus.

18 The first coördinate of each point in the locus of the function is the additive inverse of the second coördinate of the point.

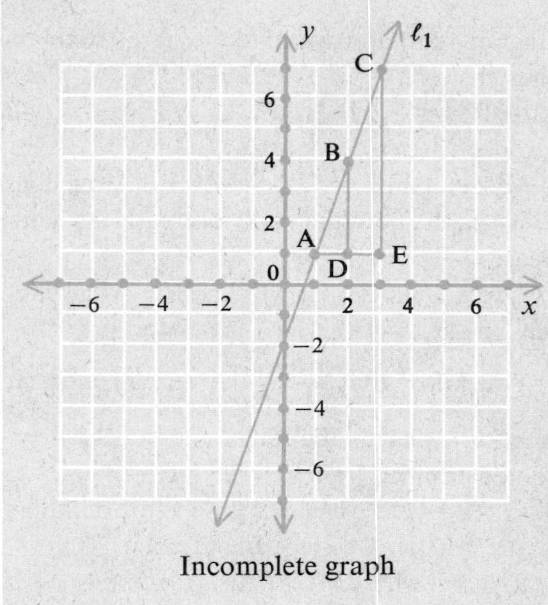

Incomplete graph

D1

slope of a segment (slōp). For any non-vertical segment AB, if the components of (x_1, y_1) are the coördinates of point A and if the components of (x_2, y_2) are the coördinates of point B, then $\frac{y_2 - y_1}{x_2 - x_1}$ is the slope of $\overline{AB}$.

23 275 Exploring ideas

Slope of a line

In the last lesson you learned how the replacement for the parameter m in a condition of the form $f(x) = mx + b$ affects the line that is the locus of the condition. In this lesson you will use the coördinates of the points in a line to find the number that is the replacement for m in $f(x) = mx + b$.

A Look at D1. Line ℓ_1 is the locus of a function determined by a condition of the form $y = mx + b$. In this case, is m less than zero, or is m greater than zero? Use the graph to explain your answer.

We will use segments AB, AC, AD, and so on, to find a number that is associated with each of these segments. Points A, B, and C are in ℓ_1.

B Is $2 - 1$, or 1, the measure of $\overline{AD}$? What is $m(\overline{BD})$?

C If you divide $m(\overline{BD})$ by $m(\overline{AD})$, what quotient do you obtain?

From the graph you can tell that point B is 1 unit to the right of point A and 3 units above point A. Now you will see how these numbers and the quotient that you obtained for exercise C are related to the coördinates of the endpoints of $\overline{AB}$.

D What number do you obtain if you subtract the second coördinate of point A from the second coördinate of point B? If you subtract the first coördinate of A from the first coördinate of B? What number do you obtain if you divide the difference of the second coördinates by the difference of the first coördinates?

E What number do you obtain if you subtract the second coördinate of point B from the second coördinate of point A? If you subtract the first coördinate of B from the first coördinate of A? If you divide the difference of the second coördinates by the difference of the first coördinates?

Notice that you obtain the same quotient when you subtract the coördinates of point A from the coördinates of point B and then divide as when you subtract the coördinates of point B from the coördinates of point A and then divide. In each case, the difference of the second coördinates is the dividend. Notice also that each quotient is the same as $\frac{m(\overline{BD})}{m(\overline{AD})}$.

The quotient 3 is called the *slope* of $\overline{AB}$. The slope of any non-vertical segment is the result of dividing the difference of the second coördinates of the endpoints by the difference of the first coördinates of the endpoints.

F Look again at D1. What is $m(\overline{AE})$? What is $m(\overline{CE})$? Point C is how many units to the right of point A and how many units above it?

G If you divide $m(\overline{CE})$ by $m(\overline{AE})$, what number do you get?

H What replacements can you make in (x_1, y_1) to obtain the coördinates of A? In (x_2, y_2) to obtain the coördinates of C?

I If you use the coördinates of points A and C as replacements in $(y_2 - y_1) \div (x_2 - x_1)$, what quotient do you get? What is the slope of $\overline{AC}$?

J Is the slope of $\overline{AC}$ the same number that you obtained for exercise G?

K What is the slope of $\overline{BC}$?

So far, you have found that each of segments AB, AC, and BC has a slope of 3. It is possible to use properties of similar triangles to prove that any two segments that are included in the same non-vertical or the same non-horizontal line have the same slope.

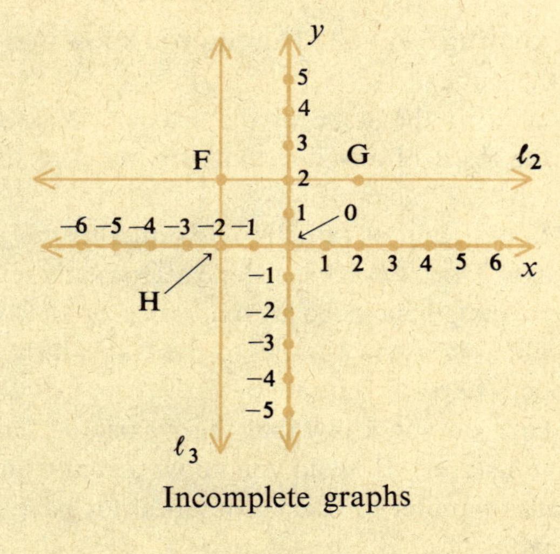

Incomplete graphs

D2

slope of a line. If ℓ is a non-vertical line in the coördinate plane, then the slope of ℓ is the slope of any segment that is included in ℓ.

L Now look at D2. Line ℓ_2 is a horizontal line. In other words, it is parallel to the x-axis. $\overline{FG}$ is included in ℓ_2. How do you know that the second coördinate of point F is the same as the second coördinate of point G? What is the slope of $\overline{FG}$?

M ? If points (x_1, y_1) and (x_2, y_2) are the endpoints of a segment that is included in the x-axis, or that is included in a line parallel to the x-axis, why is y_2 equal to y_1? Is $y_2 - y_1 = 0$?

N ? What is the slope of any segment that is included in the x-axis or in a line parallel to the x-axis?

In exercises B through N, you have developed the property that is expressed below.

If ℓ is a non-vertical line, then all segments that are included in ℓ have the same slope.

Since all the segments included in a particular non-vertical line have the same slope, we can say that the *slope of a line* is the slope of any segment included in the given line.

O Look again at D2. How do you know that 0 is the slope of ℓ_2?

P What is the slope of the x-axis? What is the slope of any line that is parallel to the x-axis?

Q Look again at D2. $\overline{FH}$ is parallel to the y-axis. Does $\overline{FH}$ have a slope? Does any segment that is included in the y-axis or that is included in a line parallel to the y-axis have a slope? Explain your answers.

R How do you know that the y-axis does not have a slope? How do you know that any line that is parallel to the y-axis does not have a slope?

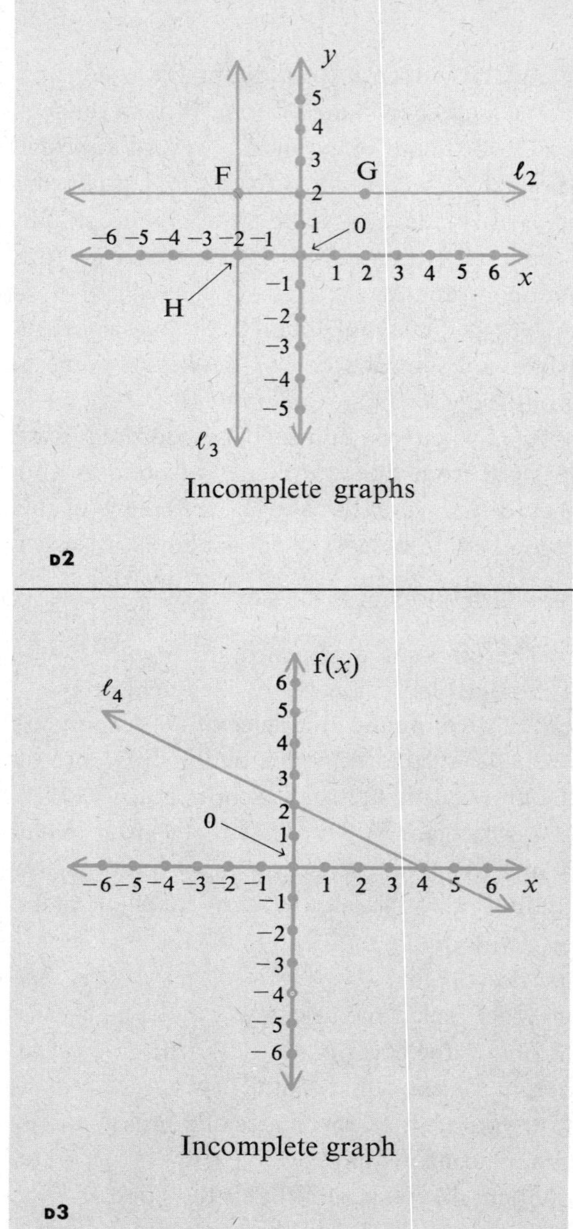

Incomplete graphs

D2

Incomplete graph

D3

You have used the slope of a segment to find the slope of a line. In the following exercises you will see that the replacement for m in $f(x) = mx + b$ is the same as the slope of the line that is the locus of a condition of the form $f(x) = mx + b$.

A Consider the function that is determined by $f(x) = -\frac{1}{2}x + 2$. What is the x-intercept of the locus of function f? What is the $f(x)$-intercept of the locus?

B The line determined by points (4, 0) and (0, 2) is represented in D3. Explain why ℓ_4 is the locus of $f(x) = -\frac{1}{2}x + 2$.

C You know that the slope of ℓ_4 is the slope of any segment that is included in ℓ_4. Use the coördinates of the intercepts of ℓ_4 to find the slope of ℓ_4.

D Now consider the function that is determined by $g(x) = 3x - 6$. How do you know that the locus of the function is a line? What is the x-intercept of the locus? What is the $g(x)$-intercept? Use the coördinates of the intercepts to find the slope of the locus.

E Think of the locus of $f(x) = mx + b$, where $b = 0$. Is point (0, 0) the only intercept of the locus? Consider (x, mx) as the coördinates of any point in the locus other than point (0, 0). How do you know that m is the slope of the segment determined by point (0, 0) and point (x, mx)? What is the slope of the locus of function f?

F Now think of the locus of $f(x) = mx + b$, where $b \neq 0$. You will recall that point

$\left(\frac{-b}{m}, 0\right)$ and point $(0, b)$ are the coördinates of the intercepts of the locus. What is the slope of the segment determined by the intercepts of the locus? What is the slope of the locus of function f?

G Is m the slope of the locus of any function that is determined by a condition of the form $f(x) = mx + b$, where $m \neq 0$?

In lesson 274 you learned that, if $m > 0$ in $f(x) = mx + b$, then the locus of function f slants upward to the right; and if $m < 0$ in $f(x) = mx + b$, then the locus slants downward to the right.

H If the slope of the locus of a function determined by $f(x) = mx + b$ is a positive number, how do you know that $f(x)$ increases as x increases? Does the locus slant upward to the right, or does the locus slant downward to the right?

I If the slope of the locus of a function determined by $f(x) = mx + b$ is a negative number, how do you know that $f(x)$ decreases as x increases? Does the locus slant upward to the right, or does the locus slant downward to the right?

J Suppose that $m = 0$ in $f(x) = mx + b$. How can you obtain $f(x) = b$ from $f(x) = mx + b$? How do you know that function f is a constant function?

K ? If $m = 0$ in $f(x) = mx + b$, what is the $f(x)$-intercept of the locus? Does the locus have an x-intercept? Is the locus either the x-axis or a line parallel to the x-axis? Explain your answers.

From the preceding exercises, you know that, if a given function is determined by a condition of the form $f(x) = mx + b$, then m is the slope of the locus of the given function. We will accept the following statement as true. The locus of a function is a non-vertical line if and only if there is exactly one condition of the form $f(x) = mx + b$ that determines the function.

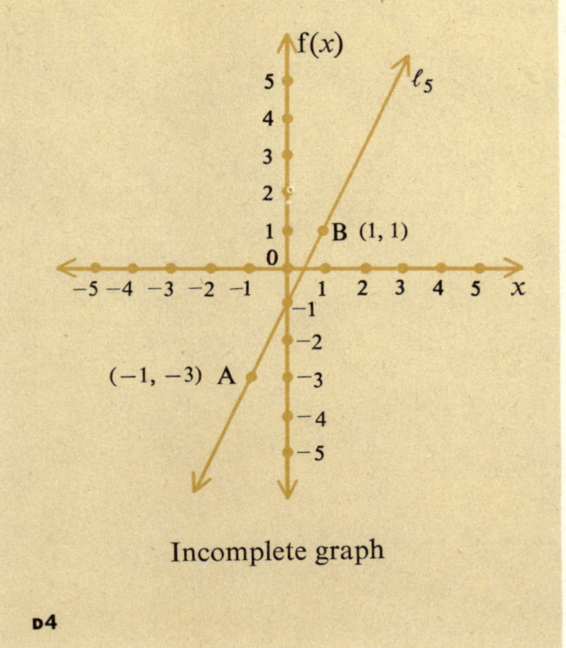

D4

In the exercises that follow, you will learn to develop a condition for the function whose locus is a given line. First you will use the coördinates of two points in the given line and the $f(x)$-intercept of the line to develop the condition.

L Look at D4. You know that ℓ_5 is the locus of a function determined by a condition of the form $f(x) = mx + b$. Use the coördinates of points A and B to find the slope of ℓ_5. How do you know that 2 is the replacement for m in the condition for the function whose locus is ℓ_5?

M Name the coördinates of the point in which ℓ_5 intersects the $f(x)$-axis. How do you know that the second coördinate of this point is the replacement for b in the condition for the function whose locus is ℓ_5?

N Is $f(x) = 2x - 1$ the condition for the function whose locus is represented in D4?

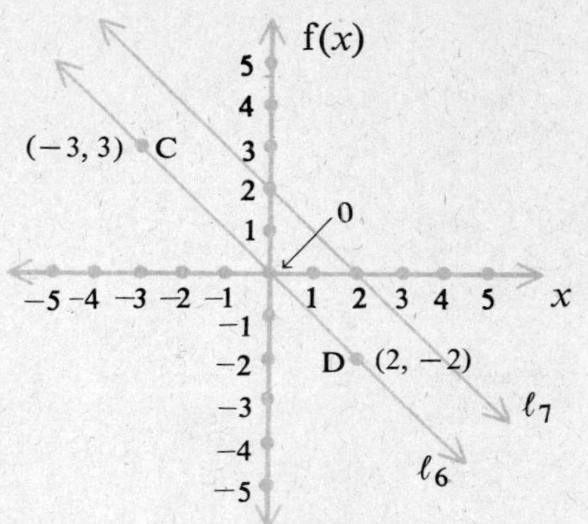

Incomplete graphs

D5

A $\dfrac{f(x) - 3}{x - 2} = 3.$

B $f(x) - 3 = 3(x - 2).$

C $f(x) - 3 = 3x - 6.$

D $f(x) = 3x - 3.$

D6

O Now look at D5. Use the coördinates of points C and D to find the slope of ℓ_6. Use the coördinates of the points in which ℓ_7 intersects the coördinate axes to find the slope of ℓ_7.

P Line ℓ_6 is the locus of what function? Line ℓ_7 is the locus of what function?

Next you will use the slope of a given line and the coördinates of one point in the line to develop a condition of the form $f(x) = mx + b$.

Q Suppose that 3 is the slope of a given line and that point (2, 3) is in the line. Let $(x, f(x))$ represent any other point in the line. How do you know that $\dfrac{f(x) - 3}{x - 2} = 3$?

R Now look at D6. How was each of conditions B, C, and D obtained?

S Is the line that has a slope of 3 and that contains point (2, 3) the locus of the function determined by $f(x) = 3x - 3$? What is the x-intercept of the locus?

T Make a graph of the locus of the function determined by $f(x) = 3x - 3$.

U The locus of what function contains point (0, 1) and has a slope of -2? Make a graph of the locus of the function.

V The locus of what function contains point $(-3, 4)$ and has a slope of 0? Make a graph of the locus of the function.

In this lesson you learned what the slope of a line is and how m in $f(x) = mx + b$ is related to the slope.

On your own

Each pair of points named in exercises 1 through 6 determines a segment. Find the slope of the segment.

1 A (2, 1), B (5, 7)

2 C $(-6, 2)$, D $(-1, -8)$

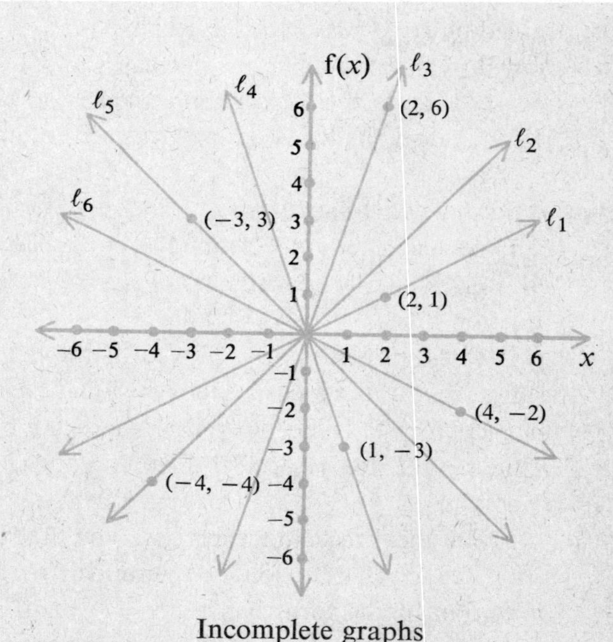

Incomplete graphs

D7

3 E (5, 5), F $(\frac{1}{2}, \frac{1}{2})$
4 G (3, 2), H (0, −4)
5 I (6, −2), J (5, −2)
6 K (−2, 4), L (−1, 2)

Find the slope of the line described in each of exercises 7 through 13.

7 The line determined by point (2, −2) and point (0, −3)

8 The line determined by point (−4, 5) and point (5, 5)

9 The line determined by point (0, 6) and point (2, 0)

10 The locus of the function determined by $f(x) = 3x + 2$

11 The locus of the function determined by $g(x) = -\frac{1}{3}x + 7$

12 The locus of the function determined by $h(x) = 8$

13 The locus of the function determined by $g(x) = 4x$

The lines named in exercises 14 through 19 are represented in D7. Find the slope of each line.

14 ℓ_1 16 ℓ_3 18 ℓ_5
15 ℓ_2 17 ℓ_4 19 ℓ_6

For each of exercises 20 through 27, find the condition for the function whose locus is described.

20 The slope of the locus is 5, and the $f(x)$-intercept is point (0, 0).

21 The slope of the locus is −3, and the $f(x)$-intercept is point (0, 0).

22 The slope of the locus is 2, and point (2, 1) is in the locus.

23 The slope of the locus is −4, and point (−8, 0) is in the locus.

24 The slope of the locus is 0, and point (7, 3) is in the locus.

25 Points (0, 0) and (2, 5) are in the locus.

26 Points (−1, 1) and (2, 2) are in the locus.

27 Points (4, 2) and (−3, 2) are in the locus.

23 276 Exploring ideas

The quadratic function

You have studied linear functions and the loci of these functions. This lesson concerns another special kind of polynomial function.

A Each condition expressed in D1 determines a function. How do you know that each of the conditions expressed in D1 determines a polynomial function? What is the degree of each function?

A second-degree polynomial function is called a *quadratic function*. The standard form of a condition that determines a quadratic function is $f(x) = ax^2 + bx + c$, where a, b, and c are parameters and $a \neq 0$.

B Look again at D1. Which conditions determine quadratic functions? What replacements were made for a, b, and c in $f(x) = ax^2 + bx + c$ to obtain each condition that determines a quadratic function?

Because condition A was obtained by replacing a by 4, b by 0, and c by 0, you can think of $f(x) = 4x^2$ as a condition of the form $f(x) = ax^2$.

C Now consider the function determined by $f(x) = 4x^2$. Is D the domain of the function? Is the set of non-negative real numbers the

A $f(x) = 4x^2$.
B $f(x) = 3x - 5$.
C $f(x) = 2x^2 + 7x + 3$.
D $f(x) = 5x^2 - 2$.

D1

range? Use the graph of the locus, which is shown in D2, to explain your answers.

D For any function f determined by a condition of the form $f(x) = ax^2$, if $a > 0$, what is the domain? What is the range? Explain your answers.

E For $f(x) = 4x^2$, find each of the following: $f(-100)$, $f(-10)$, $f(-1)$, $f(-\frac{1}{2})$.

F In $f(x) = 4x^2$, if x is replaced by successively greater negative numbers, what happens to $f(x)$? Explain why the locus of function f curves downward to the right in the second quadrant.

G For $f(x) = 4x^2$, find each of the following: $f(\frac{1}{2})$, $f(1)$, $f(10)$, $f(100)$.

H In $f(x) = 4x^2$, if x is replaced by successively greater positive numbers, what happens to $f(x)$? How is this change shown in the graph in D2?

I If $a > 0$ in $f(x) = ax^2$, does $f(x)$ decrease as x is replaced by successively greater negative numbers? If $a > 0$ in $f(x) = ax^2$, what happens to $f(x)$ as x is replaced by successively greater positive numbers? Explain your answers.

J The locus of $f(x) = 4x^2$ is symmetric with respect to which axis? Explain why the locus of any function determined by a condition of the form $f(x) = ax^2$ is symmetric with respect to the $f(x)$-axis.

K What is the x-intercept of the locus of $f(x) = 4x^2$? What is the $f(x)$-intercept? What are the intercepts of the locus of any function determined by a condition of the form $f(x) = ax^2$?

L The locus of the function determined by $f(x) = -4x^2$ is represented in D3. Describe the domain and the range of the function.

M For any function determined by $f(x) = ax^2$, if $a < 0$, what are the domain and the range of the function? Explain your answer.

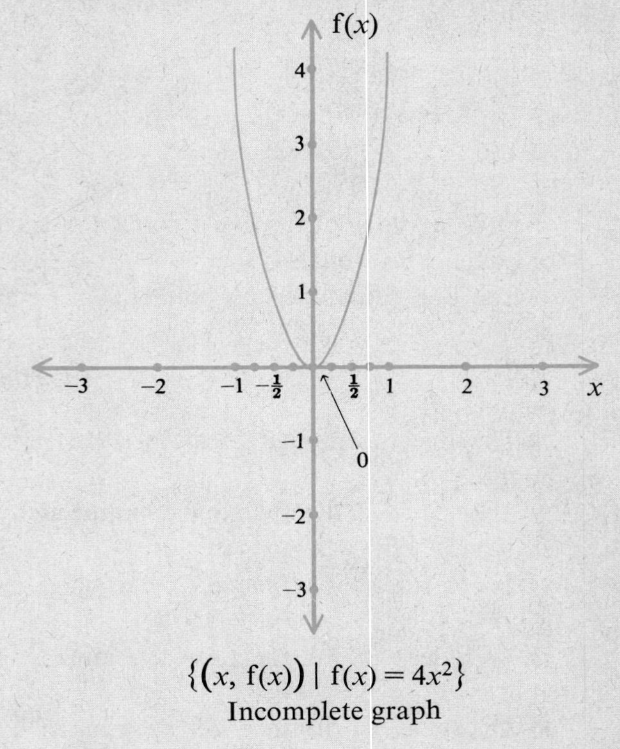

$\{(x, f(x)) \mid f(x) = 4x^2\}$
Incomplete graph

D2

$\{(x, f(x)) \mid f(x) = -4x^2\}$
Incomplete graph

D3

N In $f(x) = -4x^2$, what happens to $f(x)$ as x is replaced by successively greater negative numbers? What happens to $f(x)$ as x is replaced by successively greater positive numbers?

O For any function determined by $f(x) = ax^2$, ? if $a < 0$, what happens to $f(x)$ as x is replaced by successively greater negative numbers? What happens to $f(x)$ as x is replaced by successively greater positive numbers?

From the exercises above, you have the following information about any quadratic function determined by $f(x) = ax^2$:

The domain of the function is D. If $a > 0$, then the range is the set of non-negative real numbers. If $a < 0$, then the range is the set of non-positive real numbers.

If $a > 0$, then $f(x)$ decreases as x is replaced by successively greater negative numbers; and if $a > 0$, then $f(x)$ increases as x is replaced by successively greater positive numbers.

Also, if $a < 0$, then $f(x)$ increases as x is replaced by successively greater negative numbers; and if $a < 0$, then $f(x)$ decreases as x is replaced by successively greater positive numbers.

Point (0, 0) is both the x-intercept and the $f(x)$-intercept of the locus of a function whose condition is of the form $f(x) = ax^2$. The locus is symmetric with respect to the $f(x)$-axis.

Another form of $f(x) = ax^2 + bx + c$ is obtained by replacing b by 0. The result is a condition of the form $f(x) = ax^2 + c$. Next you will investigate the locus of a function determined by a condition of the form $f(x) = ax^2 + c$.

A The loci of two functions determined by conditions of the form $f(x) = ax^2 + c$ are represented in D4. The locus of $f(x) = 4x^2$ is also represented. Look at the graphs of the loci

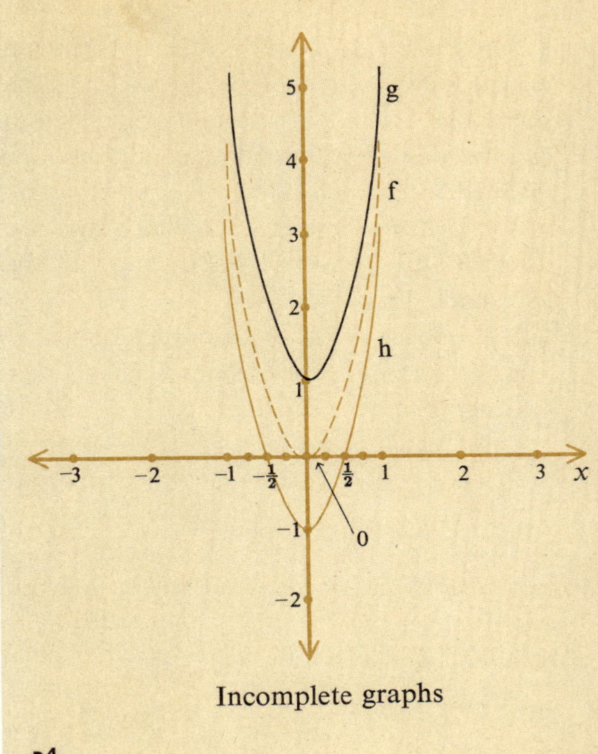

Incomplete graphs

D4

of $g(x) = 4x^2 + 1$ and $h(x) = 4x^2 - 1$. Why is each point in the locus of function g one unit directly above each corresponding point in the locus of function f? Why is each point in the locus of function h one unit below each corresponding point in the locus of function f?

B How is each point in the locus of $f(x) = ax^2 + c$, where $c > 0$, related to a corresponding point in the locus of $f(x) = ax^2$? ? How is each point in the locus of $f(x) = ax^2 + c$, where $c < 0$, related to a corresponding point in the locus of $f(x) = ax^2$?

C On the same graph of D × D, represent the loci of the functions determined by $f(x) = -x^2$, $f(x) = -x^2 + 4$, and $f(x) = -x^2 - 4$.

D How is each point in the locus of $f(x) = -x^2$ related to each corresponding point in the locus of $f(x) = -x^2 + 4$? To each corresponding point in the locus of $f(x) = -x^2 - 4$?

E Name the f(x)-intercept of each locus represented in your graph. How do you know that point (0, c) is the f(x)-intercept of the locus of any function determined by a condition of the form $f(x) = ax^2 + c$?

F Which locus represented in your graph does not have an x-intercept? For each of the other loci, name the x-intercepts.

G ? If the locus of the function determined by $f(x) = ax^2 + c$ intersects the x-axis, is there at least one x such that $ax^2 + c = 0$? If $ax^2 + c = 0$, is $x = \sqrt{\frac{-c}{a}} \vee x = -\sqrt{\frac{-c}{a}}$? Are point $\left(\sqrt{\frac{-c}{a}}, 0\right)$ and point $\left(-\sqrt{\frac{-c}{a}}, 0\right)$ the x-intercepts of the locus? Explain your answers.

H Look again at D4. In $h(x) = 4x^2 - 1$, $a = 4$, $c = -1$, $\sqrt{\frac{-c}{a}} = \sqrt{\frac{1}{4}}$, and $-\sqrt{\frac{-c}{a}} = -\sqrt{\frac{1}{4}}$. Therefore, point $(\frac{1}{2}, 0)$ and point $(-\frac{1}{2}, 0)$ are the x-intercepts of the locus of function h. What point is the x-intercept of the locus of function f?

I ? Think again about $g(x) = 4x^2 + 1$. Why are there no x-intercepts in the locus of function g?

J Now you know that point (0, c), point $\left(\sqrt{\frac{-c}{a}}, 0\right)$, and point $\left(-\sqrt{\frac{-c}{a}}, 0\right)$ are the intercepts, if they exist, of the locus of a function determined by $f(x) = ax^2 + c$. What are the intercepts of the locus of $f(x) = 4x^2 + 16$? Of $f(x) = 4x^2 - 16$? Of $f(x) = -4x^2 + 16$?

K ? Earlier in this lesson, you learned that, if the condition for a function is of the form $f(x) = ax^2$, then the locus of the function is symmetric with respect to the f(x)-axis. How do you know that, if the condition for a function is of the form $f(x) = ax^2 + c$, then the locus is symmetric with respect to the f(x)-axis?

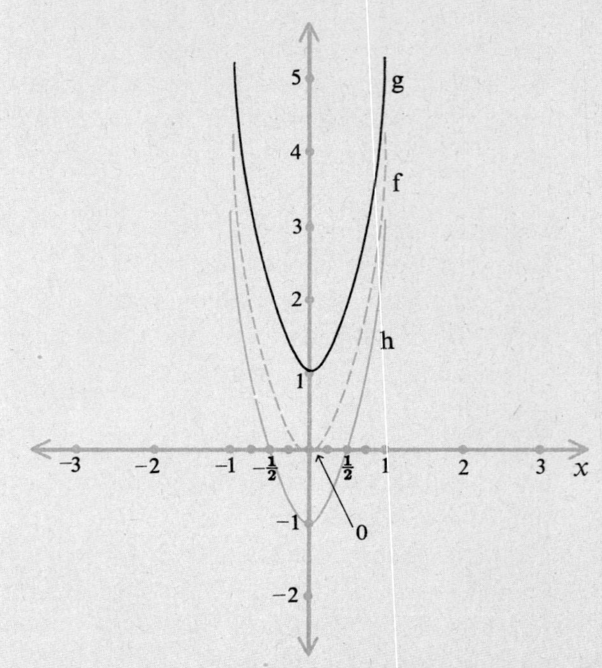

Incomplete graphs

D4

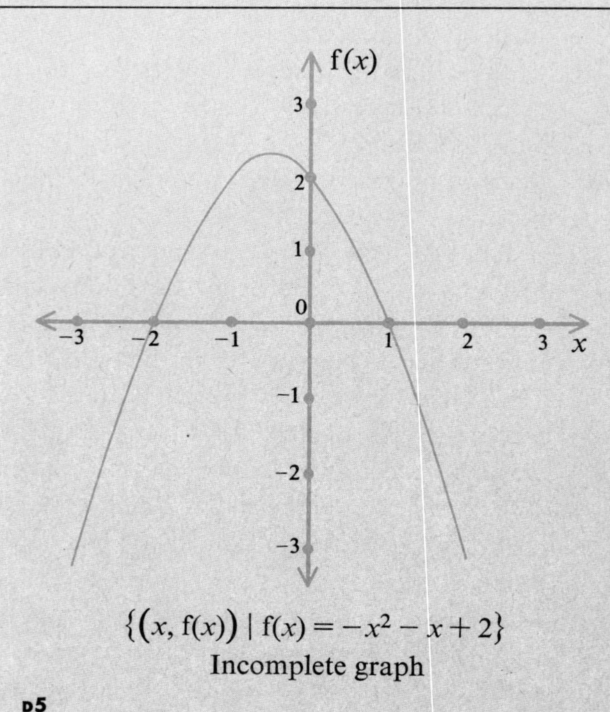

$\{(x, f(x)) \mid f(x) = -x^2 - x + 2\}$
Incomplete graph

D5

L If $a > 0$ in $f(x) = ax^2 + c$, what happens to ? $f(x)$ as x is replaced by successively greater negative numbers? What happens to $f(x)$ as x is replaced by successively greater positive numbers? Explain how $f(x)$ decreases and increases with x if $a < 0$ in $f(x) = ax^2 + c$.

The locus of each quadratic function considered so far in this lesson is a parabola. In fact, the locus of any quadratic function is a parabola. Next you will study the parabola that is the locus of a quadratic function whose condition is of the form $f(x) = ax^2 + bx + c$, where b is *not* equal to zero.

A Is $f(x) = -x^2 - x + 2$ of the form $f(x) = ax^2 + bx + c$? What replacements were made for a, b, and c in $f(x) = ax^2 + bx + c$ to obtain $f(x) = -x^2 - x + 2$?

B What is the $f(x)$-intercept of the locus of $f(x) = -x^2 - x + 2$?

C How do you know that $(0, c)$ is the $f(x)$-intercept of the locus of any function whose condition is of the form $f(x) = ax^2 + bx + c$?

D For $f(x) = -x^2 - x + 2$, find $f(1)$, $f(2)$, $f(-\frac{1}{2})$, $f(-1)$, and $f(-2)$.

E Use your answers for exercise D to help you name five points in the locus of function f.

The points that you named for exercise E are contained in the parabola that is represented in D5. This parabola is the locus of the function determined by $f(x) = -x^2 - x + 2$.

F Use the parabola represented in D5 to de- ? scribe the domain and the range of the function determined by $f(x) = -x^2 - x + 2$. $f(x)$ increases as x increases if each replacement for x is less than what number? $f(x)$ decreases as x increases if each replacement for x is greater than what number?

G Look again at D5. Is the locus of function f ? symmetric with respect to the $f(x)$-axis? Suppose that the vertical line that is the locus of $x = -\frac{1}{2}$ were represented in D5. Would the locus of function f be symmetric with respect to this vertical line? Explain your answers.

H What points are the x-intercepts of the locus of function f?

I Copy the graph in D5. In your graph, represent the locus of $f(x) = -x^2 - x$ and the locus of $f(x) = -x^2 - x - 2$. How are the points in each of these loci related to the corresponding points in the locus of the function determined by $f(x) = -x^2 - x + 2$?

J Name the intercepts of the locus of the function determined by $f(x) = -x^2 - x$. Then describe the domain and the range of the function.

K Name the intercepts of the locus of the function determined by $f(x) = -x^2 - x - 2$. Then describe the domain and the range of the function.

In this lesson you learned that a quadratic function is determined by a condition of the form $f(x) = ax^2 + bx + c$. You also observed how the replacements for the parameters a, b, and c in $f(x) = ax^2 + bx + c$ affect the locus of a quadratic function.

On your own

Each condition expressed in D6 determines a quadratic function. Use D6 in connection with exercises 1 through 10.

1 What is the domain of each function?

2 The set of non-negative real numbers is the range of which function?

E $f(x) = 9x^2$.	**H** $f(x) = -9x^2 - 1$.
F $f(x) = 9x^2 - 1$.	**I** $f(x) = 9x^2 + 1$.
G $f(x) = -9x^2$.	**J** $f(x) = -9x^2 + 1$.

D6

E $f(x) = 9x^2$.
F $f(x) = 9x^2 - 1$.
G $f(x) = -9x^2$.
H $f(x) = -9x^2 - 1$.
I $f(x) = 9x^2 + 1$.
J $f(x) = -9x^2 + 1$.

D6

3 The set of non-positive real numbers is the range of which function?

4 What is the range of the function determined by condition I?

5 What is the range of the function determined by condition J?

6 Name the $f(x)$-intercept of the locus of each function.

7 Name each x-intercept of the locus of each function.

8 The loci of which functions are symmetric with respect to the $f(x)$-axis?

9 Name the functions in which $f(x)$ increases as x is replaced by successively greater negative numbers and in which $f(x)$ decreases as x is replaced by successively greater positive numbers.

10 Name the functions in which $f(x)$ decreases as x is replaced by successively greater negative numbers and in which $f(x)$ increases as x is replaced by successively greater positive numbers.

Exercises 11 through 17 concern the function determined by $f(x) = \frac{1}{4}x^2 + 4$.

11 What is the domain of function f?

12 What is the range of function f?

13 Name the $f(x)$-intercept of the locus of the function.

14 If each replacement for x is less than 0, what happens to $f(x)$ as x increases?

15 If each replacement for x is greater than 0, what happens to $f(x)$ as x increases?

16 Each point in the locus of a function g is four units below its corresponding point in the locus of function f. What condition determines function g? Name the intercepts of the locus of function g.

17 Each point in the locus of a function h is eight units below its corresponding point in the locus of function f. What condition determines function h? Name the intercepts of the locus of function h.

18 Name the $f(x)$-intercept of the locus of the function determined by $f(x) = x^2 - x - 6$.

19 Explain why points $(3, 0)$ and $(-2, 0)$ are x-intercepts of the locus of the function determined by $f(x) = x^2 - x - 6$.

20 If points $(3, 4)$ and $(1, 4)$ are in the locus of a function determined by a condition of the form $f(x) = ax^2 + bx + c$, the locus of the function must be symmetric with respect to a vertical line. Describe the vertical line.

SPECIAL CHALLENGE

A function is said to *transform* each member of its domain onto a member of its range. For example, the function f determined by $f(x) = x + 3$ transforms 2 onto 5.

A Onto what number does function f transform -3? Onto what number does function f transform 0?

When the domain and the range of a function are sets of points, the function is called a *geometric transformation*.

B Look at D1. The transformation T_1 is determined by $T_1(x) = x + 3$. Onto what point does T_1 transform point -2? What point is $T_1(0)$?

C The domain of T_1 is the line. What is the range of T_1?

T_1 is a one-to-one transformation that transforms the line *onto itself*. You can see that, for each point a, $T_1(a) \neq a$. This means that there are no *fixed points* under T_1.

D Suppose that points a and b are the endpoints of a segment and that $a \neq b$. Then the

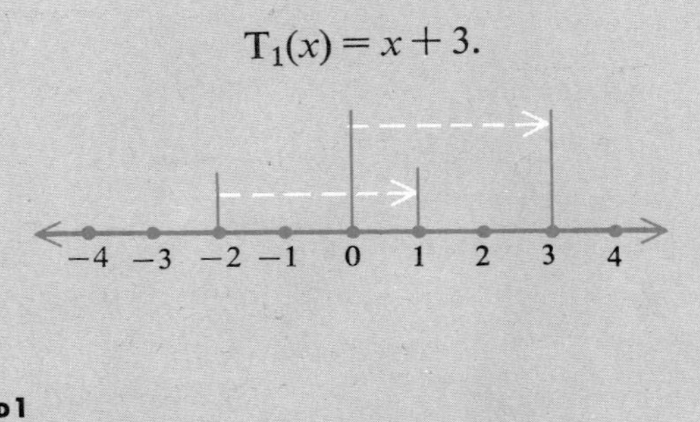

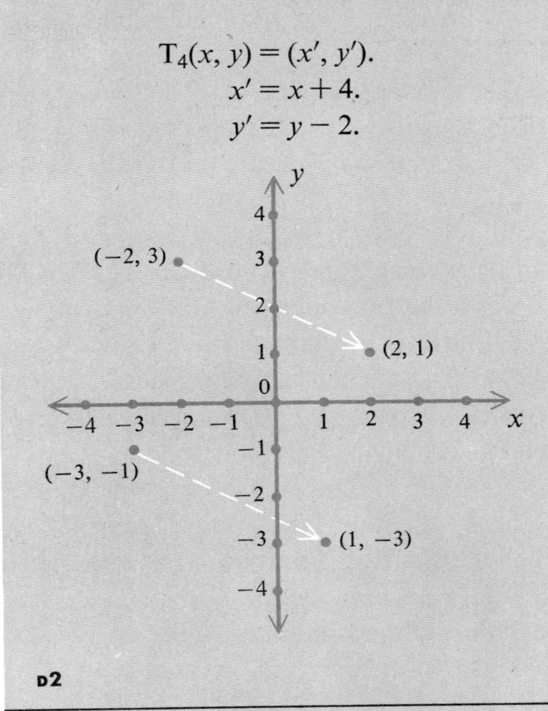

$T_5(x, y) = (x', y').$

$x' = x \cos 30 - y \sin 30.$

$y' = x \sin 30 + y \cos 30.$

D3

length of this segment is $| a - b |$. What is the length of the segment whose endpoints are $T_1(a)$ and $T_1(b)$?

T_1 is a *distance-preserving transformation.* This means that, for any two points a and b, the distance between a and b is equal to the distance between $T_1(a)$ and $T_1(b)$.

E How many points are fixed points under T_2 if $T_2(x) = 5x$? Prove that T_2 is not a distance-preserving transformation.

F How many fixed points are there under the transformation T_3 if $T_3(x) = 2x - 5$? Prove that T_3 is not a distance-preserving transformation.

The transformation given in D2 transforms a plane onto itself. Notice that more than one condition is necessary to determine T_4.

Consider point $(-2, 3)$. Since $x = -2$, $x' = -2 + 4$, or 2. (The symbol x' is read "x prime.") Since $y = 3$, $y' = 3 - 2$, or 1. Thus, $T_4(-2, 3) = (2, 1)$.

G How can you obtain $T_4(-3, -1) = (1, -3)$?

T_4 is a distance-preserving transformation that is commonly called a *translation*. There are no fixed points under T_4.

H In $\triangle ABC$, $A = (7, 10)$, $B = (-5, 2)$, and $C = (-3, -1)$. What are the vertices of the triangle onto which T_4 transforms $\triangle ABC$? Make a drawing to show this transformation in the real plane.

I What point is transformed onto the origin by T_4?

J Look at D3. Show that $T_5(5, 2)$ is approximately equal to $(3.33, 4.232)$.

K What is $T_5(-3, 0)$?

L Make a drawing to show the transformations of $(5, 2)$ and $(-3, 0)$ under T_5.

M What point remains fixed under T_5?

T_5 is a distance-preserving transformation that is commonly called a *rotation*. The origin is a fixed point under T_5. In other words, the origin is the center of rotation. T_5 is a rotation of 30 degrees.

N What two conditions determine a rotation of 45 degrees? Onto what point does this rotation transform point $(5, 0)$?

$$T_6(x, y) = (x', y').$$
$$x' = x.$$
$$y' = -y.$$

D4

$$T_8(x, y) = (x', y').$$
$$x' = 4x - 3y.$$
$$y' = x + 2y.$$

D5

O Study T_6 given in D4. Let $H = (-3, 1)$, $K = (2, 5)$, and $L = (3, 0)$. Make a drawing of $\triangle HKL$ in the real plane.

P Make a drawing of $T_6(\triangle HKL)$ in the drawing that you made for exercise O.

Q Which points are fixed points under T_6?

T_6 is a distance-preserving transformation that is commonly called a *reflection*. The x-axis is a fixed set of points under T_6. We say that T_6 is a reflection in the x-axis.

R T_7 is the transformation that is determined by $T_7(x, y) = (x', y')$, where $x' = y$ and $y' = x$. Make a drawing to show that T_7 is a reflection in the line that is the locus of $y = x$. Show the following points and their transformations in your drawing.

$(5, 3)$ $(-2, -6)$ $(8, -2)$ $(2, -7)$

Some of the most important geometric transformations are not distance-preserving transformations. T_8, given in D5, is an important kind of transformation that does not preserve distance.

S Make a drawing to show segment AB and $T_8(\overline{AB})$. Let $A = (1, -2)$ and $B = (-3, 2)$.

T Prove that the origin is a fixed point under the transformation T_8.

U Show that $T_8[(2, -1) \oplus (-4, 5)] = T_8(2, -1) \oplus T_8(-4, 5)$.

APPLYING MATHEMATICS

For each problem, write a sentence that expresses a condition. Then give the answer to the problem. Use 3.14 as an approximation of π.

1 An airplane is headed south in a wind whose velocity is 45 mi. per hour east. The speed of the airplane, with no wind, is 220 mi. per hour. What is the resultant velocity of the airplane? (Ones)

2 The regular price of a coat was \$60. During a sale, the price of the coat was reduced to \$36. The discount was what per cent of the regular price?

3 Marcia bought orange, grape, and lime popsicles for a party. Altogether, she bought 36 popsicles. She bought 4 times as many orange popsicles as grape popsicles. She bought the same number of grape popsicles as lime popsicles. How many popsicles of each flavor did Marcia buy?

4 Tim is 65 in. tall. At a certain time of day, he casts a shadow 50 in. long. At the same time of day, Edith casts a shadow 40 in. long. What is Edith's height in inches?

5 The length of an ultraviolet wave is less than 10^{-6} meters and greater than 10^{-9} meters. What is the length of an ultraviolet wave in centimeters?

6 Last year 625 girls and 800 boys were enrolled in the Lewistown High School. 1.6% of the girls and 6 of the boys had records of perfect attendance. How many more girls than boys had records of perfect attendance?

7 In eleven years, Martin will be more than 42 years old. Nineteen years ago, he was less than 23 years old. How old is Martin now?

8 A can of fruit is in the shape of a right circular cylinder. The length of a radius of a base of the cylinder is 2.5 in. The height of the can is 8 in. What is the volume of the can in cubic inches?

9 An airplane left Kennedy Airport and flew east at a rate of 510 mi. per hour. At the same time another airplane left the airport and flew west at a rate of 350 mi. per hour. After how many hours were the two airplanes 1075 mi. apart?

10 Mr. Walton has \$7230 in a savings account. The interest is compounded semiannually at a rate of $2\frac{1}{2}\%$ per 6-month period. If he makes no deposits or withdrawals, how much will Mr. Walton have in his account after drawing interest for three 6-month periods?

11 Mr. Lee invested part of \$800 at 5% and the remainder at 6%. How much did he invest at 6% if his total interest after three years amounted to \$133.17?

12 A merchant wants to make a mixture of seed to sell for \$.95 per pound from seed that sells for \$.85 per pound and seed that sells for \$1.10 per pound. How many pounds of \$.85 seed should he use in 70 lb. of the mixture?

13 A regulation baseball diamond is in the shape of a square whose sides are 90 ft. in length. How many feet must the catcher throw the ball to reach second base? (Ones)

14 $\overrightarrow{CD}$ is 85 mi. long and directed south. $\overrightarrow{DE}$ is 110 mi. long and directed west. What is the length in miles and what is the direction of the sum of $\overrightarrow{CD}$ and $\overrightarrow{DE}$? (Ones)

15 An agent collected a sum of money for the Kenman Company. The rate of commission that he received for collecting the money was 23%. After he took his commission from the sum of money, he paid the remainder, which was \$1948.87, to the Kenman Company. How much was the agent's commission?

16 A number is not greater than the difference of -236.5 and -189.7. What is the number?

CHECKING UP

If you have trouble with this test, you can find help in lessons 273 through 276.

Test 256

1 What is the degree of a linear function?

2 If $f(x) = 5x^2$, then what is $f(-3)$?

3 What is the h(x)-intercept of the locus of function h if $h(x) = 2x - 5$?

4 What replacements were made to obtain $g(x) = -8x^2 - 5$ from $g(x) = ax^2 + bx + c$?

5 What is the x-intercept of the locus of the function determined by $f(x) = 8 - 5x$?

6 What is the standard form of a condition that determines a linear function?

7 What is the slope of a line that is parallel to the x-axis?

8 At what point does the locus of $y = 3x + 2$ intersect the x-axis?

9 What is the degree of the function that is determined by $g(x) = 2x - 7 + 5x^2 - 3x^4$?

10 Name the two x-intercepts of the locus of $\{(x, y) \mid y = \sqrt{25 - x^2}\}$.

11 $h(x) = h(-x)$. With respect to which axis is the locus of function h symmetric?

12 What are the intercepts of the locus of $3y + 5 = 2x$?

13 What is the slope of the locus of the condition $3 - 5y = 4x$?

14 What is the standard form of a condition that determines a quadratic function?

15 What is the zero of the function determined by $f(x) = -2x + 5$?

16 What are the intercepts of the locus of $g(x) = 5x^2 - 45$?

17 What is the slope of a line that contains points $(-2, 5)$ and $(3, -3)$?

18 $h(x) = 3x + 2$. Make a graph of the locus of function h.

19 $f(x) = 3x^2 - 5$. Make a graph of the locus of function f.

quadratic condition for equality in one variable. A polynomial condition of the form $ax^2 + bx + c = 0$, where $a \neq 0$.

23 | 277 **Exploring ideas**

Solving quadratic conditions by factoring

This lesson concerns quadratic functions and quadratic conditions. You will use factoring to solve certain quadratic conditions for equality. Then you will discover how the solutions of a quadratic condition are related to the zeros of a quadratic function.

A How can $g(x) = 2x^2 - 3$ be obtained from $g(x) = ax^2 + bx + c$? What is the degree of the function determined by $g(x) = 2x^2 - 3$?

The condition $g(x) = 2x^2 - 3$ requires that the second component of each element of function g be 3 less than the product of 2 and the square of the first component. $(x, 2x^2 - 3)$, therefore, represents each member of function g. If the second component of an element of function g is 9, then the first component is an x that satisfies $2x^2 - 3 = 9$.

B How do you know that $\sqrt{6}$ and $-\sqrt{6}$ are the solutions of $2x^2 - 3 = 9$? Name the two elements of function g whose second components are 9.

C If the second component of $(x, 2x^2 - 3)$ is 5, then the first component satisfies what condition? How do you know that 2 and -2 are the first components of the members of function g whose second components are 5?

D Name the two elements of function g that have second components of 7.

E Name the member of the function determined by $f(x) = 9x^2 - 4$ for which $f(x) = -4$.

F If 0 is the second component of a member of function f, then the first component is a solution of $9x^2 - 4 = 0$. How do you know that $\frac{2}{3}$ and $-\frac{2}{3}$ are the solutions of $9x^2 - 4 = 0$?

A second-degree polynomial condition such as $9x^2 - 4 = 0$ is a *quadratic condition for equality in one variable.* The standard form of this kind of condition is $ax^2 + bx + c = 0$.

G In lesson 274 you learned that a zero of a function is the first component of a member whose second component is 0. Are the solutions of $9x^2 - 4 = 0$ the zeros of the function determined by $f(x) = 9x^2 - 4$?

H Explain why the zeros of the function determined by $f(x) = \frac{1}{9}x^2 - 16$ are the solutions of $\frac{1}{9}x^2 - 16 = 0$. Name the zeros of function f.

I ? If zeros exist for a function whose condition is of the form $f(x) = ax^2 + c$, why are $\sqrt{\frac{-c}{a}}$ and $-\sqrt{\frac{-c}{a}}$ the zeros? Describe a and c if function f has at least one zero.

J What quadratic condition must be satisfied by the zeros of the function determined by $g(x) = x^2 - 5x + 6$? Show that 2 and 3 are the zeros of function g.

K How do you know that $f(x) = (x - 3)^2$ determines the same function as the condition $f(x) = x^2 - 6x + 9$? What quadratic condition must be satisfied by a zero of the function determined by $f(x) = (x - 3)^2$? Show that 3 is a zero of function f.

L Explain why the quadratic condition $4x^2 - 10x + 6 = 0$ must be satisfied by the zeros of the function determined by the condition $g(x) = 2(x - 1)(2x - 3)$.

M A function h is determined by the condition $h(x) = (x - 5)^2 - 2x + 3$. What quadratic condition is satisfied by the zeros of function h?

N ? If zeros exist for a function determined by $f(x) = ax^2 + bx + c$, are the zeros the solutions of $ax^2 + bx + c = 0$?

Now you know that the zeros of quadratic functions are the same as the solutions of certain quadratic conditions. In the following exercises you will use properties of real numbers to find the solutions of these conditions.

One theorem that you will find helpful in solving quadratic conditions is the conditional $ab = 0 \Rightarrow (a = 0 \vee b = 0)$, which you proved in lesson 222. Use this theorem to explain why each of the conditionals expressed in exercises A, B, and C is true for each x.

A $3x = 0 \Rightarrow (3 = 0 \vee x = 0)$.

B $4(x - 5) = 0 \Rightarrow (4 = 0 \vee x - 5 = 0)$.

C $(x + 3)(2x - 5) = 0 \Rightarrow (x + 3 = 0 \vee 2x - 5 = 0)$.

To find the solutions of a quadratic condition like $x^2 + x = 2$, you can derive an equivalent condition. Look at D1, which shows how to derive $x = 1 \vee x = -2$ from $x^2 + x = 2$.

D How was condition B obtained from A?

E How can you use factoring to obtain C?

F Does $ab = 0 \Rightarrow (a = 0 \vee b = 0)$ justify condition D? Justify condition E.

The chain of conditions expressed in D1 is a proof of $x^2 + x = 2 \Rightarrow (x = 1 \vee x = -2)$. From this conditional, we know only that, if $x^2 + x = 2$ has any solutions, then they are the solutions of $x = 1 \vee x = -2$. However, since it is also possible to prove the conditional $(a = 0 \vee b = 0) \Rightarrow ab = 0$, we will accept $x = 1 \vee x = -2 \Leftrightarrow x^2 + x = 2$ without proof. This means that we will accept the solutions of $x = 1 \vee x = -2$ as the solutions of $x^2 + x = 2$. To make certain that we have not made an error in deriving the chain of conditions, we will also check the solutions of $x = 1 \vee x = -2$ in $x^2 + x = 2$.

A $x^2 + x = 2$.
B $x^2 + x - 2 = 0$.
C $(x - 1)(x + 2) = 0$.
D $x - 1 = 0 \vee x + 2 = 0$.
E $x = 1 \vee x = -2$.

D1

F $-2x^2 + 128 = 0$.
G $x^2 - 64 = 0$.
H $(x - 8)(x + 8) = 0$.
I $x - 8 = 0 \vee x + 8 = 0$.
J $x = 8 \vee x = -8$.

D2

G Is $1^2 + 1 = 2$? Is $(-2)^2 + (-2) = 2$? Is $x^2 + x = 2$ equivalent to $x = 1 \vee x = -2$?

H Tabulate $\{x \mid x^2 + x = 2\}$. Name the zeros of function f when $f(x) = x^2 + x - 2$.

I Why can you use $ab = 0 \Rightarrow (a = 0 \vee b = 0)$ to derive a disjunction from the condition $(2x - 3)(x + 1) = 0$? What is the disjunction?

J What is the solution of each simple condition in $2x - 3 = 0 \vee x + 1 = 0$?

K If $(2x - 3)(x + 1) = 0$ is true, explain why $x = 1.5 \vee x = -1$ is also true. How do you know that $(2x - 3)(x + 1) = 0$ is equivalent to $x = 1.5 \vee x = -1$?

L Tabulate $\{x \mid (2x - 3)(x + 1) = 0\}$. Name the zeros of the function that is determined by $g(x) = (2x - 3)(x + 1)$.

Tabulate the solution set of each quadratic condition expressed in exercises M through P.

M $(x - 4)(9x - 18) = 0$.

N $(3x + 4)(2x + 1) = 0$.

O $x^2 + 4x - 5 = 0$.

P $x^2 + 6 = -5x$.

Q If zeros exist for the function determined by $f(x) = 128 - 2x^2$, are the zeros the solutions of $-2x^2 + 128 = 0$? Explain your answer.

D2 shows how to obtain $x = 8 \vee x = -8$ from $-2x^2 + 128 = 0$. You can use these steps

F $-2x^2 + 128 = 0.$
G $x^2 - 64 = 0.$
H $(x - 8)(x + 8) = 0.$
I $x - 8 = 0 \vee x + 8 = 0.$
J $x = 8 \vee x = -8.$

D2

K $\frac{1}{25}x^2 + \frac{1}{5}x + \frac{9}{4} = 2.$
L $\frac{1}{25}x^2 + \frac{1}{5}x + \frac{1}{4} = 0.$
M $4x^2 + 20x + 25 = 0.$
N $(2x + 5)(2x + 5) = 0.$
O $2x + 5 = 0.$
P $x = -\frac{5}{2}.$

D3

to help you find the zeros of the function determined by $f(x) = 128 - 2x^2$.

R Justify each condition expressed in D2.

S The chain of conditions given in D2 is a proof of what conditional? How can you show that the converse of the conditional is true? Tabulate the solution set of the condition $-2x^2 + 128 = 0$. Name the zeros of the function determined by $f(x) = 128 - 2x^2$.

T The chain of conditions given in D3 is a proof of what conditional? Justify each step of the proof.

U Show that, for each x, if statement P is true, then statement K is true. Tabulate the solution set of condition K. What is the zero of the function that is determined by the condition $f(x) = \frac{1}{25}x^2 + \frac{1}{5}x + \frac{1}{4}$?

Tabulate the solution set of each condition expressed below.

V $2y^2 = -7y + 9.$
W $3x^2 = 4x.$
X $(x + 1)^2 + (x - 1)(x + 1) = 0.$
Y $x^2 = \frac{1}{3}x - \frac{1}{36}.$
Z $(x + 3)(x - 2) = 6x.$

In this lesson you learned that the zeros of a quadratic function determined by a condition of the form $f(x) = ax^2 + bx + c$ are the solutions of a quadratic condition of the form $ax^2 + bx + c = 0$. You also learned how the property $ab = 0 \Rightarrow (a = 0 \vee b = 0)$ can be applied in finding the solutions of certain quadratic conditions.

On your own

Tabulate the solution set of each condition expressed in exercises 1 through 15.

1 $(x + 2)(12x + 3) = 0.$
2 $x^2 - 4x - 32 = 0.$
3 $30 + 11x + x^2 = 0.$
4 $10x^2 + 15x = 8x + 12.$
5 $-20x - 2x^2 = -(5x + 50).$
6 $\frac{4}{9}x^2 + 2 = -2x.$
7 $(x - 5)(2x - 4) = (2x - 4)^2.$
8 $6x^2 = 12x.$
9 $-x^2 = 12x.$
10 $(x + \sqrt{6})(x - \sqrt{6}) = 0.$
11 $x^2 - 25 = 5 - x.$
12 $17x^2 = 17.$
13 $(x - 3)^2 - 9 = 0.$
14 $(x - 5)^2 = 25.$
15 $10x^2 + \frac{5}{4}x = -x - \frac{1}{8}.$

Each condition expressed in exercises 16 through 26 determines a quadratic function. Find the zeros of each function.

16 $g(x) = x^2 - 4x - 12.$
17 $f(x) = 9x^2 - 16.$
18 $h(x) = 4x^2 - 20x + 25.$
19 $g(x) = x^2 - 9(x - 2).$
20 $f(x) = 10x^2 - 5x.$
21 $g(x) = \frac{1}{8}x^2 - (\frac{1}{4}x + 1).$
22 $h(x) = 5x(x - 2) - 15.$
23 $h(x) = -(3x^2 + 6) + (5x^2 - 3x + 1).$
24 $f(x) = (x - \sqrt{3})(x + \sqrt{3}).$
25 $f(x) = 4x^2 - 6.$
26 $h(x) = 6x^2 + 37x - 119.$

27 Suppose that a quadratic condition is of the form $a^2x^2 + 2abx + b^2 = 0$. For example, the condition $x^2 + 6x + 9 = 0$ is of this form, where $a = 1$ and $b = 3$. First find the x that satisfies $a^2x^2 + 2abx + b^2 = 0$ in terms of a and b. Then use your answer to help you tabulate the solution set of $x^2 + 6x + 9 = 0$.

28 Suppose that P_x is a second-degree polynomial in one variable and that 2 and 3 are the only solutions of the quadratic condition $P_x = 0$. Name two binomials that are factors of P_x.

29 If $P_x = 0$ is a quadratic condition, and if $x - a$ and $x - b$ are binomial factors of P_x, what are the solutions of $P_x = 0$?

30 If 7 and -2 are the zeros of a quadratic function f, what condition determines the function?

---

23 278 Exploring ideas

Completing the square

In the last lesson you used your knowledge of factoring to solve quadratic conditions. In this lesson you will study another method of solving quadratic conditions. This new method is known as *completing the square*. It is convenient to use when you are solving conditions like $x^2 - 2x + 4 = 0$, where the factors of the polynomial that is equal to zero are not immediately apparent.

A Look at D1. How was condition B obtained from condition A? Is B a quadratic condition in standard form?

B Explain how each of conditions C, D, and E was obtained.

A $x^2 + 14x + 49 = 16.$
B $x^2 + 14x + 33 = 0.$
C $(x + 3)(x + 11) = 0.$
D $x + 3 = 0 \vee x + 11 = 0.$
E $x = -3 \vee x = -11.$

D1

A $x^2 + 14x + 49 = 16.$
F $(x + 7)^2 = 16.$
G $x + 7 = 4 \vee x + 7 = -4.$
H $x = -3 \vee x = -11.$

D2

C Show that, for each x, if $x = -3 \vee x = -11$, then $x^2 + 14x + 49 = 16$. Tabulate the solution set of condition A.

D Condition A is expressed again in D2. Is $x^2 + 14x + 49$ the square of the binomial $x + 7$? How was condition F obtained from condition A?

E What theorem justifies condition G?

> **REMINDER**
> The universe for x is D. The universe for a is the set of non-negative real numbers. For each x and a,
> $x^2 = a \Leftrightarrow x = \sqrt{a} \vee x = -\sqrt{a}.$
> *See lesson 255, page 237.*

F Justify condition H.

Notice that condition E, expressed in D1, is the same as condition H, expressed in D2. To obtain E from A, first we expressed condition A as a trinomial equal to 0. Then we factored the trinomial and applied the theorem $ab = 0 \Rightarrow (a = 0 \vee b = 0)$. To obtain H from A, first we recognized $x^2 + 14x + 49$ as the square of a binomial. Then we applied the theorem $x^2 = a \Leftrightarrow x = \sqrt{a} \vee x = -\sqrt{a}$. In both cases, we found that $\{-3, -11\}$ is the solution set of $x^2 + 14x + 49 = 16$.

G Use steps similar to those given in D2 to find $\{x \mid x^2 - 8x + 16 = 2\}$.

H How do you know that each member of ? $\{4 + \sqrt{2},\ 4 - \sqrt{2}\}$ is a zero of the function determined by $f(x) = x^2 - 8x + 14$?

In each condition expressed in exercises I through L, the left side is the square of a binomial. For each condition, first express the left side in a factored form. Then apply the theorem $x^2 = a \Leftrightarrow x = \sqrt{a} \vee x = -\sqrt{a}$ and tabulate the solution set of the original condition.

I $x^2 - \frac{5}{2}x + \frac{25}{16} = 7$. **K** $x^2 + .6x + .09 = 0$.

J $x^2 - x + \frac{1}{4} = 1$. **L** $x^2 + 16x + 64 = 100$.

In some quadratic conditions, the left side is not the square of a binomial; for each condition of this kind, we can try to find an equivalent condition in which one side is the square of a binomial. To find the equivalent condition, you will need the following information concerning the squares of binomials.

A Let $x + a$ represent a binomial such as $x + 3$ or $x - 5$. What is the square of $x + a$?

$x^2 + 2ax + a^2$ is a polynomial in x that has three terms. You can think of 1 and x^2 as factors of the first term. The factor 1 is sometimes called the *coefficient* (kō′ə fish′ənt) of x^2. The second term of $x^2 + 2ax + a^2$ contains the factors $2a$ and x. The coefficient of x is $2a$.

B Think of $x^2 + 10x$ as the first two terms of a trinomial of the form $x^2 + 2ax + a^2$. What replacement was made for a in $2ax$ to obtain $10x$? What is a^2? The trinomial $x^2 + 10x + 25$ is the square of what binomial?

C If you think of $x^2 - 10x$ as the first two terms of a trinomial of the form $x^2 + 2ax + a^2$, then $2a = -10$ and $a = -5$. This means that a^2 must be equal to 25. Therefore, 25 is the third term of the trinomial. $x^2 - 10x + 25$ is the square of what binomial?

Notice how the second term of $x^2 + 2ax + a^2$ is related to the third term. If you find one half the coefficient of x in $2ax$, you get $\frac{1}{2}(2a)$, or a. If you square this, you get a^2, or the third term of $x^2 + 2ax + a^2$. Therefore, the third term of $x^2 + 2ax + a^2$ is the square of one half the coefficient of the second term.

D Think of $x^2 - \frac{5}{3}x$ as the first two terms of a trinomial that is the square of a binomial. Then the third term of the trinomial is the square of $\frac{1}{2}(-\frac{5}{3})$. Since $(-\frac{5}{6})^2 = \frac{25}{36}$, the third term of the trinomial is $\frac{25}{36}$. What binomial can you square to obtain $x^2 - \frac{5}{3}x + \frac{25}{36}$?

In each exercise below, the first two terms of a trinomial are given. The trinomial is the square of a binomial. For each exercise, find the trinomial and the binomial.

E $x^2 + 4x$ **G** $x^2 + \frac{2}{3}x$ **I** $x^2 - .4x$

F $x^2 - 4x$ **H** $x^2 - \frac{3}{4}x$ **J** $x^2 + .3x$

A $x^2 + 14x + 49 = 16$.
F $(x + 7)^2 = 16$.
G $x + 7 = 4 \vee x + 7 = -4$.
H $x = -3 \vee x = -11$.

D2

I $x^2 - 1\frac{3}{4} = 3x$.
J $x^2 - 3x = 1\frac{3}{4}$.
K $x^2 - 3x + \frac{9}{4} = \frac{9}{4} + 1\frac{3}{4}$.
L $x^2 - 3x + \frac{9}{4} = 4$.

D3

M $(x - \frac{3}{2})^2 = 4$.
N $x - \frac{3}{2} = 2 \vee x - \frac{3}{2} = -2$.
O $x = 3\frac{1}{2} \vee x = -\frac{1}{2}$.

D4

Now you know how to find the third term of a trinomial that is the square of a binomial. In other words, you know how to "complete the square" of a binomial. Let us see how to use this information to solve $x^2 - 1\frac{3}{4} = 3x$. Although one side of $x^2 - 1\frac{3}{4} = 3x$ is not the square of a binomial, you can find an equivalent condition, in which one side is the square of a binomial. D3 shows how to obtain the condition $x^2 - 3x + \frac{9}{4} = 4$ from $x^2 - 1\frac{3}{4} = 3x$.

A Look at D3. Justify condition J. Notice that it is of the form $x^2 + px = q$, where $p = -3$ and $q = 1\frac{3}{4}$.

B ? You can think of $x^2 + px$, or $x^2 - 3x$, as the first two terms of the square of a binomial. Explain why $\frac{9}{4}$ is the term that completes the square.

C Justify conditions K and L, expressed in D3. Notice that in K, $\frac{9}{4}$ is added to $1\frac{3}{4}$ as well as to $x^2 - 3x$.

D The chain of conditions given in D3 is continued in D4. Justify each of conditions M, N, and O.

E Is condition O equivalent to condition I? Tabulate $\{x \mid x^2 - 1\frac{3}{4} = 3x\}$. Name the zeros of the function determined by $f(x) = x^2 - 3x - 1\frac{3}{4}$.

In the preceding exercises, you completed the square of a binomial and used the theorem $x^2 = a \Leftrightarrow x = \sqrt{a} \vee x = -\sqrt{a}$, along with certain other properties, to solve $x^2 - 1\frac{3}{4} = 3x$. That is, you solved a quadratic condition by the method of completing the square. Next, you will use the same method to find the solutions of $2x^2 + 3x - 1 = 0$.

F Look at D5. How was condition Q obtained from condition P? Justify each of conditions R through U.

G Which condition expressed in D5 is of the form $x^2 + px = q$? In this condition, what replacement was made for p? For q?

P $2x^2 + 3x - 1 = 0.$

Q $2x^2 + 3x = 1.$

R $x^2 + \frac{3}{2}x = \frac{1}{2}.$

S $x^2 + \frac{3}{2}x + \frac{9}{16} = \frac{9}{16} + \frac{1}{2}.$

T $x^2 + \frac{3}{2}x + \frac{9}{16} = \frac{17}{16}.$

U $(x + \frac{3}{4})^2 = \frac{17}{16}.$

V $x + \dfrac{3}{4} = \dfrac{\sqrt{17}}{4} \vee x + \dfrac{3}{4} = \dfrac{-\sqrt{17}}{4}.$

W $x = \dfrac{-3 + \sqrt{17}}{4} \vee x = \dfrac{-3 - \sqrt{17}}{4}.$

D5

H ? If $x^2 + \frac{3}{2}x$ are the first two terms of the square of a binomial, why is $\frac{9}{16}$ the term that completes the square? Notice that, in condition S, $\frac{9}{16}$ is added to $\frac{1}{2}$ as well as to $x^2 + \frac{3}{2}x$.

I Now justify conditions V and W. Is condition W equivalent to condition P? Tabulate the solution set of condition P. Why are the members of this set the zeros of the function determined by $f(x) = 2x^2 + 3x - 1$?

Now you will solve $5x^2 + 3 = -16x$.

J Show how $x^2 + \frac{16}{5}x = -\frac{3}{5}$ can be obtained from $5x^2 + 3 = -16x$. If $x^2 + \frac{16}{5}x$ are the first two terms of the square of a binomial, what number is the third term?

K What condition do you obtain when you add $\frac{64}{25}$ to both sides of $x^2 + \frac{16}{5}x = -\frac{3}{5}$? How do you know that $(x + \frac{8}{5})^2 = \frac{49}{25}$ is equivalent to the condition you obtain?

L If you apply $x^2 = a \Leftrightarrow x = \sqrt{a} \vee x = -\sqrt{a}$ to $(x + \frac{8}{5})^2 = \frac{49}{25}$, what disjunction do you obtain?

M Tabulate the solution set of $5x^2 + 3 = -16x$. What are the zeros of the function determined by $f(x) = 5x^2 + 16x + 3$?

N ? Now solve $5x^2 + 3 = -16x$ by factoring. That is, put the condition in the form

$ax^2 + bx + c = 0$ and factor the polynomial that is equal to 0. Then apply the theorem $ab = 0 \Rightarrow (a = 0 \vee b = 0)$.

Solve each of conditions O through R by completing the square.

O $x^2 + 6x = 7$.

P $3x^2 + x = \frac{1}{3}$.

Q $2x^2 + x = 10x + 5$.

R $3(4 - x) = x(4 - x)$.

S ? Now consider $x^2 + x = -2$. If $x^2 + x$ are the first two terms of the square of a binomial, why is $\frac{1}{4}$ the term that completes the square? Show that $x^2 + x = -2$ is equivalent to $(x + \frac{1}{2})^2 = -\frac{7}{4}$.

T ? How do you know that no real number satisfies $(x + \frac{1}{2})^2 = -\frac{7}{4}$?

U ? What set is the solution set of $x^2 + x = -2$? Explain why the locus of the function determined by $f(x) = x^2 + x + 2$ cannot intersect the x-axis.

In this lesson you learned how to complete a trinomial that is the square of a binomial. Then you solved quadratic conditions by completing the square of a binomial.

On your own

In each condition expressed in exercises 1 through 10, the left side is the square of a binomial. Tabulate the solution set of each condition.

1 $x^2 + 2x + 1 = 0$.

2 $x^2 + 16x + 64 = 0$.

3 $16x^2 - 64x + 64 = 49$.

4 $9x^2 - 36x + 36 = 25$.

5 $.01x^2 + .06x + .09 = 0$.

6 $x^2 + 6x + 9 = 7$.

7 $100x^2 - 10x + \frac{1}{4} = 5$.

8 $25x^2 + \frac{10}{3}x + \frac{1}{9} = -8$.

9 $x^2 + 2ax + a^2 = 0$.

10 $a^2x^2 + 2abx + b^2 = 0$.

The first two terms of a trinomial that is the square of a binomial are expressed in each of exercises 11 through 20. For each exercise, first complete the square of the binomial. Then give the binomial.

11 $x^2 + 6x$

12 $x^2 - 6x$

13 $x^2 + \frac{2}{7}x$

14 $x^2 + .6x$

15 $x^2 - \frac{4}{3}x$

16 $x^2 + \frac{8}{5}x$

17 $x^2 + 2px$

18 $x^2 + px$

19 $x^2 + (a + b)x$

20 $x^2 + 2abx$

For each condition expressed in exercises 21 through 35, use the method of completing the square to help you tabulate the solution set.

21 $x^2 + 2x = 9$.

22 $3x^2 + 18x = 12$.

23 $x(x - 1) = 30$.

24 $\frac{1}{2}x^2 = \frac{5}{2} - 2x$.

25 $\frac{x^2}{8} - \frac{x}{4} = 1$.

26 $2x^2 - 3x - 5 = 0$.

27 $2(3x^2 + 10) = 23x$.

28 $16 - x^2 = 6x$.

29 $x^2 = 5x + 14$.

30 $x^2 + 2x = 2$.

31 $x^2 + 6x = 0$.

32 $\frac{x^2}{3} - x = 18$.

33 $ax^2 + 2abx = 0$.

34 $x^2 + 4ax = 3a^2$.

35 $x^2 + 2(a - b)x = 3(a - b)^2$.

---

23 279 **Exploring ideas**

The quadratic formula

So far, you have used the methods of factoring and of completing the square to find the solutions of quadratic conditions. Now we will develop a formula that can be used to solve any condition that can be put in the form $ax^2 + bx + c = 0$, where $a \neq 0$.

A How can $2x^2 + 7x + 1 = 0$ be obtained from $ax^2 + bx + c = 0$? Solve $2x^2 + 7x + 1 = 0$ by completing the square.

B Every quadratic condition for equality in one variable is of the form $ax^2 + bx + c = 0$. For $2x^2 + 7x + 1 = 0$, the value of a is 2, the value of b is 7, and the value of c is 1. What is

A $ax^2 + bx + c = 0 \Rightarrow \left(x = \frac{-b + \sqrt{b^2 - 4ac}}{2a} \vee x = \frac{-b - \sqrt{b^2 - 4ac}}{2a}\right)$.

B $ax^2 + bx + c = 0 \Rightarrow x = \frac{-b \pm \sqrt{b^2 - 4ac}}{2a}$.

D1

the value of $\sqrt{b^2 - 4ac}$? What is the value of $-b + \sqrt{b^2 - 4ac}$? Of $-b - \sqrt{b^2 - 4ac}$?

C For $2x^2 + 7x + 1 = 0$, what is the value of $\frac{-b + \sqrt{b^2 - 4ac}}{2a}$? Of $\frac{-b - \sqrt{b^2 - 4ac}}{2a}$?

Notice that the numbers that you obtained for exercise C are the solutions of the condition $2x^2 + 7x + 1 = 0$.

D Consider the condition $2x^2 - x - 3 = 0$. What is the value of $\frac{-b + \sqrt{b^2 - 4ac}}{2a}$? What is the value of $\frac{-b - \sqrt{b^2 - 4ac}}{2a}$? Use the method of completing the square to find the solutions of $2x^2 - x - 3 = 0$.

The exercises you have just completed suggest that the solutions of a quadratic condition such as $2x^2 - x - 3 = 0$ are the values of $\frac{-b + \sqrt{b^2 - 4ac}}{2a}$ and $\frac{-b - \sqrt{b^2 - 4ac}}{2a}$. You can prove that this is so by completing the square to solve $ax^2 + bx + c = 0$, where $a \neq 0$. For certain replacements of a, b, and c, you can prove that the conditional expressed by sentence A in D1 is true.

E What two statements are the components of conditional A?

F One of the components of conditional A is a disjunction. What are the components of this disjunction?

The only difference between the components that you named for exercise F is that in one the dividend involves adding $\sqrt{b^2 - 4ac}$ and in the other the dividend involves subtracting $\sqrt{b^2 - 4ac}$. This idea can be expressed by the symbol at the right. This symbol is read "plus or minus." It is used in sentence B in D1 to express the same conditional as that expressed by sentence A.

$\pm$

Now look at D2, in which a proof of conditional B is given. Statement 1 is the hypothesis.

1 $ax^2 + bx + c = 0$.

2 $x^2 + \left(\frac{b}{a}\right)x + \frac{c}{a} = 0$.

3 $x^2 + \left(\frac{b}{a}\right)x = -\frac{c}{a}$.

4 $x^2 + \left(\frac{b}{a}\right)x + \frac{b^2}{4a^2} = \frac{b^2}{4a^2} - \frac{c}{a}$.

5 $\left(x + \frac{b}{2a}\right)^2 = \frac{b^2 - 4ac}{4a^2}$.

6 $x + \frac{b}{2a} = \pm\sqrt{\frac{b^2 - 4ac}{4a^2}}$.

7 $x + \frac{b}{2a} = \pm\frac{\sqrt{b^2 - 4ac}}{2a}$.

8 $x = -\frac{b}{2a} \pm \frac{\sqrt{b^2 - 4ac}}{2a}$.

9 $x = \frac{-b \pm \sqrt{b^2 - 4ac}}{2a}$.

D2

A $ax^2 + bx + c = 0 \Rightarrow \left(x = \frac{-b + \sqrt{b^2 - 4ac}}{2a} \vee x = \frac{-b - \sqrt{b^2 - 4ac}}{2a}\right).$

B $ax^2 + bx + c = 0 \Rightarrow x = \frac{-b \pm \sqrt{b^2 - 4ac}}{2a}.$

D1

1 $ax^2 + bx + c = 0.$

2 $x^2 + \left(\frac{b}{a}\right)x + \frac{c}{a} = 0.$

3 $x^2 + \left(\frac{b}{a}\right)x = -\frac{c}{a}.$

4 $x^2 + \left(\frac{b}{a}\right)x + \frac{b^2}{4a^2} = \frac{b^2}{4a^2} - \frac{c}{a}.$

5 $\left(x + \frac{b}{2a}\right)^2 = \frac{b^2 - 4ac}{4a^2}.$

6 $x + \frac{b}{2a} = \pm\sqrt{\frac{b^2 - 4ac}{4a^2}}.$

7 $x + \frac{b}{2a} = \pm\frac{\sqrt{b^2 - 4ac}}{2a}.$

8 $x = -\frac{b}{2a} \pm \frac{\sqrt{b^2 - 4ac}}{2a}.$

9 $x = \frac{-b \pm \sqrt{b^2 - 4ac}}{2a}.$

D2

G How can you obtain statement 2 from statement 1? How can you obtain statement 3 from statement 2? How can you obtain statements 4 and 5?

Notice that statements 1 through 5 are the steps you would use to solve $ax^2 + bx + c = 0$ by completing the square.

H ? Suppose that the replacements for a, b, and c are such that $b^2 - 4ac$ is a negative number. Is $\frac{b^2 - 4ac}{4a^2}$ also negative? In this case, how do you know that statement 5 is false for each x?

I Now suppose that the replacements for a, b, and c are such that $b^2 - 4ac$ is greater than or equal to 0. Is $\frac{b^2 - 4ac}{4a^2} \geqq 0$? In this case, how can you obtain statement 6 from statement 5?

J ? How was statement 7 obtained from statement 6? Remember that $\sqrt{a^2} = |a|$ and that $|a| = a \vee |a| = -a$.

K How was statement 8 obtained from statement 7? How was statement 9 obtained from statement 8?

The steps in D2 prove that conditional B, expressed in D1, is true if the replacements for a, b, and c are such that $b^2 - 4ac \geqq 0$. It is also possible to prove the converse of this conditional. This means that the condition $ax^2 + bx + c = 0$ is equivalent to the condition $x = \frac{-b \pm \sqrt{b^2 - 4ac}}{2a}$. Thus, the real numbers that satisfy the condition $ax^2 + bx + c = 0$ are $\frac{-b + \sqrt{b^2 - 4ac}}{2a}$ and $\frac{-b - \sqrt{b^2 - 4ac}}{2a}$.

The condition $x = \frac{-b \pm \sqrt{b^2 - 4ac}}{2a}$ is the *quadratic formula*. From now on, you can use the quadratic formula to solve quadratic conditions for equality in one variable. In the remainder of this lesson, you will use the quadratic formula to investigate the nature of the solutions of quadratic conditions.

A For $4x^2 + 20x + 25 = 0$, what is the value of $b^2 - 4ac$? What is the value of $\sqrt{b^2 - 4ac}$? What is the value of $\frac{-b + \sqrt{b^2 - 4ac}}{2a}$? What is the value of $\frac{-b - \sqrt{b^2 - 4ac}}{2a}$?

B ? Tabulate $\{x \mid 4x^2 + 20x + 25 = 0\}$. How many members are in this solution set?

C When $b^2 - 4ac = 0$, how does the value of $\frac{-b + \sqrt{b^2 - 4ac}}{2a}$ compare with the value of $\frac{-b - \sqrt{b^2 - 4ac}}{2a}$?

From exercises B and C, you can observe that, if $b^2 - 4ac = 0$ for a given condition of the form $ax^2 + bx + c = 0$, then the given condition has exactly one solution. The solution is $\frac{-b}{2a}$. The expression $b^2 - 4ac$ is called the *discriminant* (dis krim′ə nənt) of $ax^2 + bx + c = 0$. You can determine how many solutions a quadratic condition has if you know the discriminant of the condition.

D What number is the discriminant of the condition $x^2 + 2x + 1 = 0$? How many members are in the solution set of $x^2 + 2x + 1 = 0$?

E Tabulate the solution set of the condition $x^2 + 2x + 1 = 0$.

F ? Suppose that $f(x) = x^2 + 2x + 1$. In how many points does the locus of function f intersect the x-axis? Explain your answer.

G What is the discriminant of the condition $2x^2 - 8 = 0$? How does this number compare with zero?

H Tabulate the solution set of $2x^2 - 8 = 0$.

From exercises G and H, you can see that when the discriminant of a given quadratic condition is greater than zero, then the given condition has two solutions.

I What is the discriminant of the condition $2x^2 - 9x - 18 = 0$? How many solutions does the condition have?

J ? Suppose that $f(x) = 2x^2 - 9x - 18$. In how many points does the locus of function f intersect the x-axis? Explain your answer.

K Tabulate $\{x \mid 2x^2 - 9x - 18 = 0\}$.

L ? How does the discriminant of the condition $x^2 - 4x + 7 = 0$ compare with zero? Explain why there are no real numbers that satisfy $x^2 - 4x + 7 = 0$.

From exercise L you can see that when the discriminant of a given quadratic condition is less than zero, then there is no real number that is a solution of the given condition. In other words, the solution set is the empty set when the universe is D. You will recall that, earlier in this lesson, you were able to develop the quadratic formula only for conditions where $b^2 - 4ac$ is not less than zero.

M ? What can you say about the relationship between the locus of $f(x) = x^2 - 4x + 7$ and the x-axis?

For each condition expressed in exercises N through Q, find the number that is its discriminant. Then tell how many solutions the condition has.

N $x(2x + 1) - x(x + 3) = 0.$

O $10x^2 - 175 = x(x + 3).$

P $(2x - 1)^2 = 3x(4x - 6) + 100.$

Q $x(x - 2) = 3(x - 5).$

Now you have the following information concerning quadratic conditions in x, where the universe for x is D:

If the discriminant of the condition is 0, then the condition has exactly one solution. If the discriminant is positive, then the condition has exactly two solutions. If the discriminant is negative, then the condition has no solutions.

For a quadratic condition in which a, b, and c are rational numbers, you can also use the discriminant to decide if any solutions that exist are rational numbers, or if they are irrational numbers.

R What is the discriminant of each quadratic condition expressed in D3? How do you know that each of these conditions has at least one solution?

S Which conditions expressed in D3 have discriminants that are squares of rational numbers? Use the quadratic formula to determine the solutions of each of these conditions.

T Which conditions expressed in D3 have discriminants that are not the squares of rational numbers? Use the quadratic formula to determine the solutions of each of these conditions.

Exercises R, S, and T suggest the following information concerning quadratic conditions in which a, b, and c are rational numbers:

If the discriminant of a given quadratic condition is the square of a rational number, then the solution, or solutions, of the given condition are rational.

If the discriminant of a given quadratic condition is positive but is not the square of a rational number, then the solutions of the given condition are irrational.

U ? Now consider the quadratic condition $x^2 - \sqrt{2}x = 0$, in which b is an irrational number. What is the discriminant? What are the solutions? Does the information in the preceding paragraph apply to such conditions as $x^2 - \sqrt{2}x = 0$?

Determine the discriminant of each condition expressed in exercises V through Y. Then tell how many real numbers satisfy the condition. Finally, tell whether the solution or solutions are rational or irrational.

V $3x^2 + 5x = 2.$ **X** $3x^2 - 5x + 7 = 0.$

W $3x^2 - 5x - 7 = 0.$ **Y** $7x^2 + 10x = 3x.$

C $2x^2 + 5x - 3 = 0.$

D $x(x - 6) = 6x - 36.$

E $x^2 - 6x = -6.$

F $3x^2 = 15.$

D3

G $$\left(\frac{-b + \sqrt{b^2 - 4ac}}{2a}\right)\left(\frac{-b - \sqrt{b^2 - 4ac}}{2a}\right)$$

H $$\frac{(-b + \sqrt{b^2 - 4ac})(-b - \sqrt{b^2 - 4ac})}{4a^2}$$

I $$\frac{(-b)^2 - (\sqrt{b^2 - 4ac})^2}{4a^2}$$

K $$\frac{4ac}{4a^2}$$

J $$\frac{b^2 - (b^2 - 4ac)}{4a^2}$$

L $$\frac{c}{a}$$

D4

A condition of the form $ax^2 + bx + c = 0$ involves the constants a, b, and c. The quadratic formula can be used to show the relationship that exists between these constants and the product and the sum of the solutions of a quadratic condition.

A According to the quadratic formula, what are the solutions of $ax^2 + bx + c = 0$? We will assume that there are two solutions of $ax^2 + bx + c = 0$. That is, we will assume that the discriminant is a positive number.

B Look at D4. Expression G is the product of the solutions of $ax^2 + bx + c = 0$. How was expression H obtained from expression G?

C The dividend of expression H is in the form $(m + n)(m - n)$, where m is $-b$ and n is $\sqrt{b^2 - 4ac}$. What is the product of $(m + n)$ and $(m - n)$?

D What is the product of $(-b + \sqrt{b^2 - 4ac})$ and $(-b - \sqrt{b^2 - 4ac})$?

Expression I was obtained from expression H by finding the product in the dividend of expression H.

E What is the square of $-b$? What is the square of $\sqrt{b^2 - 4ac}$?

Expression J was obtained from expression I by finding the square of $-b$ and the square of $\sqrt{b^2 - 4ac}$.

F How was expression K obtained from expression J? What property was used to obtain expression L from expression K?

The steps in D4 prove the following property of quadratic conditions for equality in one variable.

For each a, b, *and* c, *if* $\mathrm{ax}^2 + \mathrm{bx} + \mathrm{c} = 0$ *has two solutions, then their product is* $\frac{\mathrm{c}}{\mathrm{a}}$.

G What are the solutions of the condition $x^2 - 11x + 24 = 0$? What is the product of these solutions? What is the value of $\frac{c}{a}$ for $x^2 - 11x + 24 = 0$?

Now you will see how $\frac{c}{a}$ is related to the solution of a quadratic condition that has just one solution.

H What is the solution of $4x^2 - 12x + 9 = 0$? For this condition, how does the value of $\frac{c}{a}$ compare with the solution?

You can see that if a quadratic condition has exactly one solution, then $\frac{c}{a}$ is equal to the square of that solution. In other words, $\frac{c}{a}$ is equal to the product of the solution and itself.

I For $1.5x^2 + 12.58x + 21.48 = 0$, what is the discriminant? How many solutions does this condition have? What is the product of these solutions? If -6 is one solution, what is the other solution?

M $$\frac{-b + \sqrt{b^2 - 4ac}}{2a} + \frac{-b - \sqrt{b^2 - 4ac}}{2a}$$

N $$\frac{(-b + \sqrt{b^2 - 4ac}) + (-b - \sqrt{b^2 - 4ac})}{2a}$$

O $$\frac{-2b}{2a}$$

P $$\frac{-b}{a}$$

D5

J What is the discriminant of the condition $\frac{2}{7}x^2 + \frac{3}{5}x - 5\frac{2}{3} = 0$? How do you know that the condition cannot have two solutions both of which are negative?

K Look at D5. Expression M is the sum of the solutions of $ax^2 + bx + c = 0$. What property enables you to obtain expression N from expression M?

L How was expression O obtained from expression N?

M What property was used to derive expression P from expression O?

The steps in D5 prove the following property of quadratic conditions for equality in one variable.

For each a, b, *and* c, *if* $\mathrm{ax}^2 + \mathrm{bx} + \mathrm{c} = 0$ *has two solutions, then their sum is* $\frac{-\mathrm{b}}{\mathrm{a}}$.

N What is the discriminant of the condition $x^2 + 2x - 35 = 0$? What are the solutions? What is the sum of these solutions? What is the value of $\frac{-b}{a}$ for $x^2 + 2x - 35 = 0$?

Now you will see how $\frac{-b}{a}$ is related to the solution of a quadratic condition that has just one solution.

O What is the discriminant of the condition $3x^2 - 30x + 75 = 0$? What is the solution?

How does the value of $\frac{-b}{a}$ for this condition compare with the solution?

You can see that if a quadratic condition has exactly one solution, then $\frac{-b}{a}$ is equal to the sum obtained when the solution is added to itself.

P Suppose that 8 is the value of $\frac{-b}{a}$ for a quadratic condition. If one solution of the condition is -2, what is the other solution?

After you have solved a quadratic condition, you can check each solution in the original condition. You can also check each solution by using the properties concerning the product and the sum of the solutions.

For example, $\{-\frac{1}{3}, 5\}$ is the solution set of $3x^2 - 14x - 5 = 0$. The value of $\frac{c}{a}$ for this condition is $-\frac{5}{3}$. This agrees with the product of $-\frac{1}{3}$ and 5. The value of $\frac{-b}{a}$ for this condition is $\frac{14}{3}$. This agrees with the sum of $-\frac{1}{3}$ and 5.

In a similar way, you can determine that $\{7, 4\}$ is *not* the solution set of the condition $x^2 - 11x + 24 = 0$. The value of $\frac{c}{a}$ for this condition is 24. This does not agree with the product of 7 and 4.

For each condition expressed below, decide if the given set is the solution set of the condition.

Q $x^2 - 6x - 27 = 0.$ $\{9, -3\}$

R $5x^2 - x = 7 - 35x.$ $\{\frac{1}{5}, -7\}$

S $4x^2 = 3.$ $\{\frac{3}{2}, -\frac{3}{2}\}$

In this lesson you derived the quadratic formula, $x = \frac{-b \pm \sqrt{b^2 - 4ac}}{2a}$, from the condition $ax^2 + bx + c = 0$. You used the formula to solve quadratic conditions and you used the discriminant, $b^2 - 4ac$, in studying the nature of the solutions of a quadratic condition.

On your own

For each of exercises 1 through 10, use the quadratic formula to help you tabulate the solution set of the condition.

1 $x^2 - 2x - 3 = 0.$

2 $x^2 = 1.$

3 $-49 + x^2 = 0.$

4 $x^2 = 5x.$

5 $x^2 = 5.$

6 $4x^2 - 4x + 1 = 0.$

7 $4x^2 + 4x + 1 = 0.$

8 $9x^2 = 7.$

9 $5x = 2x^2.$

10 $x^2 = 10(x + 350).$

The number named in each exercise below is the discriminant of a quadratic condition, where a, b, and c are rational. Tell how many solutions the condition has and whether the solutions are rational or irrational.

11 144 **13** 36 **15** 100 **17** 10 **19** -5

12 -36 **14** 0 **16** -10 **18** 16 **20** 28

Use the properties that concern the sums and products of solutions to decide if the set named in each of exercises 21 through 26 is the solution set of the condition expressed.

21 $x^2 + 6x - 7 = 0.$ $\{-7, 1\}$

22 $x^2 - 4x + 3 = 0.$ $\{3, 1\}$

23 $x^2 = 64.$ $\{8, -8\}$

24 $5x^2 + 25 = 0.$ $\{5, -5\}$

25 $12x^2 = 8x + 1.$ $\left\{\frac{2 + \sqrt{7}}{6}, \frac{2 - \sqrt{7}}{6}\right\}$

26 $x^2 + 50 = 5x + 10x.$ $\{-8, -7\}$

Without solving the conditions expressed in exercises 27 through 32, tell how many solutions each condition has. For each condition that has at least one solution, tell if the solutions are rational or irrational numbers.

27 $100x^2 + 10x + \frac{1}{4} = 0.$

28 $5x^2 + 7x + 1 = 0.$

29 $-5x^2 + 7x + 1 = 0.$

30 $12x^2 + 9x + 3 = 0.$

31 $12x^2 - 9x + 3 = 0.$

32 $x^2 + 4 = 0.$

Each condition expressed below determines a function. Tell how many x-intercepts the locus of each function has.

33 $f(x) = x^2 + 5x + 6$.

34 $f(x) = x^2 + 12x + 36$.

35 $f(x) = x^2 - 2x + 100$.

36 $f(x) = x^2 - 2x - 100$.

37 For what replacement of c does the condition $2x^2 + 4x + c = 0$ have exactly one solution? What is the solution?

38 Describe the set of replacements for b for which the locus of $f(x) = x^2 + bx + 9$ will intersect the x-axis in two points.

39 Describe the set of replacements for c for which $2x^2 + 4x + c = 0$ has no solutions.

40 What are the zeros of the function determined by $f(x) = x^2 - 2x - 15$?

---

23 | 280 Exploring ideas

Use of the quadratic formula

In this lesson you will review several methods of solving quadratic conditions. In particular, you will have more practice in using the quadratic formula.

A The development in D1 shows how to solve $x(x + 7) = 8x + 56$ by factoring. Tell how each of conditions B, C, and D was obtained.

B What property justifies condition E?

Notice that condition E is the disjunction of two linear conditions. This disjunction is equivalent to condition A.

C How was condition F obtained from condition E?

D What are the solutions of condition F? How do you know that these solutions are also solutions of condition A? Tabulate the solution set of condition A.

E The development in D2 shows how to solve condition A by completing the square. Justify conditions G and H.

F Condition H is of the form $x^2 + px = q$, where $p = -1$ and $q = 56$. Recall that p is the coefficient of x in $x^2 + px = q$. Therefore, -1 is the coefficient of x in $x^2 - x = 56$. What is the square of $\frac{1}{2}(-1)$? How was condition I obtained from condition H?

G $x^2 - x + \frac{1}{4}$ is the square of what binomial?

Condition J was obtained by factoring the left side of condition I and by finding the sum indicated in the right side of condition I.

H What property enables you to obtain condition K from condition J? How was condition L obtained from condition K?

I How do you know that condition L is equivalent to condition A? Tabulate the solution set of condition A.

A $x(x + 7) = 8x + 56$.
B $x^2 + 7x = 8x + 56$.
C $x^2 - x - 56 = 0$.
D $(x - 8)(x + 7) = 0$.
E $x - 8 = 0 \vee x + 7 = 0$.
F $x = 8 \vee x = -7$.

D1

A $x(x + 7) = 8x + 56$.
G $x^2 + 7x = 8x + 56$.
H $x^2 - x = 56$.
I $x^2 - x + \frac{1}{4} = \frac{1}{4} + 56$.
J $(x - \frac{1}{2})^2 = \frac{225}{4}$.
K $x - \frac{1}{2} = \frac{15}{2} \vee x - \frac{1}{2} = -\frac{15}{2}$.
L $x = 8 \vee x = -7$.

D2

A $x(x+7)=8x+56.$

M $x^2-x-56=0.$

N $x=\dfrac{-b\pm\sqrt{b^2-4ac}}{2a}.$

O $x=\dfrac{-(-1)\pm\sqrt{(-1)^2-4(1)(-56)}}{2(1)}.$

P $x=\dfrac{1\pm\sqrt{1+224}}{2}.$

Q $x=\dfrac{1\pm\sqrt{225}}{2}.$

R $x=\dfrac{1\pm 15}{2}.$

S $x=8 \vee x=-7.$

D3

So far, you have solved $x(x+7)=8x+56$ by factoring and by completing the square. In each case, you found that $\{8, -7\}$ is the solution set of the condition. Now you will solve the same condition by using the quadratic formula.

J Look at D3. To solve condition A by using the quadratic formula, you should first find an equivalent condition that is of the form $ax^2+bx+c=0$. How was condition M obtained from condition A?

K For condition M, what are the values of a, b, and c? What is the discriminant?

Condition N is the quadratic formula. Condition O was obtained by replacing a, b, and c in the quadratic formula by the values that you named for exercise K. The remaining conditions expressed in D3 show the steps in simplifying condition O.

L What are the solutions of condition A that are obtained by using the quadratic formula?

In comparing the three different methods of solving $x(x+7)=8x+56$, you would perhaps conclude that the factoring method is the simplest because the factors of the left side of $x^2-x+56=0$ are obvious. For a condition of the form $ax^2+bx+c=0$, where a, b, and c are non-zero, if you know the binomial factors of the left side, then you can use the factoring method to solve the condition.

If you are working with a condition of the form $ax^2+bx+c=0$, where a, b, and c are non-zero, and you do not know the binomial factors of the left side, then you can use the quadratic formula. You will also discover some cases in which the method of completing the square is convenient.

For each condition expressed below, use the method indicated to help you tabulate the solution set.

M $2x^2+9x=16x+72.$ (Factoring)

N $3x^2-2x-5=0.$ (Quadratic formula)

O $x^2+14x=120.$ (Completing the square)

P $9=4x^2.$ (Factoring)

In exercise P you solved $9=4x^2$ by factoring. This condition can be put in the form $ax^2-c=0$. Notice that the first power of x is not involved in a condition of this form. Such a condition can be solved by putting it in the form $ax^2=c$. Then $x^2=\frac{c}{a}$ and $x=\pm\sqrt{\frac{c}{a}}$. In the case of $9=4x^2$, $a=4$ and $c=9$. Therefore, $x=\pm\sqrt{\frac{9}{4}}$, or $x=\pm\frac{3}{2}$.

Q Tabulate the solution set of $2x^2-5=0$ by using the method described in the preceding paragraph.

Consider $5x^2+2x=0$. This quadratic condition can be put in the form $ax^2+bx=0$. Notice that the condition does not involve a constant term. Such a condition can be solved by the factoring method.

R What monomial and binomial are factors of $5x^2+2x$? Tabulate $\{x \mid 5x^2+2x=0\}$.

Throughout the remainder of this lesson, you will solve quadratic conditions by using the quadratic formula. When using the quadratic formula to solve a given quadratic condition, you should first put the condition in the form $ax^2 + bx + c = 0$ so that you can determine the values of a, b, and c. Then find the discriminant to determine whether or not the condition has any solutions.

A Look at D4. How was condition B obtained from condition A? Justify condition C. What are the values of a, b, and c for condition C?

B What is the discriminant of condition C? Describe the solutions of condition A. That is, tell how many solutions it has and tell whether the solutions are rational or irrational numbers.

C Use the quadratic formula to solve condition C. Then check the solutions by using them as replacements for x in condition A.

D Tabulate the solution set of condition A.

E Put $(x-3)(8x+23) = -4(x^2+17)$ in the form $ax^2 + bx + c = 0$. Find the discriminant of the condition you obtain.

F Describe the solutions of the condition $(x-3)(8x+23) = -4(x^2+17)$. Then solve the condition you obtained for exercise E.

G Check the solutions that you obtained for exercise F by using them as replacements for x in the original condition. Tabulate the solution set of the original condition.

H Look at D5. How was condition E obtained from condition D?

Condition E is easier to solve than condition D. Since these conditions are equivalent, you can use condition E to help you solve condition D.

I Use the discriminant of condition E to help you describe the solutions of condition D.

A $(2x-3)^2 = 8x.$

B $4x^2 - 12x + 9 = 8x.$

C $4x^2 - 20x + 9 = 0.$

D4

D $5x^2 + 20x - 55 = 0.$

E $x^2 + 4x - 11 = 0.$

F $x = \dfrac{-4 \pm \sqrt{4^2 - 4(1)(-11)}}{2(1)}.$

G $x = -2 \pm \sqrt{15}.$

D5

J How was condition F obtained? Tell how condition G was obtained from condition F.

The rational approximation of $\sqrt{15}$ to the nearer thousandth is 3.873. Therefore, a rational approximation of one solution of condition D is -5.873.

K What is a rational approximation of the other solution of condition D to the nearer thousandth?

L Now consider $(7x+3)(x-1) = 2x(x-6)$. Put this condition in the form of the condition $ax^2 + bx + c = 0$.

M What are the values of a, b, and c for $5x^2 + 8x - 3 = 0$? Describe the solutions of $(7x+3)(x-1) = 2x(x-6)$.

N ? Use the quadratic formula to find the solutions of $(7x+3)(x-1) = 2x(x-6)$. Then find rational approximations of these solutions to the nearer thousandth.

Use the quadratic formula to help you tabulate the solution set of each condition expressed below. Then, for the solutions that are irrational, find rational approximations to the nearer thousandth.

O $x^2 - 6x + 4 = 0.$ **Q** $x^2 = 2(x+3).$

P $x^2 = 20x.$ **R** $2x(x-1) = 5.$

In this lesson you have learned how to use the quadratic formula to solve various kinds of quadratic conditions.

On your own

Show how you can solve each condition expressed in exercises 1 through 5 by factoring. Then tabulate the solution set.

1 $x^2 + 3x - 70 = 0$.
2 $9x^2 + 44x - 5 = 0$.
3 $x^2 - 16x + 64 = 0$.
4 $x(x + 2) + 2(x - 6) = 0$.
5 $(7x - 4)(3x + 3) = -2(x + 5)$.

Show how you can solve each condition expressed in exercises 6 through 10 by completing the square. Then tabulate the solution set of the condition.

6 $x^2 - 5x = 6$.
7 $x^2 - 10x = 1$.
8 $x^2 - 3x - \frac{1}{4} = 0$.
9 $4x^2 + 4x = 7$.
10 $x^2 = (\sqrt{7})x$.

For each condition expressed in exercises 11 through 21, use the quadratic formula to help you tabulate the solution set. Then, for each irrational solution, give a rational approximation to the nearer thousandth.

11 $x^2 + 5x - 24 = 0$.
12 $100x^2 = 115x + 6$.
13 $\frac{1}{3}x^2 + 2x = 24$.
14 $\frac{2}{5}x^2 - 4x = 10 - x$.
15 $x(x + 5) = 3x^2$.
16 $2(4 + 5x) = 3x^2$.
17 $(x + 2)(3x - 11) = 2x^2 - x - 1$.
18 $x^2 - 4x = 3$.
19 $x^2 = 3(2x + 1)$.
20 $2x^2 + 10x = -11$.
21 $.5x^2 - 1.6 = 3x$.
22 Solve $2x^2 + 3(\sqrt{3})x + 15 = 0$ by using the quadratic formula.
23 Find the solutions of $| x^2 + 5x | = 4$.

CHECKING UP

If you have trouble with this test, you can find help in lessons 277 through 280.

Test 257

1 What is the coefficient of x in $-3x$?
2 What is the standard form of a quadratic condition for equality in one variable?
3 What trinomial is the square of $x - a$?
4 To obtain $3x^2 - 8x + 5 = 0$, what replacements have been made for a, b, and c?
5 What are the zeros of the function f if $f(x) = 4x^2 - 1$?
6 How can you obtain $x^2 - 2x - 35 = 0$ from $x(x + 5) = 7x + 35$?
7 Tabulate the solution set of the condition $(x + 2)(3x - 5) = 0$.
8 What trinomial is the square of $2x - 3$?
9 When you solve $x^2 - 5x = 2$ by completing the square, what number should you add to each side of the condition?
10 Suppose that $f(x) = x^2 + 6x + 9$. In how many points does the locus of function f intersect the x-axis?
11 Tabulate the solution set of $(x - 2)^2 = 25$.
12 What is the discriminant of the condition $9x^2 - 30x + 25 = 0$?
13 Tabulate $\{x \mid x^2 - 6x + 20 = 11\}$.
14 For $4x^2 + 12x + 9 = 0$, what is the value of $b^2 - 4ac$?
15 Tabulate $\{x \mid x^2 + 3x - 28 = 0\}$.
16 $x^2 + \frac{25}{24}x + \frac{1}{4} = 0$ has two solutions. What is the sum of the solutions?
17 Tabulate the solution set of $2x^2 - 3x = 0$.
18 The discriminant of a quadratic condition in one variable is -6. What do you know about the solution set of this condition?
19 $x^2 + 3.3x - 31.5 = 0$ has two solutions. What is the product of the solutions?
20 A given quadratic condition has one solution. What is the discriminant?

23 281 Exploring ideas

Rational conditions for equality

The linear and quadratic conditions that have been considered so far in this unit are special kinds of polynomial conditions. In this lesson you will study rational conditions for equality that are *not* polynomial conditions.

A Consider condition A expressed in D1. Are $\frac{x+5}{x-10}$ and 0 both rational expressions?

> REMINDER
>
> A rational expression is a polynomial, a quotient of two polynomials, or a sum each of whose terms is a polynomial or a quotient of two polynomials.
>
> *See lesson 251, page 218.*
>
> A condition in which both sides are rational expressions is a rational condition.
>
> *See lesson 258, page 253.*

B Is condition A a rational condition? A polynomial condition? Explain your answers.

You know that $\frac{x+5}{x-10}$ is the quotient of $x+5$ and $x-10$. You can use information that you have concerning the quotient of two numbers to help you find the solutions of rational conditions like $\frac{x+5}{x-10}=0$.

C What is the quotient of zero and any given number? Is there a real number that is the quotient of a given number and zero?

D1

A $\frac{x+5}{x-10}=0.$

D2

B $\frac{x^2-9}{x}=0.$

D Think of a and b as any two real numbers.

? If $\frac{a}{b}=0$, how do you know that $a=0$ and $b\neq 0$? If $a=0$ and $b\neq 0$, how do you know that $\frac{a}{b}=0$?

We can apply the information concerning the quotient of two numbers to conditions that involve the quotient of two polynomials. We will accept the following property of rational conditions without proof.

For each A *and* B, *where* A *and* B *are polynomials,* $\frac{\mathrm{A}}{\mathrm{B}}=0 \Leftrightarrow \mathrm{A}=0 \wedge \mathrm{B}\neq 0.$

E Think again about the condition expressed in D1. How was $\frac{x+5}{x-10}=0$ obtained from $\frac{A}{B}=0$? How do you know that $\frac{x+5}{x-10}=0$ if and only if $x+5=0 \wedge x-10\neq 0$?

F What is the solution of $x+5=0$? Does this solution satisfy $x-10\neq 0$?

G How do you know that $\{-5\}$ is the solution set of $\frac{x+5}{x-10}=0$?

H Now think about condition B expressed in D2. What polynomials have been used as replacements for A and B in $\frac{A}{B}=0$ to obtain condition B?

B $\dfrac{x^2-9}{x}=0.$

D2

C $\dfrac{x^2-x-6}{x^2-4}=0.$

D3

D $\dfrac{x^2}{x+3}-\dfrac{5}{x+3}=0.$

E $\dfrac{3}{x+1}+\dfrac{2}{x-5}=0.$

F $\dfrac{8}{x-1}=\dfrac{3}{x^2+x-2}.$

D4

I You know that $\dfrac{x^2-9}{x}=0$ if and only if $x^2-9=0 \wedge x \neq 0$. What two binomials are factors of x^2-9? What are the solutions of $x^2-9=0$?

J Next you must decide if the solutions of $x^2-9=0$ also satisfy $x \neq 0$. If you replace x by 3 in $x \neq 0$, do you obtain a true statement? Does -3 satisfy $x \neq 0$?

K From exercises I and J, you know that 3 and -3 are the solutions of $x^2-9=0 \wedge x \neq 0$. Tabulate the solution set of condition B.

For each condition of the form $\dfrac{A}{B}=0$ that you have solved so far, each solution of $A=0$ is also a solution of $B \neq 0$. Now you will consider a case in which one of the solutions of $A=0$ is not a solution of $B \neq 0$.

L Look at D3. What replacements have been made for A and B in $\dfrac{A}{B}=0$ to obtain condition C? If $\dfrac{x^2-x-6}{x^2-4}=0$, how do you know that $x^2-x-6=0 \wedge x^2-4 \neq 0$?

M Use the factoring method to find the solutions of $x^2-x-6=0$.

N Which solution of $x^2-x-6=0$ also satisfies $x^2-4 \neq 0$?

O How do you know that $\{3\}$ is the solution set of condition C?

Tabulate the solution set of each condition expressed below.

P $\dfrac{x+3}{x+2}=0.$

Q $\dfrac{x^2-x-12}{x-5x-6}=0.$

R $\dfrac{x+5}{x^2+3x-10}=0.$

S $\dfrac{x^2-4x+4}{x^2+7x+10}=0.$

Next you will solve rational conditions that involve sums and differences of quotients.

A Look at D4. Does each quotient in condition D have the same divisor? How can you obtain $\dfrac{x^2-5}{x+3}$ from $\dfrac{x^2}{x+3}-\dfrac{5}{x+3}$? Put condition D in the form $\dfrac{A}{B}=0$.

B Use the quadratic formula to show that $\sqrt{5}$ and $-\sqrt{5}$ are the solutions of $x^2-5=0$. Are $\sqrt{5}$ and $-\sqrt{5}$ solutions of $x+3 \neq 0$? By what property do you know that $\{\sqrt{5}, -\sqrt{5}\}$ is the solution set of condition D?

C What are the divisors of the quotients in condition E? Explain why $(x+1)(x-5)$, or x^2-4x-5, is the least common multiple of the two divisors.

> REMINDER
>
> A least common multiple of two or more divisors is the simplest expression that has each of the divisors as a factor.
>
> *See lesson 254, page 231.*

G $\dfrac{8}{x+1} + \dfrac{x}{1-x} = \dfrac{-2}{x^2-1}$.

H $\dfrac{8}{x+1} - \dfrac{x}{x-1} = \dfrac{-2}{x^2-1}$.

I $\dfrac{8(x-1) - x(x+1)}{(x+1)(x-1)} = \dfrac{-2}{(x+1)(x-1)}$.

J $\dfrac{-x^2+7x-8}{(x+1)(x-1)} + \dfrac{2}{(x+1)(x-1)} = 0$.

K $\dfrac{-x^2+7x-6}{(x+1)(x-1)} = 0$.

D5

L $\dfrac{4}{x} - 1 = \dfrac{x}{2}$.

M $\dfrac{4-x}{x} = \dfrac{x}{2}$.

N $\dfrac{4-x}{x} - \dfrac{x}{2} = 0$.

O $\dfrac{8-2x}{2x} - \dfrac{x^2}{2x} = 0$.

P $\dfrac{8-2x-x^2}{2x} = 0$.

D6

D Show the steps that you can use to obtain $\dfrac{5x-13}{(x+1)(x-5)}$ from $\dfrac{3}{x+1} + \dfrac{2}{x-5}$.

E Put condition E, expressed in D4, in the form $\dfrac{A}{B} = 0$. What is the solution of $A = 0$? Is the solution of $A = 0$ a solution of $B \neq 0$? Tabulate the solution set of condition E.

F Explain how $\dfrac{8}{x-1} - \dfrac{3}{x^2+x-2} = 0$ can be derived from condition F. What is the least common multiple of $x-1$ and x^2+x-2? What steps can you use to obtain the expression $\dfrac{8x+13}{(x-1)(x+2)}$ from $\dfrac{8}{x-1} - \dfrac{3}{x^2+x-2}$?

G Put condition F in the form $\dfrac{A}{B} = 0$. What is the solution of $A = 0$? Does the solution of $A = 0$ satisfy $B \neq 0$? Tabulate the solution set of condition F.

H The development in D5 shows how to obtain a condition of the form $\dfrac{A}{B} = 0$ from condition G. What are the divisors of the quotients in condition G?

I How was condition H obtained from G? Are the divisors in the left side of H factors of the divisor in the right side of H?

J Justify conditions I, J, and K.

K Is condition K of the form $\dfrac{A}{B} = 0$? Use the quadratic formula to determine the solutions of $-x^2 + 7x - 6 = 0$. Which solution is also a solution of $(x+1)(x-1) \neq 0$? How do you know that $\{6\}$ is the solution set of condition G, expressed in D5?

L The development in D6 shows how you can obtain a condition of the form $\dfrac{A}{B} = 0$ from condition L. Explain how condition M was obtained from L.

M Justify condition N. What is the least common multiple of x and 2?

N How was condition O obtained from N? Justify condition P.

O Use the factoring method to find the solutions of $8 - 2x - x^2 = 0$. Which solutions of $8 - 2x - x^2 = 0$ satisfy $2x \neq 0$? Tabulate the solution set of condition L expressed in D6.

In this lesson you accepted the property $\dfrac{A}{B} = 0 \Leftrightarrow A = 0 \wedge B \neq 0$ and used the property to help find the solutions of rational conditions for equality.

On your own

For each of exercises 1 through 8, tell what replacements have been made for A and B in $\frac{A}{B}=0$ to obtain the condition expressed. Then use $\frac{A}{B}=0 \Leftrightarrow A=0 \wedge B\neq 0$ to help you tabulate the solution set of the given condition.

1 $\frac{x}{2x+1}=0.$

2 $\frac{3x}{x-4}=0.$

3 $\frac{2x+10}{3x}=0.$

4 $\frac{x+3}{x+7}=0.$

5 $\frac{2(x-6)+4x}{7x}=0.$

6 $\frac{2(x-7)+3(x+9)}{(x-7)(x+9)}=0.$

7 $\frac{x^2+10x+21}{x+3}=0.$

8 $\frac{8x^2+2x-15}{2x^2+5x+3}=0.$

For each of the following exercises, first put the given condition in the form $\frac{A}{B}=0.$ Then tabulate the solution set of the given condition.

9 $\frac{5}{x-1}+\frac{x}{x-1}=0.$

10 $\frac{10}{x+10}=\frac{x}{x+10}.$

11 $\frac{2}{x-3}=\frac{x}{3-x}.$

12 $\frac{x^2}{x+2}-\frac{8}{x+2}=0.$

13 $\frac{6}{x-3}-\frac{2x-5}{3-2x}=0.$

14 $\frac{x^2+4}{x+1}+\frac{5x}{x+1}=0.$

15 $6+\frac{18}{x}=0.$

16 $\frac{8}{x-4}=-4.$

17 $\frac{14}{x}-2=x-7.$

18 $\frac{2}{x}-\frac{x}{8}=\frac{3}{4}.$

19 $\frac{4}{x^2}=\frac{8}{3x+2}.$

20 $\frac{1}{x+5}=\frac{x}{50}.$

21 $\frac{8x+16}{x-6}=\frac{5x}{x-6}+\frac{10}{x-6}.$

22 $\frac{3}{x-4}=\frac{1}{x-2}.$

23 $\frac{3}{x^2-4}=8+\frac{5}{4-x^2}.$

24 $\frac{1-2x}{1-x}=\frac{2x}{1+x}.$

25 $\frac{x+2}{2x-6}+\frac{3}{3-x}=\frac{x}{2}.$

26 $\frac{360}{x-2}=\frac{360}{x}+2.$

27 $\frac{700}{x}+15x=\frac{700}{x-6}.$

28 $\frac{x-2}{x+4}+\frac{13}{70}=\frac{x}{x+3}.$

KEEPING SKILLFUL

For each of exercises 1 through 5, the ordered pairs given satisfy either a condition of the form $f(x)=kx$ or of the form $f(x)=kx^2$. Write a sentence that expresses the appropriate condition.

1 $(0, 0)$, $(4, -48)$, $(12, -144)$, $(15, -180)$
2 $(-3, 81)$, $(-1, 9)$, $(6, 324)$, $(10, 900)$
3 $(-240, -30)$, $(-400, -50)$, $(16, 2)$, $(64, 8)$
4 $(-2, -5)$, $(-2.5, -6.25)$, $(0, 0)$, $(.8, 2)$
5 $(-\frac{1}{3}, -\frac{2}{3})$, $(2, -24)$, $(6, -216)$, $(8, -384)$

For each of exercises 6 through 9, the ordered pairs given satisfy either a condition of the form $f(x)=\frac{k}{x}$ or of the form $f(x)=\frac{k}{x^2}$. Write a sentence that expresses the appropriate condition.

6 $(-5, -10)$, $(2, 25)$, $(2\frac{1}{2}, 20)$, $(10, 5)$
7 $(-4, 4\frac{3}{8})$, $(-2, 18)$, $(1, 72)$, $(2, 18)$
8 $(-6, -4)$, $(-4, -6)$, $(8, 3)$, $(12, 2)$
9 $(-.5, 32)$, $(-.25, 128)$, $(2, 2)$, $(8, .125)$

The conditions expressed in the exercises below determine functions. For each function, find $f(-4)$, $f(0)$, and $f(4)$.

10 $f(x)=-2.$

11 $f(x)=[x]+3.$

12 $f(x)=-4\,|\,x\,|.$

13 $f(x)=5\,|\,x+1\,|.$

23 282 **Exploring ideas**

Conditions involving radicals

You will recall that in the last lesson you found solution sets of rational conditions that were not polynomial conditions. Now you will learn how to find solution sets of irrational conditions.

A Look at D1. What two operations have been performed in $\sqrt{x+3}$? Which of these operations is not a rational operation? How do you know that $\sqrt{x+3}$ is not a rational expression?

B Explain why taking an even root is closed in the set of non-negative real numbers. How do you know that $\sqrt{x+3}$ is an algebraic expression?

> REMINDER
>
> An algebraic expression is an expression formed from constants or variables or both by means of a finite number of algebraic operations.
>
> *See lesson 257, page 244.*

The condition for equality expressed in D1 is formed from two algebraic expressions, one of which is not a rational expression. A condition for equality that is formed from two algebraic expressions, at least one of which is not a rational expression, is an *irrational condition for equality*.

C Explain why $\sqrt{x+3}=7$ is an irrational condition for equality. Is $x+\sqrt{2}=5$ an irrational condition for equality?

$$\sqrt{x+3}=7.$$

D1

> **irrational condition for equality.** A condition of the form $A=B$, where A and B are algebraic expressions, and where either A or B, or both, are not rational expressions.

The property expressed below can be used to help find the solution sets of irrational conditions for equality.

For each a *and* b, $a=b \Rightarrow a^2=b^2$.

You will recall from your previous work that the property given above means that, if two numbers are equal, then the squares of these numbers are equal. For example, if $a=5$, then $a^2=25$.

D What is the converse of $a=b \Rightarrow a^2=b^2$? If $a^2=25$, does a necessarily equal 5? Is the converse of $a=b \Rightarrow a^2=b^2$ true for each a and b? Explain your answers.

Now you will use $a=b \Rightarrow a^2=b^2$ to help find the solution set of the irrational condition $\sqrt{x+3}=7$.

E How do you know that if $\sqrt{x+3}=7$, then $(\sqrt{x+3})^2=7^2$?

F What property can you use to obtain $x+3$ from $(\sqrt{x+3})^2$? How do you know that $\sqrt{x+3}=7 \Rightarrow x+3=49$? Tabulate the solution set of $x+3=49$.

G ? How do you know that if $\sqrt{x+3}=7$ has a solution, then that solution must satisfy $x+3=49$?

H If $\sqrt{x+3}=7$ has a solution, then what is the solution?

I ? Now check 46 in $\sqrt{x+3}=7$. Is 46 a solution of $\sqrt{x+3}=7$? How do you know that 46 is the only solution of the condition $\sqrt{x+3}=7$?

A $x - 9 = \sqrt{x - 3}$.
B $(x - 9)^2 = (\sqrt{x - 3})^2$.
C $x^2 - 18x + 81 = x - 3$.
D $x^2 - 19x + 84 = 0$.

D2

E $2\sqrt{x + 1} + 7 = 15$.
F $2\sqrt{x + 1} = 8$.
G $\sqrt{x + 1} = 4$.

D3

H $3\sqrt{2x - 5} = 7\sqrt{2x - 5} - 12$.
I $12 = 7\sqrt{2x - 5} - 3\sqrt{2x - 5}$.
J $12 = (7 - 3)\sqrt{2x - 5}$.
K $12 = 4\sqrt{2x - 5}$.
L $3 = \sqrt{2x - 5}$.

D4

J Explain why condition A, expressed in D2, is an irrational condition. What property was used to obtain condition B from A?

K How was condition C obtained? How was D obtained from C?

L The development in D2 is a proof of what conditional?

M From $x - 9 = \sqrt{x - 3} \Rightarrow x^2 - 19x + 84 = 0$, you know that, if $x - 9 = \sqrt{x - 3}$ has a solution, then that solution must be a solution of $x^2 - 19x + 84 = 0$. Use the factoring method to find the solutions of $x^2 - 19x + 84 = 0$.

N Why are 7 and 12 the only numbers that can be solutions of $x - 9 = \sqrt{x - 3}$? Why is it necessary to check to see if these numbers are solutions of $x - 9 = \sqrt{x - 3}$?

O Explain why $\{12\}$, and not $\{7, 12\}$, is the solution set of $x - 9 = \sqrt{x - 3}$.

For each of exercises P through S, first square the expression in each side of the condition. Next, find the solutions of the condition that you obtain. Then check each solution in the original condition and tabulate the solution set of the original condition.

P $\sqrt{x + 2} = 5$.　　**R** $\sqrt{x^2 - 1} = -x$.

Q $\sqrt{-x - 5} = 1$.　　**S** $\sqrt{\frac{x}{6}} = 6x$.

To solve an irrational condition for equality, it is convenient first to put the condition in the form $A = B$, where either A or B, or both, are radicals. For example, the development in D3 shows how to obtain condition G from condition E. Notice that condition G is of the form $A = B$, and A is a radical.

A Explain how each of conditions F and G was obtained. How do you know that G is equivalent to condition E?

B Solve $\sqrt{x + 1} = 4$. How do you know that the solution of $\sqrt{x + 1} = 4$ is also the solution of $2\sqrt{x + 1} + 7 = 15$? Tabulate the solution set of $2\sqrt{x + 1} + 7 = 15$.

C The development in D4 is similar to the development in D3. Justify each step in D4.

D How do you know that condition L is equivalent to condition H? What condition do you obtain by squaring each side of $3 = \sqrt{2x - 5}$?

E What is the solution of $9 = 2x - 5$? Check this solution in $3 = \sqrt{2x - 5}$. How do you know that the solution of $9 = 2x - 5$ is also the solution of $3\sqrt{2x - 5} = 7\sqrt{2x - 5} - 12$?

Tabulate the solution set of each condition expressed below.

F $20 = 5\sqrt{2x}$.　　**I** $\sqrt{16x^2} - 2x - 1 = 0$.

G $12 - \sqrt{x} = -15$.　　**J** $5\sqrt{x} = 40 - 5\sqrt{x}$.

H $\sqrt{x} - \frac{1}{2}x = 0$.　　**K** $5 + \sqrt{x + 7} = x$.

Now you will solve irrational conditions for equality that involve different radicals. Condi-

M $\sqrt{x+5} = \sqrt{3x+4}$.

N $(\sqrt{x+5})^2 = (\sqrt{3x+4})^2$.

O $(x+5) = (3x+4)$.

D5

P $\sqrt{x+4} + \sqrt{x+11} = 7$.

Q $\sqrt{x+4} = 7 - \sqrt{x+11}$.

R $(\sqrt{x+4})^2 = (7 - \sqrt{x+11})^2$.

S $x+4 = 49 - 14\sqrt{x+11} + (x+11)$.

T $x+4 = 60 + x - 14\sqrt{x+11}$.

U $4 = 60 - 14\sqrt{x+11}$.

V $14\sqrt{x+11} = 56$.

W $\sqrt{x+11} = 4$.

D6

tion M, expressed in D5, for example, is of the form $A = B$, where A and B are two different radicals.

A What property justifies condition N? How was condition O obtained from N?

B The development in D5 is a proof of what conditional?

C What is the solution of condition O? Why is it necessary to check this solution in condition M?

D Tabulate the solution set of condition M.

Tabulate the solution set of each condition expressed below. Show each step of your work.

E $\sqrt{3x+2} = \sqrt{x+6}$.

F $\sqrt{\frac{1}{3}x} = \frac{1}{2}\sqrt{x-8}$.

G $\sqrt{x^2+2} = \sqrt{3x}$.

H $2\sqrt{3x-2} = \sqrt{2x-3}$.

Condition P, expressed in D6, involves the radicals $\sqrt{x+4}$ and $\sqrt{x+11}$. To obtain condition Q, the radical $\sqrt{x+11}$ was subtracted from each side of $\sqrt{x+4} + \sqrt{x+11} = 7$. Notice that, in Q, we obtained a condition of the form $A = B$, where both A and B involve just one radical.

I What property justifies condition R, expressed in D6?

J How do you know that $(\sqrt{x+4})^2 = x+4$? Use $(a-b)^2 = a^2 - 2ab + b^2$ to explain why $(7 - \sqrt{x+11})^2 = 49 - 14\sqrt{x+11} + (x+11)$. How was condition S obtained? Justify condition T.

K How was condition U obtained from T? Justify conditions V and W.

L If you square each side of the condition $\sqrt{x+11} = 4$, what condition do you obtain? What is the solution of the condition that you obtained?

M Why is it necessary to check the solution of $x + 11 = 16$ in condition P? How do you know that $\{5\}$ is the solution set of condition P?

N Put $\sqrt{x+13} - \sqrt{x-3} = 2$ in the form $A = B$, where A is $\sqrt{x+13}$. What is B? Square each side of the condition that you obtain.

O Now put $x + 13 = 4 + 4\sqrt{x-3} + (x-3)$ in the form $A = B$, where B is $\sqrt{x-3}$. What is A? Square each side of the condition that you obtain. What is the solution set of this condition?

P If $\sqrt{x+13} - \sqrt{x-3} = 2$ has a solution, what is the solution? Now check this solution in $\sqrt{x+13} - \sqrt{x-3} = 2$. What is the solution set of this condition?

Tabulate the solution set of each condition expressed below.

Q $\sqrt{x-2} + \sqrt{x+3} = 3$.

R $\sqrt{x+5} = 9 - \sqrt{x-4}$.

S $\sqrt{x+5} + \sqrt{x} = 5$.

T $\sqrt{x} + \sqrt{x+1} = 7$.

X $\sqrt{x}+1=0$.

Y $\sqrt{x}=-1$.

Z $x=1$.

D7

U Now look at D7. How was condition Y obtained from condition X? How was Z obtained from Y?

V What is the solution of condition Z? Why is it necessary to check the solution of condition Z in $\sqrt{x}+1=0$?

W Explain why $\emptyset$ is the solution set of $\sqrt{x}+1=0$.

In this lesson you have learned how to solve certain irrational conditions.

On your own

Tabulate the solution set of each condition expressed below. Show the steps in your work.

1 $\sqrt{x}=-11$.

2 $\sqrt{4x}=8$.

3 $4\sqrt{x}=8$.

4 $\sqrt{x+4}=8$.

5 $\sqrt{2x-3}=5$.

6 $8-\sqrt{x-1}=6$.

7 $\sqrt{x-1}-2=0$.

8 $\sqrt{x^2-3x}=2$.

9 $\sqrt{-x+22}=x-2$.

10 $\sqrt{x^2-5}=5$.

11 $x+4=\sqrt{16x^2+9}$.

12 $\sqrt{2x^2-5x-3}=2x-5$.

13 $\sqrt{2x+6}=\sqrt{2x-5}$.

14 $\sqrt{x+2}=2\sqrt{x}$.

15 $\sqrt{x+10}=\sqrt{5x-7}$.

16 $\sqrt{x^2-8}+4=x$.

17 $\sqrt{x}-\sqrt{x+21}=-3$.

18 $\sqrt{x}+3=\sqrt{x+6}$.

19 $\sqrt{x+5}-\sqrt{x-5}=2$.

20 $\sqrt{x^2+5}=x-5$.

21 $x=\sqrt{2x+15}$.

22 $\sqrt{x+23}-\sqrt{x+2}=3$.

23 $x+7=11+\sqrt{x-2}$.

23 283 **Exploring ideas**

Quadratic conditions for inequality

You have studied several methods of solving quadratic conditions for equality in one variable. In this lesson you will work with quadratic conditions for inequality.

A Which condition expressed in D1 is of the form $ax^2+bx+c<0$? Which condition is of the form $ax^2+bx+c>0$?

B ? What can you add to each side of condition B to obtain an equivalent condition of the form $ax^2+bx+c<0$? What can you add to each side of condition D to obtain an equivalent condition of the form $ax^2+bx+c>0$?

Each condition expressed in D1 is a *quadratic condition for inequality in one variable.* Any condition that is of either the form $ax^2+bx+c<0$ or the form $ax^2+bx+c>0$, where $a\neq 0$, is a quadratic condition for inequality in one variable.

For each condition expressed in exercises C through F, find an equivalent condition that is of the form of a quadratic condition for inequality.

C $x^2-2x<8$.

D $x(x-2)>35$.

E $120>x(23-x)$.

F $(2x-7)^2>x^2-6x+9$.

We can develop a theorem of real numbers that will be helpful in solving quadratic conditions that involve the idea of "greater than," such as $x^2+6x+8>0$. This theorem concerns the product of two negative numbers or two positive numbers.

G Suppose that the product of two numbers is positive. Can the two numbers both be posi-

A $x^2 + 16x + 55 < 0.$
B $2x^2 + 8x < -3.$
C $3x^2 + 39x + 36 > 0.$
D $x^2 + 4 > 5x.$

D1

-6 -5 -4 -3 -2 -1 0 1 2

$\{x \mid (x+4)(x+2) > 0\}$

D2

E $x(x-6) > 7.$
F $x^2 - 6x > 7.$
G $x^2 - 6x - 7 > 0.$
H $(x-7)(x+1) > 0.$
I $(x - 7 > 0 \wedge x + 1 > 0) \vee (x - 7 < 0 \wedge x + 1 < 0).$
J $(x > 7 \wedge x > -1) \vee (x < 7 \wedge x < -1).$
K $x > 7 \vee x < -1.$

D3

quadratic condition for inequality in one variable. A condition of either the form $ax^2 + bx + c < 0$ or the form $ax^2 + bx + c > 0$, where $a \neq 0$.

tive? Can they both be negative? Can one be positive and the other negative?

H Suppose that two numbers are either both positive or both negative. What do you know about the product of the two numbers?

Exercises G and H suggest the theorem that is expressed below. You can use this theorem in solving quadratic conditions for inequality.

For each a *and* b, ab > 0 *if and only if* $(a > 0 \wedge b > 0) \vee (a < 0 \wedge b < 0)$.

I Think again about $x^2 + 6x + 8 > 0$. By factoring the left side of this condition, you can obtain $(x+4)(x+2) > 0$. Is the product of $x + 4$ and $x + 2$ positive, or is it negative?

J How do you know that $x + 4$ and $x + 2$ are either both positive or both negative?

K ? Describe the set of replacements for x for which $x + 4$ is positive. Describe the set of replacements for x for which $x + 2$ is positive. How do you know that both $x + 4$ and $x + 2$ are positive if $x > -2$? Explain why every real number that is greater than -2 satisfies $(x+4)(x+2) > 0$.

L ? Describe the set of replacements for x for which $x + 4$ is negative. Describe the set of replacements for x for which $x + 2$ is negative. How do you know that both $x + 4$ and $x + 2$ are negative if $x < -4$? Explain why every real number that is less than -4 satisfies $(x+4)(x+2) > 0$.

M The locus of $(x+4)(x+2) > 0$ is represented in D2. Why are point -4 and point -2 and the points between them not contained in the locus?

N ? Explain why every point that is not in the locus of $(x+4)(x+2) > 0$ is in the locus of $(x+4)(x+2) \leqq 0$.

O ? Give a standard description of the solution set of $x^2 + 6x + 8 > 0$.

Now you will use factoring to find the solution set of condition E, expressed in D3.

P How was condition F obtained from E? Justify conditions G and H.

Q Notice that condition H involves a product that is greater than zero. From what theorem do you know that, if $(x-7)(x+1) > 0$, then $x - 7$ and $x + 1$ are either both positive or both negative?

R Justify condition I. Justify condition J.

S ? If $x - 7$ and $x + 1$ are both positive, then x is greater than what number? If $x - 7$

and $x+1$ are both negative, then x is less than what number? How was condition K obtained?

T You know that each x that satisfies condition K is either greater than 7 or less than -1. Give a standard description of the solution set of $x(x-6)>7$. Make a graph that represents the locus of $x(x-6)>7$.

U ? Give a standard description of the solution set of $x(x-6) \leqq 7$. The solution set of this condition is what kind of interval?

V Put the condition $x(2x-3)>3(2x-3)$ in the form $ax^2+bx+c>0$.

W What are the factors of the trinomial that is the left side of the condition you obtained for exercise V?

X If $(2x-3)(x-3)>0$, then x is greater than what number or x is less than what number? Give a standard description of the solution set of $x(2x-3)>3(2x-3)$.

Y Give a standard description of the solution set of $5x^2-10x>10(x-2)$. Show each step of your work.

So far, you have been solving quadratic conditions that involve the idea of "greater than." Next, you will consider conditions that involve the idea of "less than." First you will study a theorem that will help you solve such conditions.

A If the product of two numbers is negative, can both numbers be positive? Can both numbers be negative? Can one number be positive and the other negative?

B What kind of number, a negative number or a positive number, is the product of a negative number and a positive number?

Exercises A and B suggest the theorem that is expressed below.

For each a *and* b, ab <0 *if and only if* (a $>0 \wedge$ b <0) $\vee$ (a $<0 \wedge$ b >0).

E $x(x-6)>7$.
F $x^2-6x>7$.
G $x^2-6x-7>0$.
H $(x-7)(x+1)>0$.
I $(x-7>0 \wedge x+1>0) \vee (x-7<0 \wedge x+1<0)$.
J $(x>7 \wedge x>-1) \vee (x<7 \wedge x<-1)$.
K $x>7 \vee x<-1$.

D3

A $x(x-7)<-10$.
B $x^2-7x<-10$.
C $x^2-7x+10<0$.
D $(x-5)(x-2)<0$.
E $(x-5>0 \wedge x-2<0) \vee (x-5<0 \wedge x-2>0)$.
F $(x>5 \wedge x<2) \vee (x<5 \wedge x>2)$.
G $2<x<5$.

D4

H $-6x^2-9x+6>0$.
I $6x^2+9x-6<0$.
J $2x^2+3x-2<0$.
K $(2x-1)(x+2)<0$.
L $(2x-1>0 \wedge x+2<0) \vee (2x-1<0 \wedge x+2>0)$.
M $(x>\frac{1}{2} \wedge x<-2) \vee (x<\frac{1}{2} \wedge x>-2)$.
N $-2<x<\frac{1}{2}$.

D5

C The development in D4 shows how to obtain the solution set of $x(x-7)<-10$. Justify each of conditions B, C, and D.

D By what theorem do you know that, if $(x-5)(x-2)<0$, then either $x-5$ is positive and $x - 2$ is negative, or $x - 5$ is negative and $x - 2$ is positive? How was condition E obtained? Justify condition F.

E Is there an x that satisfies $x > 5 \wedge x < 2$? Each x that satisfies $x < 5 \wedge x > 2$ is less than 5 and greater than 2. Justify condition G.

F Is $\{x \mid 2 < x < 5\}$ the solution set of condition A? What are the limits of the interval? Make a graph of the locus of condition A.

Now look at D5. Condition H involves a trinomial that is greater than 0. Notice that the coefficient of x^2 is negative and that 3 is a common factor of the terms of the trinomial. To solve a condition such as condition H, it is convenient first to find an equivalent condition in which the coefficient of x^2 is positive and the terms have no common factors. The development in D5 shows how such a condition can be obtained from condition H.

G Justify conditions I and J, expressed in D5.

H How was condition K obtained? What theorem was used to obtain condition L?

I Explain how condition M was obtained. Is there an x that satisfies $x > \frac{1}{2} \wedge x < -2$? How was condition N obtained?

J Give a standard description of the solution set of $-6x^2 - 9x + 6 > 0$. Make a graph of the locus of $-6x^2 - 9x + 6 > 0$.

K Put $3(2x^2 + x) < -5(1 + 2x)$ in the form $ax^2 + bx + c < 0$. Then factor the trinomial in the condition that you obtain.

L If $(2x + 1)(3x + 5) < 0$, then x is between what two numbers? Give a standard description of the open interval that is the solution set of $3(2x^2 + x) < -5(1 + 2x)$.

M Give a standard description of the solution set of $x^2 + 3x - 70 < 0$. Show each step that you use to obtain this description.

We can also obtain the solution set of a quadratic condition for inequality by using the

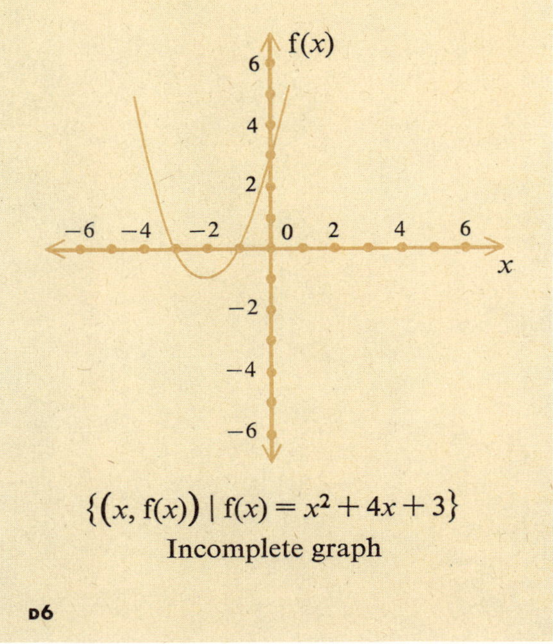

$\{(x, f(x)) \mid f(x) = x^2 + 4x + 3\}$
Incomplete graph

D6

locus of a quadratic function. For example, to solve either the condition $x^2 + 4x < -3$ or the condition $x^2 + 4x > -3$, we first can put each condition in standard form, thus obtaining $x^2 + 4x + 3 < 0$ and $x^2 + 4x + 3 > 0$. Then we can determine the solution sets of the two conditions for inequality by working with the function determined by $f(x) = x^2 + 4x + 3$.

A What numbers satisfy $x^2 + 4x + 3 = 0$? ? How do you know that each of these numbers is a zero of the function determined by $f(x) = x^2 + 4x + 3$? Name the x-intercepts of the locus of function f.

The locus of function f is the parabola represented in D6.

B Use the locus of $f(x) = x^2 + 4x + 3$ to determine when $f(x) < 0$. How do you know that the interval $\{x \mid -3 < x < -1\}$ is the solution set of $x^2 + 4x < -3$?

C Use the locus of $f(x) = x^2 + 4x + 3$ to de- ? termine when $f(x) > 0$. How do you know that $\{x \mid x < -3 \vee x > -1\}$ is the solution set of $x^2 + 4x > -3$?

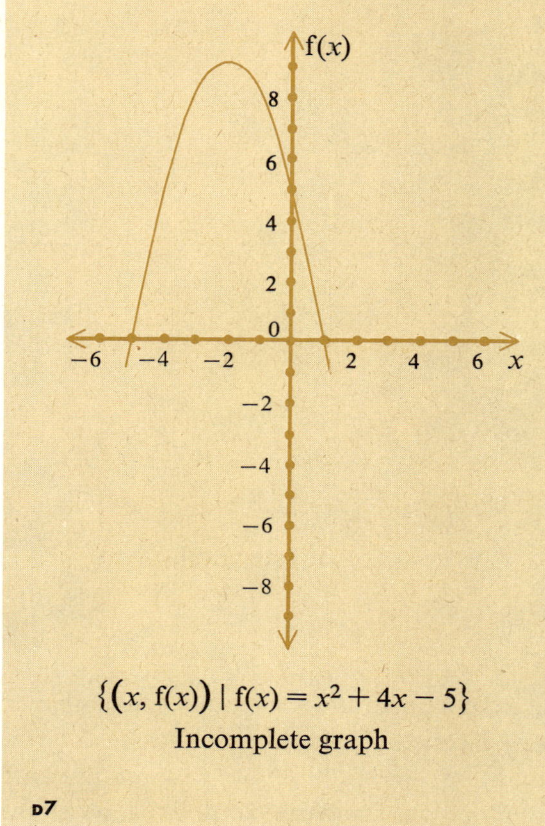

$\{(x, f(x)) \mid f(x) = x^2 + 4x - 5\}$

Incomplete graph

D7

D What condition for a quadratic function can you use to help solve $x^2 + x - 12 < 0$?

E What are the x-intercepts of the locus of the function determined by $f(x) = x^2 + x - 12$? Make a graph of the locus.

F How can you use the locus of the function determined by $f(x) = x^2 + x - 12$ to get the solution set of $x^2 + x - 12 < 0$? Give a standard description of the solution set.

G Use the locus of the function determined by $f(x) = x^2 + x - 12$ to help describe the solution set of $x^2 + x - 12 > 0$.

H The graph in D7 represents the locus of the function determined by $f(x) = x^2 + 4x - 5$. Use the locus of function f to help describe the solution set of $-x^2 - 4x + 5 < 0$. Use the locus of function f to help describe the solution set of $-x^2 - 4x > -5$.

In this lesson you have used your knowledge of factoring to solve quadratic conditions for inequality. You have also learned how to use the locus of a quadratic function to determine the solution sets of quadratic conditions for inequality.

On your own

Tell whether each statement expressed below is true or false.

1 $x(x + 3) < 0 \Leftrightarrow -3 < x < 0$.

2 $x(x + 3) > 0 \Leftrightarrow x > 0 \wedge x < -3$.

3 $x(x + 3) > 0 \Leftrightarrow x > 0 \vee x < -3$.

4 $(x + 1)(x + 7) > 0 \Leftrightarrow x < -1 \vee x < -7$.

5 $(x + 3)(x + 5) < 0 \Leftrightarrow x < -3 \vee x > -5$.

6 $(x - 5)(x - 3) > 0 \Leftrightarrow x > -5 \vee x < 3$.

7 $\{x \mid x^2 + 9x + 14 < 0\}$ is an open interval.

8 $\{x \mid x^2 + 13x + 30 > 0\}$ is an open interval.

Give a standard description of the solution set of each condition expressed in exercises 9 through 22. Show each step of your work.

9 $x^2 - 9x + 8 < 0$.

10 $x^2 + 9x + 8 < 0$.

11 $x^2 + 9x + 8 > 0$.

12 $x^2 + 7x - 8 > 0$.

13 $x^2 - 7x - 8 > 0$.

14 $9x^2 - 4 < 0$.

15 $x^2 + 6x + 9 > 0$.

16 $x^2 > x + 12$.

17 $x^2 + 2 < 3x$.

18 $x^2 < 4x + 45$.

19 $x(x - 3) < 18$.

20 $2(3x^2 - 1) > 11x$.

21 $4x(x + 1) + 3 < -4x$.

22 $(x + 6)(x - 1) > x(x + 1) - 2x^2$.

For each exercise below, give a condition for the function that you can use to find the solution set of the condition expressed. Determine the x-intercepts of the locus of the function. Make a graph of the locus. Then use the graph to help describe the solution set of the original condition.

23 $(x + 5)(x - 6) < 0$.

24 $(x + 5)(x - 6) > 0$.

25 $x^2 - 10x + 24 < 0$.

26 $-x^2 - 5x + 24 > 0$.

27 $x^2 - 3x < 0$.

Problems involving quadratic and rational conditions

In this lesson you will apply quadratic and rational conditions to problem solving. First you will solve problems that involve quadratic conditions for equality.

Read the problem in D1.

A Let x represent the lesser of the two consecutive integers. Explain why you can use the expression $x+1$ to represent the greater of the two consecutive integers.

B Does the sentence at the right express a condition for the problem in D1?

$$x(x+1)=132.$$

C The development in D2 shows how you can obtain the solution set of $x(x+1)=132$. Justify each of conditions B through F.

D What are the solutions of condition F? Tabulate the solution set of $x(x+1)=132$.

E You know that each member of $\{-12, 11\}$ satisfies $x(x+1)=132$. If x is -12, what is $x+1$? If x is 11, what is $x+1$?

You can use $\{-12, 11\}$ and the information that you obtained for exercise E to get the answer to the problem in D1.

The consecutive integers are -12 and -11 or 11 and 12.

F Now verify the answer to the problem. Are -12 and -11 consecutive integers? Are 11 and 12 consecutive integers? Is the product of -12 and -11 equal to 132? Is the product of 11 and 12 equal to 132?

Read the problem in D3.

The product of two consecutive integers is 132. What are the integers?

D1

A $x(x+1)=132.$
B $x^2+x=132.$
C $x^2+x-132=0.$
D $(x+12)(x-11)=0.$
E $x+12=0 \vee x-11=0.$
F $x=-12 \vee x=11.$

D2

The width and the length of a rectangle in feet are two consecutive odd integers. The area is 255 sq. ft. What are the width and the length of the rectangle in feet?

D3

G If x represents an odd integer, how can you represent the next greater odd integer?

H For the problem in D3, let x represent the width of the rectangle in feet. What does $x+2$ represent?

I Use the formula $A=lw$ to explain why the sentence at the right expresses a condition for the problem in D3.

$$255=(x+2)x.$$

J What are the solutions of $255=(x+2)x$?

K Although -17 and 15 each satisfy the condition for the problem, one of these numbers does not provide a sensible answer to the problem. You will recall that x represents the width of the rectangle in feet. Can you use a number that is less than or equal to zero to get a sensible answer?

Because the width of the rectangle is a positive number, we could have used the compound condition expressed below for the problem in D3.

$$255 = (x + 2)x \wedge x > 0.$$

It is not necessary to include $x > 0$ in the condition, however, if you remember that you must reject the solutions of $255 = (x + 2)x$ that do not provide a sensible answer. That is, you must reject -17 and conclude that 15 is the width of the rectangle in feet.

L For the problem in D3, you are also asked to find the length of the rectangle in feet. Remember that $x + 2$ represents this number. If x is 15, what is $x + 2$?

Now you can give the answer to the problem in D3.

The width of the rectangle is 15 feet and the length is 17 feet.

M You can verify the answer to the problem. Are 15 and 17 consecutive odd integers? Are 15 ft. and 17 ft. the width and the length of a rectangle whose area is 255 sq. ft.?

Now read the problem in D4 and study the accompanying sketch.

N ? From the problem, how do you know that George used a square piece of cardboard to make the box? Let x represent the length of the cardboard in inches. How can you represent the width of the cardboard in inches?

O ? You know that 3 inches is the length of a side of the piece that was cut from each corner of the cardboard. How do you know that $x - 6$ represents the length of each side of the base of the box in inches?

P What was the height of the box in inches?

Q Use the formula $V = lwh$ to explain why $(x - 6)(x - 6)3$ represents the volume of the box in cubic inches. Does the sentence below express a condition for the problem in D4?

$$243 = (x - 6)(x - 6)3.$$

The width and the length of a rectangle in feet are two consecutive odd integers. The area is 255 sq. ft. What are the width and the length of the rectangle in feet?

D3

George made a box from a piece of cardboard. From each corner of the cardboard, he cut a piece in the shape of a 3-inch square. The base of the box was in the shape of a square and the volume was 243 cu. in. What were the dimensions in inches of the piece of cardboard that he used for the box?

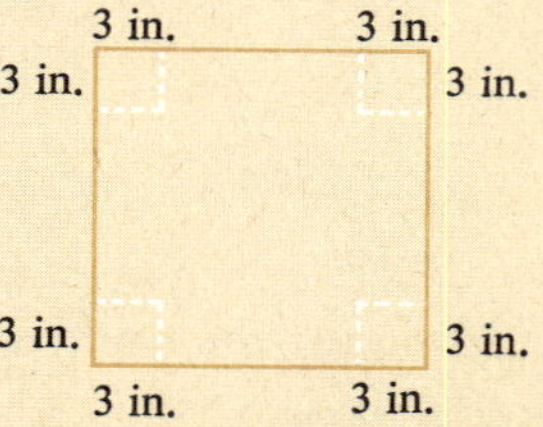

D4

A baseball was popped straight up in the air with an initial velocity of 60 feet per second. After how many seconds was the ball 50 feet from the ground?

D5

R Tabulate the solution set of the condition expressed in exercise Q.

S Which member of $\{15, -3\}$ provides an answer to the problem in D4? What were the dimensions of the piece of cardboard?

For the problems in D5 and D6, you will use some formulas that may be new to you.

Read the problem in D5.

When an object is projected either upward or downward, it is pulled downward by gravity a distance of $16t^2$ feet in t seconds. An object projected upward is affected by two forces that act on it in opposite directions: the force that gives the object its initial velocity upward and the force of gravity, which pulls it downward. The condition expressed below in color is a formula that can be used to solve problems concerning an object that is projected upward.

$$d = v_0t - 16t^2.$$

In the formula, d represents the distance from the ground; v_0 represents the initial velocity; t represents the number of seconds.

A Let t represent the number of seconds it took the ball to reach a height of 50 feet from the ground. Suppose that there were no gravity. Would $60t$ represent the distance of the ball from the ground?

B Think again about the problem in D5. Use the formula $d = v_0t - 16t^2$ to explain why $60t - 16t^2$ represents the distance of the ball from the ground. Does the sentence below in color express a condition for the problem?

$$50 = 60t - 16t^2.$$

C Tabulate the solution set of $50 = 60t - 16t^2$.

Notice that each solution of the condition for the problem is a positive number. Now you will see why you can use each solution to get a sensible answer to the problem.

D Why could the ball be 50 feet above the ground at two different times?

As the ball traveled upward, it was 50 feet above the ground after $1\frac{1}{4}$ seconds. After the ball reached its maximum height, it began to fall and was 50 feet above the ground for the second time. That is, it was 50 feet above the ground after $2\frac{1}{2}$ seconds.

A given polygon has 27 diagonals. How many sides has the polygon?

$$d = \frac{n^2 - 3n}{2}.$$

D6

A side of square ABCD is 1 in. longer than twice the length of a side of square EFGH. The difference of the areas of the two squares is less than 85 sq. in. What is the length of a side of square EFGH in inches?

D7

Read the problem in D6. The condition expressed in D6 is a formula for finding the number of diagonals of any polygon.

E In the formula expressed in D6, n represents the number of sides of a given polygon. What does $\frac{n^2 - 3n}{2}$ represent?

F Why does the sentence below in color express a condition for the problem in D6?

$$27 = \frac{n^2 - 3n}{2}.$$

G Tabulate the solution set of $27 = \frac{n^2 - 3n}{2}$.

Which member of this set can you use to get a sensible answer to the problem?

H If a polygon has 27 diagonals, how many sides does it have?

For each of the problems considered so far, you have developed a quadratic condition for equality. You will now consider a problem that requires a quadratic condition for inequality.

Read the problem in D7.

A side of square ABCD is 1 in. longer than twice the length of a side of square EFGH. The difference of the areas of the two squares is less than 85 sq. in. What is the length of a side of square EFGH in inches?

D7

A $(2x+1)^2 - x^2 < 85.$
B $4x^2 + 4x + 1 - x^2 < 85.$
C $4x^2 + 4x + 1 - x^2 - 85 < 0.$
D $3x^2 + 4x - 84 < 0.$
E $(3x - 14)(x + 6) < 0.$
F $(3x - 14 > 0 \wedge x + 6 < 0) \vee$
$(3x - 14 < 0 \wedge x + 6 > 0).$
G $-6 < x < \frac{14}{3}.$

D8

A Let x represent the length of a side of square EFGH in inches. How can you represent the length of a side of square ABCD in inches?
B Does x^2 represent the area of square EFGH in square inches? How can you represent the area of square ABCD in square inches?
C What does $(2x+1)^2 - x^2$ represent? Is the condition expressed below in color a condition for the problem in D7?

$$(2x+1)^2 - x^2 < 85.$$

D The development in D8 shows how the solution set of $(2x+1)^2 - x^2 < 85$ can be obtained. Justify each of conditions B through G.
E ? Is $\{x \mid -6 < x < \frac{14}{3}\}$ the solution set of $(2x+1)^2 - x^2 < 85$? Must the length of a side of square EFGH be a positive number? Describe the subset of $\{x \mid -6 < x < \frac{14}{3}\}$ that can be used to get an answer to the problem.
F What is the length of a side of square EFGH in inches?

In the remainder of this lesson you will solve problems that involve rational conditions for equality.

Read the problem in D9.

A From the problem, you know that John can paint $\frac{1}{12}$ of the garage in one hour. What part of the garage can Bob paint in one hour?
B What does $\frac{1}{12} + \frac{1}{20}$ represent?
C Let x represent the number of hours that it will take John and Bob to paint the garage if they work together. What does $\frac{1}{x}$ represent?

Since $\frac{1}{12} + \frac{1}{20}$ and $\frac{1}{x}$ both represent the part of the garage that the boys can paint in one hour if they work together, the sentence below in color expresses a condition for the problem in D9.

$$\frac{1}{12} + \frac{1}{20} = \frac{1}{x}.$$

D What real number cannot be a solution of a condition that involves $\frac{1}{x}$?
E How can you obtain $\frac{8}{60} - \frac{1}{x} = 0$ from $\frac{1}{12} + \frac{1}{20} = \frac{1}{x}$?
F What is the least common multiple of 60 and x? How can you obtain $\frac{8x - 60}{60x} = 0$ from $\frac{8}{60} - \frac{1}{x} = 0$?
G What is the solution of $8x - 60 = 0$? Does this solution also satisfy $60x \neq 0$?
H Tabulate the solution set of $\frac{1}{12} + \frac{1}{20} = \frac{1}{x}$. Give the answer to the problem in D9.

John can paint Mr. Harvey's garage in 12 hr. and Bob can paint it in 20 hr. If John and Bob work together, how many hours will it take them to paint the garage?

D9

Harris rowed 20 mi. upstream to a camp. Later in the day he returned to his starting point. The return trip downstream took $6\frac{2}{3}$ hr. less time than the trip upstream. Harris can row 4 mi. per hour in still water. What was the rate of the current in miles per hour?

D10

I Think again about the problem in D9. Again, let x represent the number of hours that it will take John and Bob to paint the garage if they work together. Since John can paint the garage in 12 hours, he can paint $\frac{1}{12}$ of the garage in 1 hour. Hence, $\frac{1}{12}x$ represents the part he can paint in x hours. What does $\frac{1}{20}x$ represent? What does $\frac{1}{12}x + \frac{1}{20}x$ represent?

Since $\frac{1}{x}$ represents the part of the work that the boys can do in 1 hour if they work together, $\frac{1}{x}(x)$ represents the part of the work they can do in x hours if they work together. The sentence below in color expresses a condition that you can use for the problem in D9.

$$\frac{1}{12}x + \frac{1}{20}x = \frac{1}{x}(x).$$

J How can you obtain $\frac{5x + 3x}{60} = 1$ from $\frac{1}{12}x + \frac{1}{20}x = \frac{1}{x}(x)$? What steps can you use to obtain $8x = 60$ from $\frac{5x + 3x}{60} = 1$?

K Tabulate $\left\{x \mid \frac{1}{12}x + \frac{1}{20}x = \frac{1}{x}(x)\right\}$. Is this set the same set that you obtained for exercise H? Can the boys paint the garage in $7\frac{1}{2}$ hours if they work together?

Read the problem in D10.

L Let r represent the rate of the current. You know that Harris can row at a rate of 4 miles per hour in still water. Does $4 - r$ represent the rate at which he rowed upstream? What does $4 + r$ represent?

M ? Use the formula $d = rt$ to explain what $\frac{20}{4 - r}$ and $\frac{20}{4 + r}$ represent.

N Does the sentence below in color express a condition for the problem in D10?

$$\frac{20}{4 - r} - \frac{20}{4 + r} = 6\frac{2}{3}.$$

O Tabulate the solution set of the condition expressed above.

P Which member of {2, −8} provides a sensible answer to the problem? What was the rate of the current in miles per hour?

In this lesson you used quadratic conditions for equality and inequality to solve problems. You also solved problems that involved rational conditions that were not polynomial conditions.

On your own

For each problem, first write a sentence that expresses a condition. Tabulate the solution set of the condition, if possible. Otherwise, give a standard description of the solution set. Finally, give the answer to the problem.

1 A certain theater has 5152 seats. There are 36 more seats per row than there are rows of seats. How many rows of seats are there in the theater?

2 If a number is decreased by 20 times its reciprocal, the difference is 8. What is the number?

3 The difference of the square of a given number and the number itself is 240. What is the number?

4 A skyrocket was shot directly upward with an initial velocity of 48 ft. per second. After how many seconds was the rocket 32 ft. from the ground and moving downward?

5 A given polygon has 170 diagonals. How many sides does the polygon have?

The number of telephone connections that are possible on a switchboard can be found by using the formula $c = \frac{n(n-1)}{2}$, where c represents the number of connections and n represents the number of telephones connected to the switchboard.

6 On a certain switchboard, 253 connections are possible. How many telephones are connected to the switchboard?

7 The product of two consecutive odd integers is 1159 less than the sum of the squares of the two integers. What are the two integers?

8 A side of a square is 5 units longer than a side of another square. The sum of the areas is 433 square units. What is the length of a side of the larger square in units?

9 The difference of the square of a number and the number itself is less than 72. What is the number?

10 Tom and Harold were hired to wash the 28 windows in Mr. Baker's house. Tom can wash 5 windows per hour and Harold can wash 3 windows per hour. How many hours will it take both boys to wash all 28 windows?

11 A Boy Scout troop planned a canoe trip. They figured that their total expenses would be \$55, which they would share equally. At the last minute, three of the boys could not go. As a result, the expense for each of the remaining boys was increased by \$.30. How many boys went on the canoe trip?

12 Steve can build a stage set in 4 days. Paul can build the stage set in $5\frac{1}{2}$ days. If the boys work together, how many days will it take them to build the stage set?

13 A plane made a round trip between two airports that are 800 miles apart. Throughout the flight, the speed of the wind was 30 miles per hour. The flight against the wind took $\frac{2}{3}$ hr. longer than the flight with the wind. In still air, what was the plane's speed in miles per hour?

14 Two hoses can be used to fill a wading pool. When both hoses are used, the pool can be filled in 2 hr. When just the larger hose is used, the pool can be filled in 3 hr. How long will it take to fill the pool if only the smaller hose is used?

SPECIAL CHALLENGE

Frequently in mathematics, we are given a curve, and our problem is to find a condition that "fits" the curve. In many cases, when it is possible to develop a compound condition that fits a curve, it is also possible to use the idea of absolute value to develop a simple condition that fits the same curve.

A The geometric curve represented in D1 is an angle that is the union of ray BA and ray BC. What are the coördinates of the vertex?

B The slope of line BA is -3 and the y-intercept is point $(0, 9)$. Explain why $\overrightarrow{BA}$ is the locus of $\{(x, y) \mid y = -3x + 9 \wedge x \leqq 2\}$.

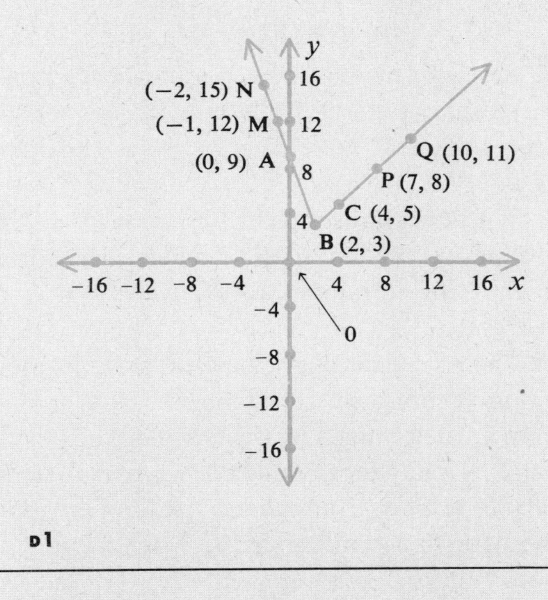

D1

A $y = M\,|\,x-2\,| + m(x-2) + 3.$
B $y = 2\,|\,x-2\,| - 1(x-2) + 3.$

D2

C The slope of line BC is 1 and the y-intercept is point (0, 1). Explain why $\overrightarrow{BC}$ is the locus of $\{(x, y) \mid y = x + 1 \wedge x \geqq 2\}$.

D What compound condition fits $\angle$ABC?

Condition A expressed in D2 can also fit $\angle$ABC if you choose the proper replacements for M and m.

E Does the first coördinate of each point in $\overrightarrow{BA}$, other than the endpoint, satisfy $x < 2$? If you replace x by a number that is less than 2, is $|\,x-2\,| = x - 2$, or is $|\,x-2\,| = -(x-2)$? If $x < 2$, explain why you obtain the condition $y = (m - M)(x-2) + 3$ from condition A.

F If m and M are replaced by real numbers, will $y = (m - M)(x-2) + 3$ yield a condition whose locus is a line? How do you know that the slope of the locus of this condition will be $m - M$? How do you know that point (2, 3) will be in the locus?

G Now suppose that you let $m - M$ be equal to the slope of the line that includes $\overrightarrow{BA}$. That is, let $m - M = -3$. How do you know that each (x, y) associated with a point in $\overrightarrow{BA}$ will satisfy $y = (m - M)(x-2) + 3$?

H Does the first coördinate of each point in $\overrightarrow{BC}$ satisfy $x \geqq 2$? Now suppose that, in condition A, x is replaced by a number that is greater than or equal to 2. In this case, how do you know that $|\,x-2\,| = x - 2$? How can you obtain $y = (m + M)(x-2) + 3$ from condition A?

I If m and M are replaced by real numbers, will $y = (m + M)(x-2) + 3$ yield a condition whose locus is a line? Why will $m + M$ be the slope of the locus? How do you know that point (2, 3) will be in the locus?

J Now suppose that you let $m + M$ be equal to the slope of the line that includes $\overrightarrow{BC}$. That is, let $m + M = 1$. How do you know that each (x, y) associated with a point in $\overrightarrow{BC}$ will satisfy $y = (m + M)(x-2) + 3$?

K Exercise G suggests that $m - M$ should be equal to -3. Exercise J suggests that $m + M$ should be equal to 1. Tabulate the solution set of $m - M = -3 \wedge m + M = 1$.

If you use your answer to exercise K to help you make replacements for M and m in condition A, you obtain condition B.

L In D1, the coördinates of several points in $\angle$ABC are given. Show that the ordered pairs associated with these points satisfy condition B.

Exercise L suggests that condition B is a condition that fits the curve represented in D1. In a similar way, by making appropriate replacements for M and m in condition A, you can obtain conditions for other angles that have point (2, 3) as a vertex.

M Suppose that $\angle$DBF is in the first and second quadrants and has point (2, 3) as its ver-

A $y = M|x-2| + m(x-2) + 3$.
B $y = 2|x-2| - 1(x-2) + 3$.

D2

tex. The slope of line BD is -2; the slope of line BF is 0. Make a graph of $\angle DBF$.

N You obtain $y = (m - M)(x - 2) + 3$ from condition A when x is less than what number? How do you know that $m - M$ must equal -2 if $y = (m - M)(x - 2) + 3$ is to be satisfied by each (x, y) associated with a point in $\overrightarrow{BD}$?

O You obtain $y = (m + M)(x - 2) + 3$ from condition B when x is greater than or equal to what number? What number must $m + M$ equal if $y = (m + M)(x - 2)$ is to be satisfied by each (x, y) associated with a point in $\overrightarrow{BF}$?

P What replacements can you make for m and M in condition A to obtain a condition that fits $\angle DBF$?

Q Suppose that $\angle GBH$ contains points (1, 4), (2, 3), and (3, 4). Point (2, 3) is the vertex. Develop a condition involving absolute value that fits $\angle GBH$.

R Suppose that $\angle RST$ contains points (0, 0), $(-1, -2)$, and $(-3, 0)$. Point $(-1, -2)$ is the vertex. Develop a condition involving absolute value that fits $\angle RST$.

KEEPING SKILLFUL

Find the product of the scalar and the vector named in each exercise.

1 $-8 \odot (4, 3)$
2 $6.8 \odot (3.2, 7)$
3 $\frac{1}{4} \odot (-6, 8\frac{1}{2})$
4 $10 \odot (-3\frac{1}{4}, -9)$
5 $0 \odot (1\frac{3}{4}, 1\frac{3}{4})$
6 $1 \odot (\sqrt{17}, -8.53)$
7 $-15 \odot (-4, -6)$
8 $3\frac{1}{8} \odot (-\frac{1}{4}, 3\frac{1}{8})$
9 $.75 \odot (72, 64)$
10 $-12 \odot (-6.5, -7.2)$
11 $12\frac{3}{8} \odot (8, -2\frac{1}{2})$
12 $-1.52 \odot (0, 6)$
13 $0 \odot (\sqrt{23}, \sqrt{5})$
14 $2.7 \odot (-3.5, -10)$
15 $2\frac{1}{7} \odot (2\frac{1}{5}, 1\frac{1}{5})$
16 $5 \odot (3.7, 8.9)$

APPLYING MATHEMATICS

For each problem, write a sentence that expresses a condition. Then give the answer to the problem. Use 3.14 as an approximation of π.

1 The temperature at which water boils at sea level is 100° C. On the Fahrenheit scale, what is the temperature at which water boils at sea level?

2 There are ten given points in a plane, and no three of them are collinear. How many lines are determined by the ten points?

3 How many foot-pounds of work are necessary to raise a 77-pound air conditioner from the floor to a window that is $5\frac{1}{2}$ feet from the floor?

4 The first term of an arithmetic progression is $2\frac{1}{2}$. The common difference of the progression is $-\frac{3}{4}$. What is the sum of the first nine terms of the progression?

5 The measures of the bases of a trapezoid are 6.8 in. and 4.9 in. The area of the trapezoid is 11.7 sq. in. What is the measure of an altitude of the trapezoid in inches?

6 Both a baseball diamond and a softball diamond are in the shape of a square. The area of a regulation baseball diamond is 4500 sq. ft. greater than the area of a regulation softball diamond. The distance between first base and second base of a baseball diamond is 30 ft. greater than the distance between first and second base of a softball diamond. What is the distance in feet between first and second base for both a baseball diamond and a softball diamond?

7 The distance between Greenville and Carson City is 440 mi. On Tuesday, Mr. Murray drove from Greenville to Carson City, and on Friday he made the return trip. By increasing his speed 15 miles per hour, he made the re-

turn trip in 3 hr. less time than he had made the trip to Carson City. How many hours did it take him to drive from Greenville to Carson City?

8 The top of a $15\frac{1}{2}$-foot ladder is placed against the side of a building. The measure of the angle formed by the ladder and the side of the building is 30 degrees. How many feet from the side of the building is the bottom of the ladder?

9 A projectile was fired straight up in the air with an initial velocity of 240 feet per second. In how many seconds was the projectile 875 ft. above the ground?

10 After one year, Mr. Long received a total of $154.60 in dividends on two investments. One of the investments pays a $4\frac{3}{4}\%$ dividend per year. The other investment is $500 more than the first and it pays a $5\frac{1}{2}\%$ dividend per year. How much money does Mr. Long have invested at each rate?

11 A high school basketball coach must choose a member of his team to play each of the five positions. There are twelve members on the team. If the coach considers all the possible arrangements, how many choices does he have for assigning the five positions?

12 Mrs. White plans to make covers for two sofa cushions. The cushions are in the shape of rectangular right prisms and are the same size. The length of each cushion is 35 in., the width is 20 in., and the height is 4 in. What is the total surface area of the two cushions in square inches?

13 On an algebra test containing 20 problems, 2 students received a grade of 100; 4 received a grade of 90; 3 received a grade of 85; 2 received a grade of 80; 15 received a grade of 75; 5 received a grade of 70; and 1 received a grade of 60. What was the mean grade received on the test?

CHECKING UP

The small numerals within parentheses tell what pages to turn to for help if you need it.

Test 258

Tell what words or symbols best complete exercises 1 through 15.

1 You obtain _____ when you factor the left side of $x^2 - 5x + 6 = 0$. (357)

2 When x is replaced by -3 in $y = -2x - 6$, _____ satisfies the condition you obtain. (334)

3 When you subtract _____ from each side of $x^2 + 9x = 2x + 8$, you obtain $x^2 + 7x - 8 = 0$. (356)

4 The least common multiple of $x + 4$ and $x^2 + x - 12$ is _____. (374)

5 The quotient of 0 and any non-zero number is _____. (373)

6 The first coördinate of a y-intercept of a locus is _____. (334)

7 The discriminant of $6x^2 - 11x - 10 = 0$ is _____. (365)

8 The _____ side of $\sqrt{x} + 2 = 0$ is a polynomial. (377)

9 The solution of $\sqrt{x - 4} = 3$ is _____. (377)

10 The second coördinate of an x-intercept of a locus is _____. (335)

11 If $f(x) = ax^2$ and $a < 0$, then the range of function f is _____. (348)

12 If you replace x in $y = 7x + 2$ by successively greater numbers, then y _____. (340)

13 The discriminant of $ax^2 + bx + c = 0$ is _____. (365)

14 $f(x) = -6x + 5$. The locus of function f intersects the x-axis in point _____. (340)

15 For each A and B, where A and B are polynomials, $\frac{A}{B} = 0 \Leftrightarrow A = 0 \wedge$ _____. (373)

Test 259

16 If x is replaced by -4 in $y = 3x - 5$, what replacement for y do you obtain? (334)

17 $x^2 - \frac{4}{3}x + \frac{4}{9}$ is the square of what binomial? (360)

18 Put $(3x - 4)(x + 7) = 5(x + 7)$ in the form $ax^2 + bx + c = 0$. (356)

19 Name the member of the function determined by $f(x) = 3x^2 + 5$ for which $f(x) = 5$. (356)

20 Tabulate $\{x \mid (x - 5)(x + 7) = 0\}$. (357)

21 What is the least common multiple of 5, $x^2 - 4$, and $x + 2$? (374)

22 What is the x-intercept of the locus of any function determined by a condition of the form $f(x) = ax^2$? (349)

23 Tabulate $\{x \mid \frac{x^2 - 5x - 14}{x + 2} = 0\}$. (373)

24 Put $\frac{3}{x - 3} + \frac{5}{x + 1} = 0$ in the form $\frac{A}{B} = 0$. (374)

25 Tabulate $\{x \mid \frac{x^2 - 4}{x} = 0\}$. (373)

26 Describe the range of the function determined by $f(x) = -2x^2$. (348)

27 Tabulate $\{x \mid 2\sqrt{x^2 + 7} - 3 = 5\}$. (378)

28 For $y = \frac{1}{2}x + 5$, describe y when x is replaced by any number greater than -10. (341)

29 Tabulate the solution set of $\sqrt{3x} = 2x$. (378)

Test 260

From the list below each exercise, choose the correct answer for the exercise.

30 A second-degree polynomial function is called a ~~~ function. (347)

a linear   c quadratic
b constant   d non-negative

31 The trinomial ~~~ is not the square of a binomial. (360)

a $x^2 + \frac{4}{5}x + \frac{4}{25}$ c $x^2 + 3x + \frac{9}{4}$
b $x^2 - \frac{2}{3}x + \frac{1}{9}$ d $x^2 + \frac{5}{2}x + \frac{25}{4}$

32 The solution set of ~~~ is $\{-2, 3\}$. (369)

a $x^2 + x - 6 = 0$ c $(x - 2)(x + 3) = 0$
b $x(x + 1) = 6$ d $x^2 - x = 6$

33 For a given quadratic condition, a, b, and c are rational and the discriminant is 6. The condition has ~~~. (366)

a two rational solutions
b no real solutions
c two irrational solutions
d one real solution

34 The solution set of ~~~ has just one member that is a real number. (365)

a $x^2 - x - 6 = 0$ c $x^2 - x + 6 = 0$
b $x^2 - 2x + 1 = 0$ d $x^2 - 2x - 2 = 0$

35 The condition $x =$ ~~~ is the quadratic formula. (364)

a $\frac{-b^2 \pm \sqrt{b - 4ac}}{2a}$ c $\frac{\pm a^2 - \sqrt{b^2 - 2ac}}{4b}$
b $\frac{-b \pm \sqrt{b^2 - 4ac}}{2a}$ d $\frac{2c^2 + \sqrt{a^2 - 4bc}}{\pm 2a}$

36 ~~~ is not satisfied by 3. (377)

a $(x - 3)(x + 4) = 0$ c $x^2 = 9$
b $5 - \sqrt{x^2} = 2$ d $\sqrt{-3x + 1} = 4$

37 The locus of ~~~ is symmetric with respect to the $f(x)$-axis. (349)

a $f(x) = 3x^2$ c $f(x) = 3x$
b $f(x) = 3x - 2$ d $f(x) = 3x^2 + x$

38 The discriminant of ~~~ is 41. (365)

a $3x^2 + 4x - 2 = 0$ c $2x^2 - 4x + 3 = 0$
b $2x^2 + 3x - 4 = 0$ d $4x^2 - 2x + 3 = 0$

39 If x^2 and $-\frac{6}{5}x$ are the first two terms of the square of a binomial, then the third term is ~~~. (360)

a $\frac{9}{25}$ b $\frac{3}{5}$ c $\frac{3}{10}$ d $\frac{9}{50}$

40 If $ax^2 + bx + c = 0$ has two solutions, then the product of those solutions is ~~~. (367)

a $\frac{a}{b}$ b $\frac{-b}{c}$ c $\frac{c}{a}$ d $\frac{-c}{b}$

41 There are replacements for a and b for which ~~~ is not true. (381)

a $a < 0 \wedge 0 < b \Rightarrow ab < 0$
b $a < 0 \wedge b < 0 \Rightarrow ab > 0$
c $a < 0 \wedge b < 0 \Rightarrow 0 > ab$
d $0 < a \wedge 0 < b \Rightarrow 0 < ab$

CHECKING UP

The small numerals within parentheses tell what pages to turn to for help if you need it.

Test 261

Tell what words or symbols best complete exercises 1 through 10.

1 The starting point of vector RT is point ~~~~. (7)

2 The condition $8 - x = 3$ is satisfied by the number ~~~~. (254)

3 Any ~~~~ noncollinear points determine a triangle. (15)

4 If you multiply the reciprocal of $-\frac{2}{3}$ by ~~~~, you obtain 6. (316)

5 The domain of a relation in A × B is a subset of ~~~~. (297)

6 In △HIJ, $\angle J^\circ = 90$. Side ~~~~ is the hypotenuse of △HIJ. (15)

7 The solution set of ~~~~ is an open interval whose limits are -5 and 7. (268)

8 ~~~~ is the vector sum of $(-7, 5)$ and $(4, 3)$. (49)

9 If a vector that is 2 in. long represents a displacement of 75 mi. in a scale drawing, then a vector that is 5 in. long represents a displacement of ~~~~. (12)

10 $f = \{(1, 2), (2, 4), (3, 2), (4, 4)\}$. The image of 2 in function f is ~~~~. (305)

Test 262

From the list below each exercise, choose the item that correctly completes the exercise.

11 The difference ~~~~ is a positive real number. (91)

a $-5 - 7$ c $-7 - (-5)$
b $-5 - (-7)$ d $5 - 7$

12 Vector AB represents a given force. The magnitude of the given force is represented by the ~~~~ of the vector. (26)

a horizontal component c direction
b vertical component d length

13 Of the numbers expressed below, ~~~~ is not a rational number of arithmetic. (65)

a $\frac{3}{4}$ b $-\frac{1}{2}$ c 2 d $4\frac{5}{9}$

14 If x is a negative real number and y is a positive real number, then ~~~~. (89)

a $x = y$ c $y > x$
b $0 < x < y$ d $x > y$

15 The contrapositive of "If there is smoke, then there is fire" is ~~~~. (127)

a "If there is not fire, then there is not smoke"
b "If there is fire, then there is smoke"
c "If there is not smoke, then there is not fire"
d "If there is smoke, then there is not fire"

16 The greatest common factor of ~~~~ is $3xy$. (195)

a $9x^2y^2$, $18x^3$, and $39y^3$
b $27xy$, $-12x^2y$, and $15xy^2$
c $3yx$, $-24xyz$, and $33yz$
d $-6xy^2$, $25x^2y$, and $21xyz$

17 When x is replaced by 5, the statement ~~~~ is false. (125)

a "If $x > 4$, then $x > 6$"
b "If $x < 6$, then $x > 4$"
c "If $x < 4$, then $x < 3$"
d "If $x > 6$, then $x < 6$"

18 The expression ~~~~ is a factored form of $6 - 4n + 15m - 10mn$. (198)

a $(3 - 10m)(2 + n)$ c $(5m + 2)(3 - 2n)$
b $(6 - 4n)(2m + 1)$ d $(2n - 3)(2 + 5m)$

19 When the antecedent and the consequent of a conditional are interchanged, the resulting conditional is the ~~~~ of the given conditional. (126)

a contrapositive c negation
b denial d converse

20 The set of ~~~~ does not form a commutative group under addition. (53)

a real numbers
b rational numbers
c positive integers
d ordered pairs of real numbers

Test 263

21 Tabulate $\{x \mid (x+3)^2 = (1-x)^2\}$. (260)

22 Name the similar terms in the expression $\frac{2}{3}x^2y + 4 + 6.2x^2y^2 - 3\frac{1}{2}xy^2 + 4\sqrt{7}$. (182)

23 What condition determines a function each of whose members can be represented by $(x, \frac{3}{4}x)$? (311)

24 Tabulate $\{x \mid |x| = 5\}$. (275)

25 $R_1 = \{(0, 1), (1, 3), (2, 5), (4, 7)\}$. Tabulate the range of R_1. (297)

26 Simplify $2(3x^2 - 4) - 5(7 + 2x) + 4x^2 - 1$. (189)

27 Put $6(3 - x) + \frac{2}{3}(12x + 9) < 0$ in standard form. (262)

28 What is the range of $\{(x, y) \mid y = -2\}$? (326)

29 What is the standard form of a fifth-degree polynomial in one variable? (182)

Test 264

For each of problems 30 through 33, write a sentence that expresses a condition. Then give the answer to the problem.

30 The mathematics club at Hanley High School has $\frac{2}{3}$ as many members as the camera club. The camera club has 12 more members than the mathematics club. How many members does each club have? (280)

31 Cloverdale Junior College has an enrollment of 910 students. The number of girls enrolled is 1.8 times the number of boys enrolled. How many boys are enrolled? (280)

32 Mr. Thurley, the chemistry teacher, has 250 grams of a 3% salt solution. How many grams of pure salt must he add to the solution to obtain a 5% salt solution? Give the answer to the nearer tenth of a gram. (280)

33 A jet airplane made a flight of 1560 mi. in scheduled time. If the average speed of the airplane had been 40 mi. per hour faster, the flight would have been $\frac{1}{4}$ hr. shorter. What was the scheduled time of the flight in hours? (385)

Unit 24

Systems of conditions

24 285 Exploring ideas

Graphic analysis of systems of conditions

You are familiar with the idea of a compound condition involving the connective "and." A compound condition of this kind makes up a system of conditions. In this unit you will study methods of solving systems of conditions that involve two and three variables. Then you will use systems of conditions to solve problems.

This lesson concerns the graphs that represent the loci of systems of conditions in two variables. In this lesson, as well as in the remaining lessons of this unit, you may assume that the universe for each variable is D, unless you are told otherwise.

A Look at D1. Which (x, y) that satisfies condition A has 0 as its first component? Which solution of A has 0 as its second component?

B Which (x, y) that satisfies condition B has 2 as its first component? Which solution of B has $\frac{1}{2}$ as its second component?

C Show the steps that are necessary to obtain condition E from A and justify each step.

D Show the steps that are necessary to obtain condition F from B and justify each step.

E How can condition G be obtained from C? How can condition H be obtained from D?

F Each of conditions E through H is in the form $ax + by + c = 0$. What are the values of a, b, and c in each of these conditions?

$ax + by + c = 0$, where a or b is not zero, is the standard form of a *linear condition for equality in two variables*. Since each of conditions A through D can be put in the form

A $3x + 5 = -2y$.
B $6 - 2y = x$.
C $3x = 5$.
D $y = 2$.
E $3x + 2y + 5 = 0$.
F $-1x - 2y + 6 = 0$.
G $3x + 0y - 5 = 0$.
H $0x + 1y - 2 = 0$.

D1

I $x + 2y = 6$.
J $3y = 9$.
K $4x = 12$.

D2

linear condition for equality in two variables. A condition of the form $ax + by + c = 0$, where a or b is not zero.

$ax + by + c = 0$, each is a linear condition for equality in two variables.

G Put $y - x = 7$ in the form $ax + by + c = 0$. Put $4y + 7 = 0$ in this form. Put $\frac{1}{2}x = 13$ in this form. In each case, give the values of a, b, and c.

H Look at D2. How can $x + 2y - 6 = 0$ be obtained from condition I? Is $x + 2y - 6 = 0$ in the form $ax + by + c = 0$? What are the values of a, b, and c in $x + 2y - 6 = 0$?

Notice that when condition I is put in the form $ax + by + c = 0$, neither a nor b is zero.

I How can you obtain $2y = -x + 6$ from condition I? How can you obtain $y = -\frac{1}{2}x + 3$ from $2y = -x + 6$? When you put condition I in the form $y = mx + b$, what are the values of m and b?

J You know that the locus of $y = -\frac{1}{2}x + 3$ is a line. What is the slope of this line? What is the y-intercept?

K Study the graphs in D3. Which line is the locus of condition I, expressed in D2?

L Think about the condition $ax + by + c = 0$, where $a \neq 0$ and $b \neq 0$. How can you obtain $y = \left(\frac{-a}{b}\right)x + \left(\frac{-c}{b}\right)$ from $ax + by + c = 0$? Is $\frac{-a}{b}$ the slope of the locus of $ax + by + c = 0$? Is point $\left(0, \frac{-c}{b}\right)$ its y-intercept?

M Put condition J, expressed in D2, in the form $ax + by + c = 0$.

N Which line represented in D3 is the locus of condition J?

O ? Consider $ax + by + c = 0$, where $a = 0$ and $b \neq 0$. How can you obtain $y = \frac{-c}{b}$ from $ax + by + c = 0$? Describe the locus of the condition $y = \frac{-c}{b}$.

P Show that condition K, expressed in D2, is of the form $ax + by + c = 0$. In this case, which is equal to 0, a or b?

Q Which line represented in D3 is the locus of K?

R Consider $ax + by + c = 0$, where $a \neq 0$ and $b = 0$. How can you obtain $x = \frac{-c}{a}$ from this condition? Describe the locus of $x = \frac{-c}{a}$.

S Suppose that the slope of ℓ_4 is 3 and its y-intercept is point (0, 1). Give a condition of the form $ax + by + c = 0$ that has ℓ_4 as its locus.

T Suppose that ℓ_5 is parallel to the x-axis. Point (0, 2) is the y-intercept of ℓ_5. Give a condition of the form $ax + by + c = 0$ that has ℓ_5 as its locus.

U Suppose that ℓ_6 is a vertical line with point $(\frac{1}{2}, 0)$ as its x-intercept. Give a condition of the form $ax + by + c = 0$ that has ℓ_6 as its locus.

I $x + 2y = 6$.

J $3y = 9$.

K $4x = 12$.

D2

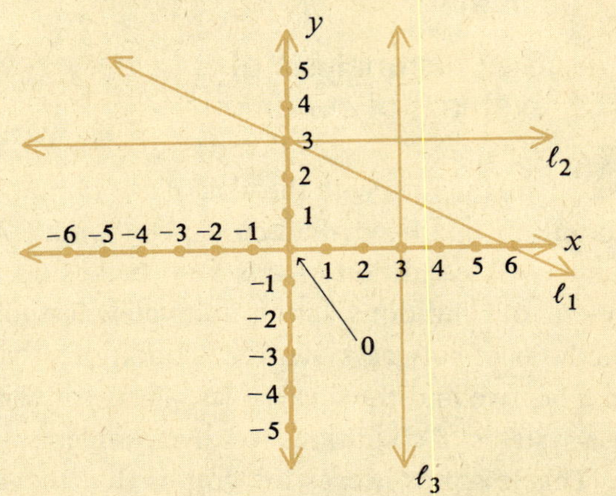

Incomplete graphs

D3

L $x + y - 5 = 0 \wedge 3x - 2y = 0$.

M
$2x - y + 3 = 0$
$2x - y + 1 = 0$.

N
$x - y + 2 = 0$
$3x - 3y + 6 = 0$.

D4

Next you will consider the loci of compound conditions that are formed from two linear conditions in two variables and the connective "and."

A For condition L, expressed in D4, why is $\{(x, y) \mid x + y - 5 = 0\} \cap \{(x, y) \mid 3x - 2y = 0\}$ the solution set?

A compound condition involving "and" is sometimes called a *system of conditions*. You can see that system L involves two linear conditions for equality in two variables. The solution set of system L is the intersection of the solution sets of the conditions in the system. That is, the solution set of system L is the intersection of the solution sets of the conditions $x + y - 5 = 0$ and $3x - 2y = 0$.

You know that the locus of a linear condition for equality in two variables is a line. To find the slope and the y-intercept of this line, you will find it convenient first to put the condition in the form $y = mx + b$. Then, the value of m is the slope and point $(0, b)$ is the y-intercept.

B What is the y-intercept of the locus of $x + y - 5 = 0$? What is the slope of this locus?

C Which line represented in D5 is the locus of $x + y - 5 = 0$?

D What is the y-intercept of the locus of $3x - 2y = 0$? What is the slope of this locus? Which line represented in D5 is the locus of $3x - 2y = 0$?

E What is the point of intersection of ℓ_7 and ℓ_8? How do you know that $\{(2, 3)\}$ is the solution set of system L?

D4 shows another way that a system of conditions can be expressed. System M is expressed in this way. Notice that the symbol for the connective "and" is omitted and one simple condition is expressed directly below the other. From now on, we will express compound conditions involving "and" in this way whenever it is convenient.

F Which line represented in D6 is the locus of $2x - y + 3 = 0$? Of $2x - y + 1 = 0$?

G ℓ_9 and ℓ_{10} are parallel. What can you say about $\ell_9 \cap \ell_{10}$? Tabulate the solution set of system M.

H Look again at D4. How is the solution set of system N related to the solution sets of the simple conditions in N?

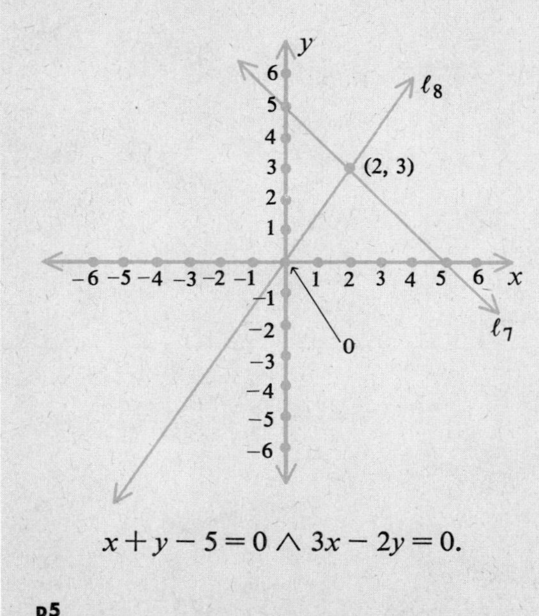

$x + y - 5 = 0 \wedge 3x - 2y = 0.$

D5

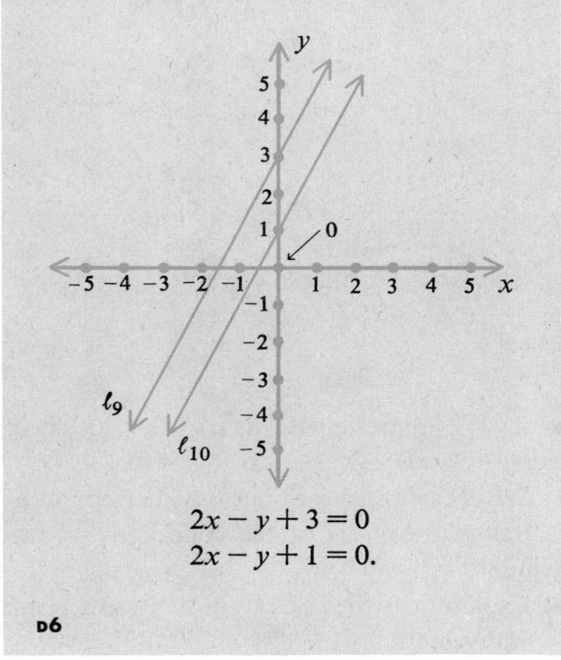

$2x - y + 3 = 0$
$2x - y + 1 = 0.$

D6

I Put $x - y + 2 = 0$ in the form $y = mx + b$. What is the slope of the locus of $x - y + 2 = 0$? What is the y-intercept of this locus?

J Find the slope and the y-intercept of the locus of $3x - 3y + 6 = 0$.

L $x + y - 5 = 0 \wedge 3x - 2y = 0.$

M $2x - y + 3 = 0$
$2x - y + 1 = 0.$

N $x - y + 2 = 0$
$3x - 3y + 6 = 0.$

D4

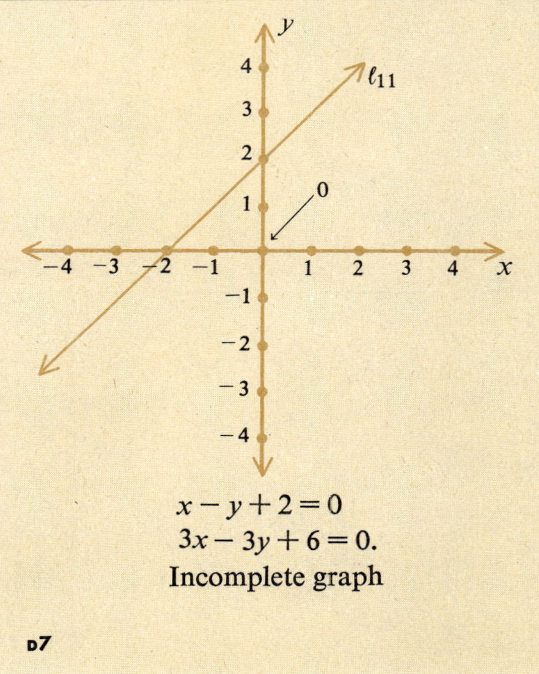

$x - y + 2 = 0$
$3x - 3y + 6 = 0.$
Incomplete graph

D7

K Is ℓ_{11}, represented in D7, the locus of $x - y + 2 = 0$? Of $3x - 3y + 6 = 0$?

L What can you say about the intersection of **?** the solution sets of the conditions in system N?

M Explain why the conditions in system N are **?** equivalent.

Exercises A through M show how the loci of two linear conditions for equality in two variables are related to the solution set of the system that is formed from the two conditions.

If the loci of the two linear conditions intersect in exactly one point, then the solution set of the system contains exactly one ordered pair. System L, expressed in D4, is an example of such a system.

If the loci of the two linear conditions are parallel, then the solution set of the system is the empty set. System M, expressed in D4, is an example of this kind of system.

If the two linear conditions have the same locus, then the solution set of the system is an infinite set and is the same as the solution set of either condition in the system. System N, expressed in D4, is an example of this kind of system.

In this lesson you have studied systems of conditions that involve two linear conditions for equality in two variables. You have also learned how the loci of the conditions in such systems are related to the solution sets of the systems.

On your own

For each condition expressed below, tell whether or not it is a linear condition for equality in two variables. If it is a linear condition for equality in two variables, put it in the form $y = mx + b$. Then determine the slope and the y-intercept of its locus.

1 $x + y = 2.$ **4** $2x + y - x = 2y + x - y.$
2 $3x = y - 10.$ **5** $x = 0.$
3 $y = 5x.$ **6** $y^2 + 2 = 0.$

For each exercise below, make a graph of the set of (x, y) that is the solution set of the condition expressed.

7 $x - y + 5 = 0.$ **10** $7x + 2y - 6 = 0.$
8 $4x + y = 0.$ **11** $7y - 14 = 0.$
9 $-3x + 6y - 1 = 0.$ **12** $2x + 5 = 0.$

For each of exercises 13 through 26, first make a graph to represent the locus of each condition in the system expressed. If possible, tabulate the solution set of the system. Otherwise, describe the solution set in words.

13 $x - 12 = 0$
$y + 7 = 0.$

14 $2x - y + 5 = 0$
$x - \frac{1}{2}y + \frac{5}{2} = 0.$

15 $3x - y + 1 = 0$
$-3x - y + 1 = 0.$

16 $5x - 2y + 4 = 0$
$10x - 4y + 24 = 0.$

17 $x - y - 2 = 0$
$3y + 6 = 0.$

18 $7x + y + 5 = 0$
$x + y + 11 = 0.$

19 $2x + y + 1 = 0$
$4x - 3y - 13 = 0.$

20 $10x + 5y = 0$
$x + 10 = 0.$

21 $x + y + 10 = 0$
$-x - y - 10 = 0.$

22 $3x - 9y = 0$
$x + y + 8 = 0.$

23 $-x + y + 7 = 0$
$3x - 3y - 6 = 0.$

24 $4x + 7y - 6 = 0$
$x + 5y + 5 = 0.$

25 $13x + 3y + 4 = 0$
$6x + y + 3 = 0.$

26 $2x + 5y = 0$
$x + 2y - 1 = 0.$

24 286 Exploring ideas

Equivalent systems of conditions

In this lesson you will learn how to decide if two systems of linear conditions for equality in two variables are equivalent. You will be concerned primarily with systems whose solution sets contain exactly one element.

Two systems of conditions are expressed in D1. First you will consider the locus of each condition in system A.

A Give the slope and the y-intercept of the locus of $x + y - 2 = 0$. Which line represented in D2 is this locus?

A $x + y - 2 = 0$
$x - y = 0.$

B $5x - y - 4 = 0$
$5x + y - 6 = 0.$

D1

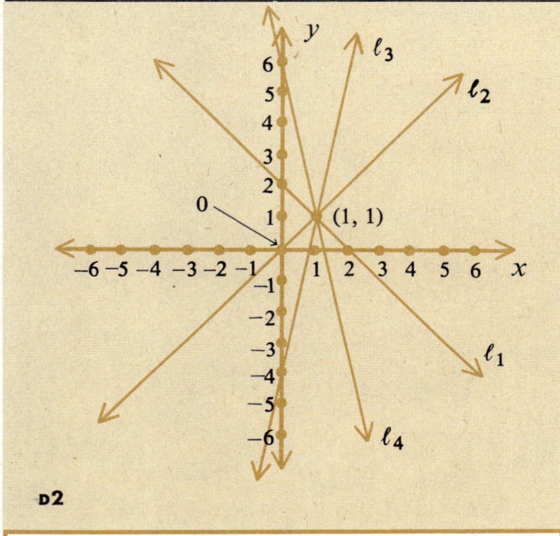

D2

equivalent systems of conditions. Systems that have the same solution set.

B Give the slope and y-intercept of the locus of $x - y = 0$. Which line represented in D2 is this locus?

C What is the point of intersection of ℓ_1 and ℓ_2? Tabulate the solution set of system A.

Next you will consider the locus of each condition in system B, expressed in D1.

D Which line represented in D2 is the locus of $5x - y - 4 = 0$?

E Which line represented in D2 is the locus of $5x + y - 6 = 0$?

F What is the point of intersection of ℓ_3 and ℓ_4? Tabulate the solution set of system B.

G How does the solution set of system A compare with the solution set of system B?

Systems A and B are equivalent. *Equivalent systems of conditions* are systems that have the same solution set.

C $x - 3y = 0$
$2x - y = 0.$

E $x = 0$
$y = 0.$

D $x - y = 0$
$x + y = 0.$

D3

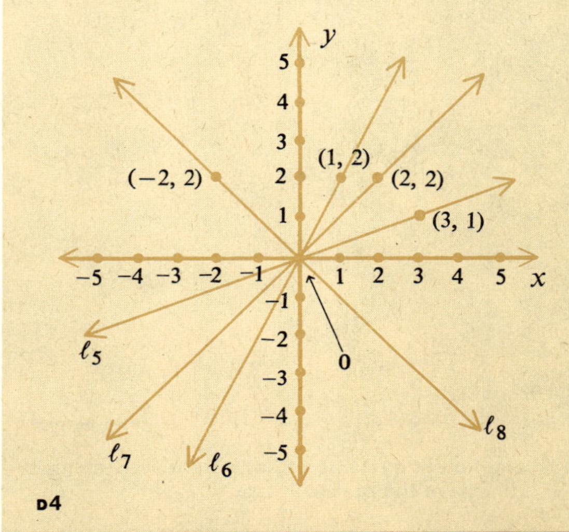

D4

F $x - 3y - 3 = 0$
$x + y + 5 = 0.$

G $x + 3 = 0$
$y + 2 = 0.$

D5

H Study system C, expressed in D3. How do you know that the locus of $x - 3y = 0$ contains the origin?

I Does the locus of $2x - y = 0$ contain the origin?

J Look at D4. Which line is the locus of $x - 3y = 0$? Which line is the locus of $2x - y = 0$?

K How do you know that $\{(0, 0)\}$ is the solution set of system C?

L Now study system D. Which line represented in D4 is the locus of $x - y = 0$? Which line is the locus of $x + y = 0$?

M Tabulate the solution set of system D. Why are systems D and C equivalent?

N ? Look again at D3. Describe the locus of each condition in system E. Is system E equivalent to system C?

O ? Consider the system that is made up of the conditions $2x - y = 0$ and $y - 5 = 0$. Is this system equivalent to system C? Explain your answer.

P Look at D5. Give the slope and the y-intercept of the locus of each condition in system F.

Q Now look at D6. Which lines are the loci of the conditions in system F?

R Tabulate the solution set of system F.

S Notice ℓ_{11} and ℓ_{12}, represented in D6. Which of these lines is parallel to the x-axis? Which line is parallel to the y-axis?

T ? How do you know that ℓ_{11} and ℓ_{12} are loci of the conditions in a system that is equivalent to system F?

U ? Study system G, expressed in D5. Which condition in G has ℓ_{11} as its locus? Which condition has ℓ_{12} as its locus?

V ? How do you know that $\{(-3, -2)\}$ is the solution set of system G?

Now that you know how to decide if two systems are equivalent, you will study a property that will enable you to derive a system that is equivalent to a given system.

Study system H, expressed in D7. Then study condition I. Notice how the left side of condition I is related to the left sides of the conditions in system H. The left side of condition I is the sum of two expressions. One of these expressions is 4 times the left side of $x + y - 2 = 0$. The other expression is -2 times the left side of $5x + y - 6 = 0$.

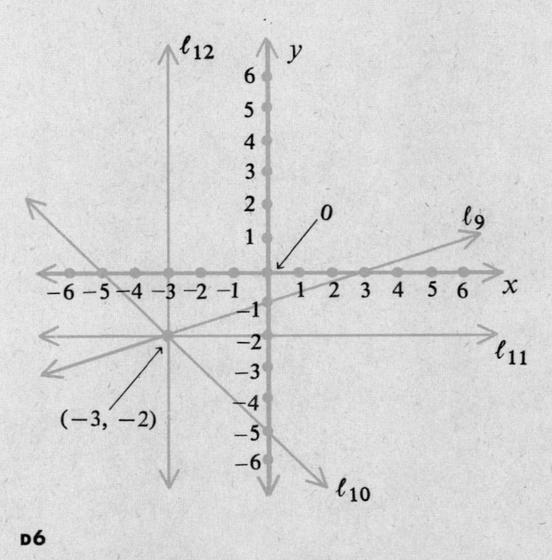

D6

H $x+y-2=0$
$5x+y-6=0.$

I $4(x+y-2)+(-2)(5x+y-6)=0.$

D7

A Suppose that a given (x, y) is a solution of system H. If you use the components of the given (x, y) as replacements for x and y in condition I, will $4(x+y-2)$ yield $4(0)$? Will $-2(5x+y-6)$ yield $-2(0)$? Explain your answers.

B What is a standard name of $4(0)-2(0)$? Is the solution of system H also a solution of condition I?

C The solution set of system H is $\{(1, 1)\}$. Show that $(1, 1)$ satisfies both conditions in system H and also satisfies condition I.

D What steps can you use to put condition I in the form $-6x+2y+4=0$?

Now look at D8. Lines ℓ_{13} and ℓ_{14} are the loci of the conditions in system H. ℓ_{15} is the locus of condition I.

E Does the locus of condition I contain the point of intersection of ℓ_{13} and ℓ_{14}?

System H and condition I are expressed again in D9. Notice condition J, which is of the same form as condition I.

F By what numbers can you replace m and n in condition J to obtain condition I?

G You have already seen that the solution of system H satisfies condition I. Suppose that the components of the (x, y) that satisfies system H are used as replacements for x and y in condition J. When these replacements are made, how do you know that $m(x+y-2)$ will yield $m \cdot 0$ for each m? How do you know that $n(5x+y-6)$ will yield $n \cdot 0$ for each n?

H For each m and n, is $m \cdot 0 + n \cdot 0 = 0$? Will the solution of system H satisfy any condition that is in the form of condition J?

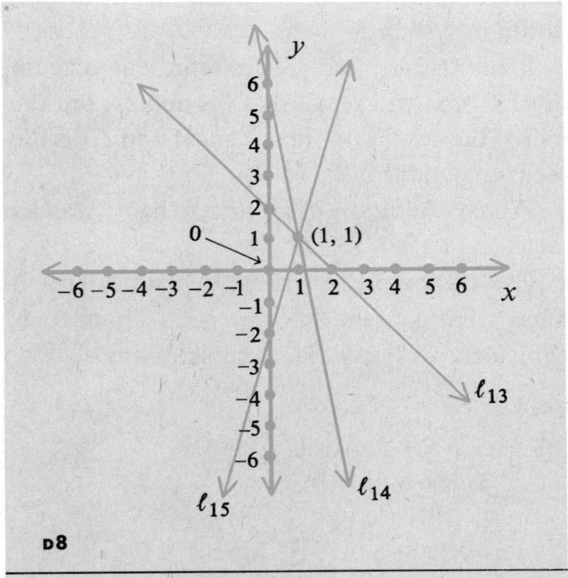

D8

H $x+y-2=0$
$5x+y-6=0.$

I $4(x+y-2)+(-2)(5x+y-6)=0.$
J $m(x+y-2)+n(5x+y-6)=0.$

D9

Exercises F, G, and H illustrate the property that is expressed below.

For each m *and* n, *each solution of the system* ax + by + c = *0* ∧ dx + ey + f = *0 is a solution of* m(ax + by + c) + n(dx + ey + f) = *0*.

I Look again at D9. What condition do you obtain if you replace m by -3 and n by 1 in condition J? How do you know that the solution of system H is a solution of the condition that you just obtained?

System K, which is composed of condition I and the condition that you obtained for exercise I, is expressed in D10.

J Remember that condition I, which is one of the conditions in system K, can be put in the form $-6x + 2y + 4 = 0$. What steps can you use to obtain $2x - 2y = 0$ from the other condition in system K?

Lines ℓ_{13}, ℓ_{14}, and ℓ_{15} are represented again in D11. You will recall that ℓ_{13} and ℓ_{14} are the loci of the conditions in system H and ℓ_{15} is the locus of condition I.

K Which condition in system K has ℓ_{16} as its locus?

L Use the graph in D11 to explain how you know that system K, expressed in D10, is equivalent to system H, expressed in D9.

H $x + y - 2 = 0$
$5x + y - 6 = 0.$

I $4(x + y - 2) + (-2)(5x + y - 6) = 0.$

J $m(x + y - 2) + n(5x + y - 6) = 0.$

D9

K $4(x + y - 2) + (-2)(5x + y - 6) = 0$
$-3(x + y - 2) + 1(5x + y - 6) = 0.$

D10

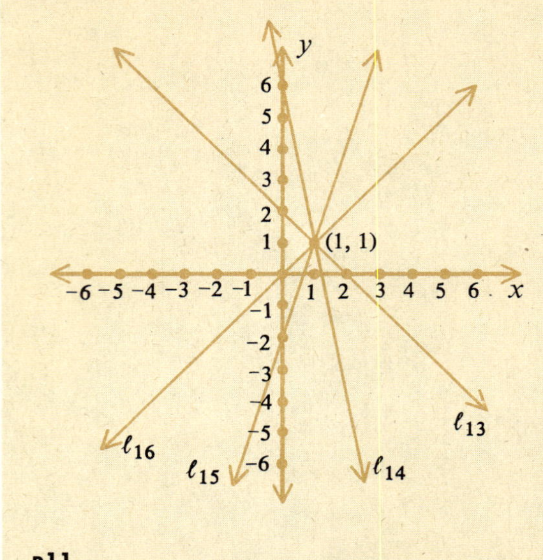

D11

L $x + y + 7 = 0$
$x - y = 0.$

M $1(x + y + 7) + 1(x - y) = 0.$

N $(-1)(x + y + 7) + 1(x - y) = 0.$

D12

M Look at D12. How can you use the left side of each condition in system L to obtain the left side of condition M? How can you use the left side of each condition in system L to obtain the left side of condition N?

N Put each of conditions M and N in the form $ax + by + c = 0$.

O Make a graph to represent the locus of system L. Then make graphs of the loci of conditions M and N.

P Use conditions M and N to form a system that is equivalent to system L.

In this lesson you learned the meaning of equivalent systems of conditions. Then you studied a property that you can use to obtain equivalent systems.

On your own

In each of exercises 1 through 5, two systems, A and B, are expressed. First, make one graph in which you represent the loci of the conditions in each system. Next, tabulate the solution set of each system. Then tell whether or not systems A and B are equivalent.

1 A $-3x + y - 2 = 0$, $y - 5 = 0.$ B $y - 5 = 0$, $x - 1 = 0.$

2 A $x - y - 5 = 0$, $x + y - 5 = 0.$ B $x = 0$, $x + y - 5 = 0.$

3 A $x - 3y + 3 = 0$, $2x - 3y - 6 = 0.$ B $5x - 3y + 15 = 0$, $x - \frac{3}{5}y + 1 = 0.$

4 A $3x - 2y + 6 = 0$, $-x + y - 3 = 0.$ B $x + y - 3 = 0$, $3x + 5y - 15 = 0.$

5 A $4x - 5y - 20 = 0$, $-x + 5y + 5 = 0.$ B $3x + 2y + 4 = 0$, $x - 4y - 22 = 0.$

6 Develop a system of conditions that is equivalent to the system expressed below.

$$6x - 7y + 12 = 0$$
$$-5x - 3y + 20 = 0.$$

KEEPING SKILLFUL

For each exercise below, copy and complete the chart. Then make a graph of the locus of the condition.

1

$f(x) = 4x^2.$					
x	-2	-1	0	1	2
$f(x)$					

2

$f(x) = \frac{64}{x}.$								
x	-16	-8	-4	-2	2	4	8	16
$f(x)$								

24 287 Exploring ideas

Systems of two conditions in two variables

You are accustomed to finding the solution set of a simple condition by a method that involves obtaining an equivalent condition whose solution set is obvious. In this lesson you will learn how to employ the same general method to find the solution set of a system of linear conditions.

A Look at D1. Then study the graph in D2. Which lines are the loci of the conditions in

A $3x - y = 0$, $4x + y - 7 = 0.$ B $x = 1$, $y = 3.$

D1

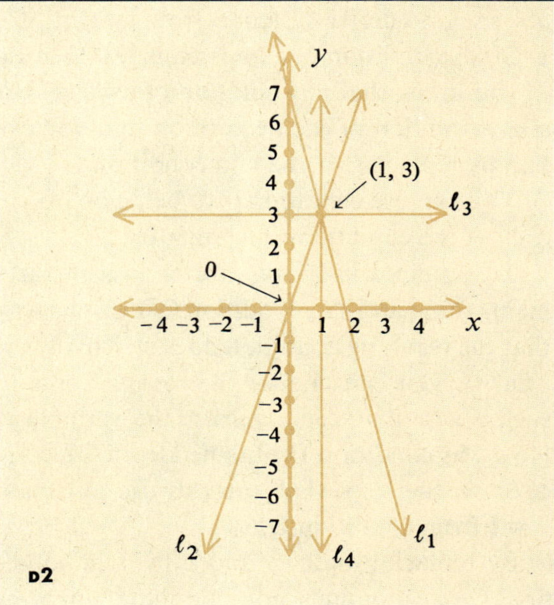

D2

system A? Which lines are the loci of the conditions in B?

B Tabulate the solution set of system A. Tabulate the solution set of system B.

C How do you know that systems A and B are equivalent?

Notice that, although A and B are equivalent systems, the solution set of B is easier to determine than the solution set of A. This is because each condition in B involves only one variable. The condition $x = 1$ requires that the first component of each solution of B must be 1; the condition $y = 3$ requires that the second component of each solution of B must be 3.

D Look again at D2. Notice that the locus of $x = 1$ is parallel to the y-axis. How is the locus of $y = 3$ located with respect to the x-axis?

For each system like A, there is an equivalent system like B, whose solution set is easy to determine because each condition involves only one variable. The loci of the conditions in a system like B are lines that are parallel to the coördinate axes. Now you will see how the property that you studied in the last lesson enables you to derive system B from system A.

E ? Study condition C, expressed in D3. How do you know that any solution of system A is also a solution of each condition that you obtain by replacing m and n in condition C?

You can use condition C to help you obtain each of the conditions in system B.

F To obtain $x = 1$, you can choose replacements for m and n in condition C in such a way that the resulting condition does not involve y. That is, you can choose the replacements in such a way that you *eliminate* the variable y. How was condition D obtained from C?

G Show the steps that you can use to obtain $x = 1$ from condition D.

By replacing both m and n by 1 in condition C, we obtain a condition that involves

A $3x - y = 0$
$4x + y - 7 = 0.$

B $x = 1$
$y = 3.$

D1

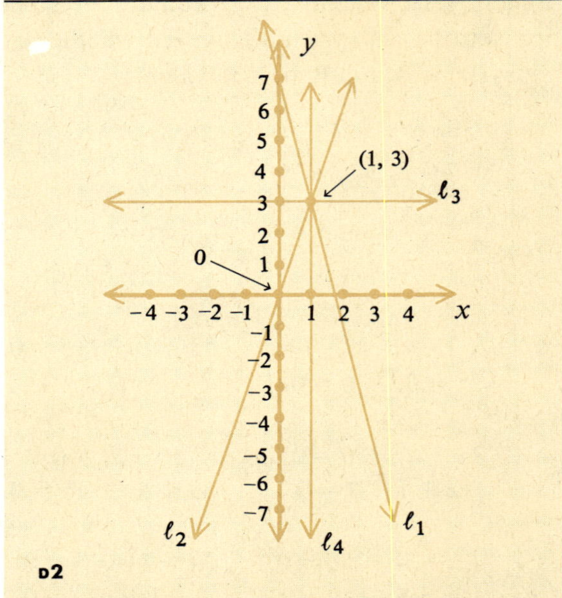

D2

C $m(3x - y) + n(4x + y - 7) = 0.$

D $1(3x - y) + 1(4x + y - 7) = 0.$

E $4(3x - y) + (-3)(4x + y - 7) = 0.$

D3

the similar terms $-y$ and y. Since $-y + y = 0$, the resulting condition involves only x.

H To obtain $y = 3$, you can choose replacements for m and n in condition C in such a way that you eliminate x. How was condition E obtained from C?

I Show the steps that you can use to obtain $y = 3$ from condition E.

By replacing m by 4 and n by -3 in condition C, we obtain a condition that involves the similar terms $12x$ and $-12x$. Since $12x + (-12x) = 0$, the resulting condition involves only y.

J What (x, y) satisfies both $x = 1$ and $y = 3$? How do you know that this ordered pair is the only solution of system A?

K To make certain that you did not make an error in obtaining system B from A, you can check (1, 3) in system A. Is $3(1) - 3 = 0$? Is $4(1) + 3 - 7 = 0$?

Next you will derive a system that is equivalent to system F, expressed in D4. Then you will use this new system to determine the solution set of F.

L Study systems F and G and condition H. Is each condition in system G a standard form of a condition in system F? Is system G equivalent to system F? How do you know that any solution of system G is also a solution of each condition that you obtain by replacing m and n in condition H?

M If you use condition H to obtain a condition in which you can eliminate x, why must you replace m and n so that $m(4x) + n(x) = 0$?

N If you replace m by 1 and n by -4 in $m(4x) + n(x)$, what do you obtain?

O What condition do you obtain if you replace m by 1 and n by -4 in condition H? Show how you can obtain $y = 2$ from this condition.

P If you use condition H to obtain a condition in which you can eliminate y, how do you know that you must replace m and n so that $m(-y) + n(y) = 0$?

Q What replacements should you make for m and n in $m(-y) + n(y)$ to obtain 0? If you use these same replacements for m and n in condition H, what condition do you obtain?

R Derive $x = 1$ from the condition that you obtained for exercise Q.

S In exercises M through R, you have derived a system of conditions that is equivalent to system F. What (x, y) satisfies $y = 2 \wedge x = 1$? How do you know that this ordered pair is the only solution of system G? Of system F?

F $\begin{cases} 4x - y = 2 \\ x + y = 3. \end{cases}$

G $\begin{cases} 4x - y - 2 = 0 \\ x + y - 3 = 0. \end{cases}$

H $m(4x - y - 2) + n(x + y - 3) = 0.$

D4

I $\begin{cases} x - 4y + 4 = 0 \\ x + y - 6 = 0. \end{cases}$ **J** $\begin{cases} x - 4y + 4 = 0 \\ y = 2. \end{cases}$

D5

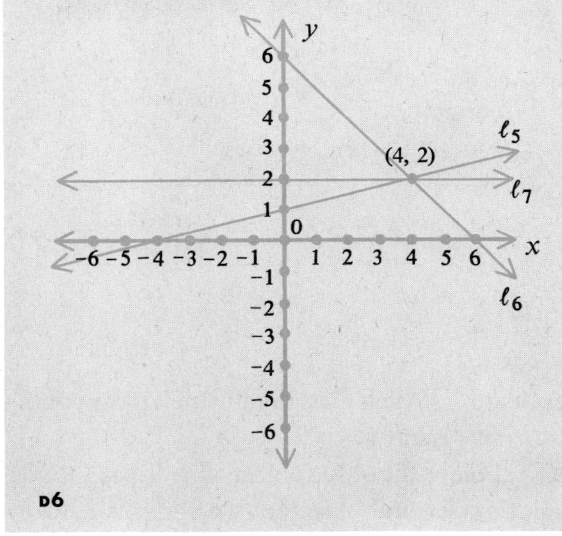

D6

T Now you can check (1, 2) in system F. Is $4(1) - 2 = 2$? Is $1 + 2 = 3$?

U Tabulate the solution set of system F.

You know how to determine the solution set of a given system by deriving an equivalent system in which each condition involves one variable. In the following exercises, you will learn another way of determining such solution sets.

A Look at D5. Then study the graph in D6. Which lines are the loci of the conditions in

I $x - 4y + 4 = 0$
$x + y - 6 = 0.$

J $x - 4y + 4 = 0$
$y = 2.$

D5

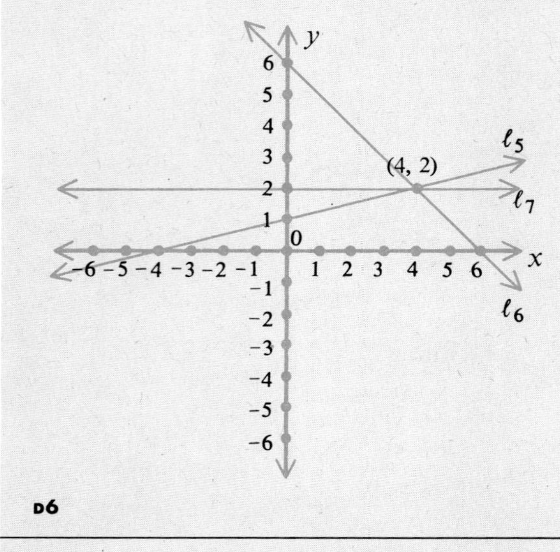

D6

K $m(x - 4y + 4) + n(x + y - 6) = 0.$

D7

system I? Which lines are the loci of the conditions in system J?

B Tabulate the solution set of I. Tabulate the solution set of J. Are the two systems equivalent?

Now you will learn how to determine the solution set of system I without making a graph.

You know that any solution of system I must satisfy $x - 4y + 4 = 0$. Notice that this condition is in both system I and system J.

C The other condition in system J involves only one variable. Which variable does this condition involve? It is possible to use condition K, expressed in D7, to obtain this condition from system I.

D Explain why any solution of system I is also a solution of each condition that you obtain by replacing m and n in condition K.

E ? What replacements can you make for m and n in condition K to obtain a condition that involves only y? Make these replacements and show the steps that you can use to obtain $y = 2$. How do you know that any (x, y) that satisfies system I also satisfies $y = 2$?

F Think again about system J, expressed in D5. What condition do you obtain if you replace y by 2 in $x - 4y + 4 = 0$? What x satisfies this condition?

G What is the only (x, y) that satisfies both $x - 4y + 4 = 0$ and $y = 2$? Tabulate the solution set of system I.

H Now look at D8. Is each condition in system M a standard form of a condition in system L? Is system M equivalent to system L?

To determine the solution set of M, you can derive a system that is equivalent to M.

I ? Suppose that you want to derive an equivalent system that has $3x - 4y - 12 = 0$ as one of its conditions and that has a condition involving only x as its other condition. Show how you can use condition N, expressed in D8, to obtain the condition that involves only x.

L $3x - 12 = 4y$
$3x + 5y = -15.$

M $3x - 4y - 12 = 0$
$3x + 5y + 15 = 0.$

N $m(3x - 4y - 12) + n(3x + 5y + 15) = 0.$

O $3x - 4y - 12 = 0$
$x = 0.$

D8

J What is the solution of system O, expressed in D8? How do you know that $\{(0, -3)\}$ is the solution set of system M? How do you know that $\{(0, -3)\}$ is the solution set of system L?

In this lesson you learned how to find the solution set of a system of two conditions for equality in two variables by deriving an equivalent system.

On your own

For each of exercises 1 through 20, first derive an equivalent system that will help you determine the solution set of the system expressed. Then tabulate the set of (x, y) that is the solution set of the given system.

1 $x - y - 3 = 0$, $x + y + 2 = 0.$

2 $2x + y - 1 = 0$, $x + 3y + 2 = 0.$

3 $5x + y = 0$, $10x + 3y - 1 = 0.$

4 $\frac{1}{2}x + y - 2 = 0$, $x + 4y - 6 = 0.$

5 $4x + y + 3 = 0$, $x - 2y - 10 = 0.$

6 $\frac{2}{9}x - \frac{2}{3}y + 2 = 0$, $\frac{2}{3}x + \frac{1}{2}y - 39 = 0.$

7 $.3x + .2y = 0$, $x + .5y + .5 = 0.$

8 $3x - 8y - 11 = 0$, $x + 6y - 8 = 0.$

9 $x + 2y - 1 = 0$, $6x - 5y - 3\frac{1}{6} = 0.$

10 $2x + 4y - 7 = 0$, $3x - y + 5 = 0.$

11 $6y = 5 + 2x$, $y = 3x.$

12 $10x - 7 = y$, $3x + y = 5.$

13 $5x = y - 13$, $\frac{1}{8}x + y + 2 = 0.$

14 $10x + y + 1 = 0$, $\frac{1}{8}x + y + 2 = 0.$

15 $\frac{3}{4}x + \frac{1}{3}y = 16$, $\frac{1}{2}x - \frac{5}{6}y = 36.$

16 $2x - 5y + 10 = x + y - 6$, $x + 3y - 17 = 2y + 17 - x.$

17 $4(x - 2) = 2(y + 1)$, $y + \frac{1}{3}(x + 1) = y + x - 3.$

18 $4x - 5y = 2$, $x = \dfrac{y + 7}{3}.$

19 $\dfrac{x + 3}{2} - \dfrac{4y - 11}{3} = x + 2y$, $\dfrac{x + 1}{6} - \dfrac{2y + 1}{3} = \dfrac{x - 6y}{2}.$

20 $\frac{1}{2}(x + y - 7) - \frac{2}{3}(2x + y) = -10$, $2y - \frac{1}{3}(3y - x) = \frac{1}{4}(x - 6y + 65).$

KEEPING SKILLFUL

A condition that determines a linear function is expressed in each of exercises 1 through 8. For each exercise, first tell what replacements were made for m and b in $f(x) = mx + b$ to obtain the given condition. Next, give the coördinates of the intercepts of the locus of function f. Finally, give the zero of the function.

1 $f(x) = 3x - 12.$

2 $f(x) = 12x + 24.$

3 $f(x) = -2x + 2.$

4 $f(x) = 10x - 7.$

5 $f(x) = \frac{1}{5}x.$

6 $f(x) = .5x + 1.$

7 $f(x) = -6x + 4.$

8 $f(x) = .66x + .33.$

Find the slope of the line described in each of exercises 9 through 13.

9 The line determined by point $(6, -6)$ and point $(0, 4)$

10 The line determined by point $(0, 5)$ and point $(5, 0)$

11 The line determined by point $(-3, 2)$ and point $(4, 5)$

12 The locus of the function determined by $f(x) = 6x + 2$

13 The locus of the function determined by $f(x) = \frac{1}{4}x - 7$

Problems involving systems of linear conditions in two variables

In this lesson you will apply what you have learned about systems of linear conditions in two variables. You will develop systems of this kind to help you find answers to problems.

Read the problem in D1.

A Let x represent the number of adults' tickets sold and let y represent the number of children's tickets sold. What does $x + y$ represent?

B Explain why $x + y = 424$ is one of the simple conditions for the problem.

C $.25x$ represents the total receipts from adults' tickets. What does $.10y$ represent?

D How can you represent the sum of the receipts from adults' tickets and from children's tickets? Is $.25x + .10y = 77.80$ a simple condition for the problem?

E Explain why the system expressed below in color can be used to solve the problem in D1.

$$x + y = 424$$
$$.25x + .10y = 77.80.$$

F Tabulate the set of (x, y) that satisfy the system for the problem.

G To what does the first component of (236, 188) refer? To what does the second component refer?

H Read the problem in D1 again. Notice that you are asked to find only the number of adults' tickets that were sold. Which component of (236, 188) do you use to get the answer to the problem?

Read the problem in D2.

The receipts from the sale of 424 tickets for a school play were \$77.80. Tickets for adults were \$.25 each and tickets for children were \$.10 each. How many tickets for adults were sold?

D1

A bakery mixed cookies selling at \$.50 per pound with cookies selling at \$.80 per pound to make a 75-pound mixture to sell at \$.60 per pound. How many pounds of each kind of cooky were used in the \$.60 mixture?

D2

A city playground is 20 ft. longer than 2 times its width. It is enclosed by a fence whose total length is 1450 ft. What are the length and the width of the playground in feet?

D3

I Use x to represent the number of pounds of \$.50 cookies. If you use y to represent the number of pounds of \$.80 cookies, explain why $x + y = 75$ is one of the simple conditions for the problem.

J Use the formula $c = np$ to explain what $.50x$ represents. What does $.80y$ represent? To what does .60(75) refer?

K Is $.50x + .80y = .60(75)$ a simple condition for the problem? How do you know that the system expressed below in color can be used to solve the problem in D2?

$$x + y = 75$$
$$.50x + .80y = .60(75).$$

L Tabulate the set of (x, y) that satisfy the system for the problem. How many pounds of each kind of cooky were used in the \$.60 mixture?

M You can verify your answer to the problem. If 50 pounds of \$.50 cookies are mixed with 25 pounds of \$.80 cookies, will the \$.60 mixture contain 75 pounds of cookies? Is the total cost of 50 pounds of cookies at \$.50 per pound and 25 pounds of cookies at \$.80 per pound equal to \$.60(75)?

Now read the problem in D3.

N Let l represent the length of the playground and let w represent its width. How can you represent the perimeter of the playground? Explain why $2l + 2w = 1450$ is one of the simple conditions for the problem.

O You know that the length of the playground is 20 ft. greater than 2 times the width. Is $l - 2w = 20$ a simple condition for the problem?

P Explain why the system expressed below in color can be used to solve the problem in D3.

$$2l + 2w = 1450$$
$$l - 2w = 20.$$

Q Tabulate the set of (l, w) that satisfy the system for the problem in D3. Then give the answer to the problem.

Read the problem in D4. When we say "sum of the digits," we mean, of course, the sum of the numbers that the digits represent.

R **?** Let t represent the tens' digit and let u represent the units' digit. In previous work we have referred to the units' digit as the ones' digit. Explain why $10t + u$ represents a number whose numeral has two digits.

S How can you represent the sum of the digits? What does $3(t + u)$ represent?

T Explain why $(10t + u) - 3(t + u) = 2$ is one of the simple conditions for the problem.

The numeral for a given number has two digits. The number is 2 greater than 3 times the "sum of the digits." The "difference" of the units' digit and the tens' digit is 4. What is the given number?

D4

Mr. Greene invested \$400 at one rate of interest and \$500 at another rate of interest. His total yearly income from the two investments was \$44. If the rates of interest had been interchanged, the yearly income from the investments would have been \$46. At what rate did Mr. Greene invest \$400 and at what rate did he invest \$500?

D5

What is another simple condition for the problem?

U Tabulate the set of (t, u) that satisfy the system expressed below in color.

$$(10t + u) - 3(t + u) = 2$$
$$u - t = 4.$$

V What is the answer to the problem in D4?

W Is 26 a number that is 2 greater than 3 times the sum of 2 and 6? Is the difference of 6 and 2 equal to 4?

Now you will use the interest formula to develop a system of conditions for the problem in D5.

Read the problem in D5.

A Let x represent the rate of interest on the \$400 investment and let y represent the rate of interest on the \$500 investment. What does $400x + 500y$ represent?

Mr. Greene invested \$400 at one rate of interest and \$500 at another rate of interest. His total yearly income from the two investments was \$44. If the rates of interest had been interchanged, the yearly income from the investments would have been \$46. At what rate did Mr. Greene invest \$400 and at what rate did he invest \$500?

D5

Mrs. Bell is 5 times as old as her daughter Mary. In 5 years, Mrs. Bell will be 3 times as old as Mary. How old are Mrs. Bell and Mary at the present time?

D6

Dave and his brother Jerry decided to ride their bicycles to the beach. Jerry left home $\frac{1}{4}$ hr. after Dave and he traveled $1\frac{1}{2}$ miles per hour faster than Dave. After traveling for $\frac{1}{2}$ hr., Jerry overtook Dave. At what average rate in miles per hour was each of the boys traveling?

D7

B What simple condition for the problem involves $400x + 500y$?

C How can you represent the total income from the two investments if the rates of interest are interchanged? Is $500x + 400y = 46$ a simple condition for the problem?

D Tabulate the set of (x, y) that satisfy the system expressed below in color.

$$400x + 500y = 44$$
$$500x + 400y = 46.$$

E Did Mr. Greene invest \$400 at 6% and \$500 at 4%?

Now read the problem in D6.

F Let x represent Mrs. Bell's present age and let y represent Mary's present age. Is $x = 5y$ a simple condition for the problem?

G If x represents Mrs. Bell's present age, how can you represent her age 5 years from now? What does $y + 5$ represent?

H Is $x + 5 = 3(y + 5)$ a simple condition for the problem?

I Tabulate the set of (x, y) that satisfy the system expressed below in color.

$$x = 5y$$
$$x + 5 = 3(y + 5).$$

J Give the answer to the problem in D6.

Read the problem in D7.

K ? Let x represent Dave's rate and let y represent Jerry's rate. How long did Jerry ride his bicycle before he overtook Dave? How do you know that Dave rode his bicycle for $\frac{3}{4}$ hr.?

L Use the distance formula, $d = rt$, to help explain what $\frac{3}{4}x$ represents. How can you represent the distance that Jerry traveled?

M Did the two boys travel the same distance?

N What are two simple conditions for the problem in D7?

O Tabulate the set of (x, y) that satisfy the system expressed below in color.

$$\tfrac{3}{4}x = \tfrac{1}{2}y$$
$$y - x = 1\tfrac{1}{2}.$$

P Give the answer to the problem in D7.

In this lesson you used systems of conditions in two variables to solve problems.

On your own

For each problem, first express a system of conditions. Then tabulate the solution set of the system and give the answer to the problem.

1 The sum of the digits in a two-digit numeral is 12. If the digits were interchanged, the number expressed by the numeral would be increased by 54. What is the number?

2 Mr. Taylor invested a total of $6900 in two corporations. One investment paid $4\frac{1}{2}\%$ interest and the other paid 5% interest. The interest on the 5% investment was $41 more than the interest on the $4\frac{1}{2}\%$ investment. How much money was invested at each rate?

3 Jim paid a total of $6.44 for $.05 stamps and $.08 air-mail stamps. He bought 4 times as many $.05 stamps as $.08 stamps. How many of each kind of stamp did Jim buy?

4 A merchant wishes to mix nuts selling at $.50 per pound with nuts selling at $.75 per pound. He wants a mixture of 100 lb. to sell at $.66 per pound. How many pounds of each kind of nut must he use in the mixture?

5 Johnson City and Richfield are 350 mi. apart. A passenger train left Johnson City for Richfield at the same time that a freight train left Richfield for Johnson City. After each train had traveled for $3\frac{1}{2}$ hr., the two trains passed. The passenger train traveled $1\frac{1}{2}$ times as fast as the freight train. What was the average rate of each train in miles per hour?

6 Mrs. O'Connor and Mrs. Benson went to the dairy store together to buy eggs and milk. Mrs. O'Connor's bill for 3 dozen eggs and 2 quarts of milk was $2.14. Mrs. Benson's bill for 2 dozen eggs and 3 quarts of milk was $1.81. What was the price of a dozen eggs and what was the price of a quart of milk?

7 A rectangle whose perimeter is 65 ft. is 4 ft. longer than it is wide. What are the dimensions of the rectangle in feet?

8 The sum of Jane's age and her sister's age is 61. Twenty-three years ago, Jane was 4 times as old as her sister. What are the present ages of Jane and her sister?

9 In a certain right triangle, the measure in degrees of one acute angle is 27 greater than the measure of the other acute angle. What is the measure in degrees of each acute angle of the right triangle?

10 Bob defeated Jim in an election for president of the Student Council. Bob received 19 fewer than 2 times as many votes as Jim. The total number of votes cast was 398. How many votes did each of the boys receive?

11 A first integer is 9 greater than 8 times a second integer. One-fifth of the first integer is 111 greater than the second integer. What are the integers?

12 One day a collector took $2.03 from a parking meter. He found that the number of pennies in the meter was 16 greater than 6 times the number of nickels. How many nickels and how many pennies were in the meter?

KEEPING SKILLFUL

For each of exercises 1 through 4, name the intercepts of the locus of the function determined by the given condition.

1 $f(x) = 10x^2$. **3** $f(x) = -16x^2 + 1$.

2 $f(x) = 25x^2 - 4$. **4** $f(x) = 3x^2$.

For each of exercises 5 and 6, name the $f(x)$-intercept of the locus of the function determined by the given condition.

5 $f(x) = x^2 - 3x - 4$.

6 $f(x) = x^2 + 3x + 2$.

For each of exercises 7 and 8, describe the range of the function determined by the condition.

7 $f(x) = 6x^2$. **8** $f(x) = 6x^2 + 1$.

For each exercise below, use factoring to help you tabulate the solution set of the given condition.

9 $x^2 + 2x - 15 = 0$. **11** $(x - 6)^2 = 36$.

10 $10x^2 = 40x$. **12** $2x^2 - 98 = 0$.

24 289 Exploring ideas

Systems of three conditions in three variables

In this lesson you will solve systems of three linear conditions in three variables. To solve such systems, you will use ideas that you studied in connection with systems of two conditions in two variables.

A Notice that system A, expressed in D1, involves three simple conditions. Each of these conditions is of the form $ax + by + cz + d = 0$. What are the values of a, b, c, and d for each of these conditions?

$ax + by + cz + d = 0$, where a, b, or c is not zero, is the standard form of a *linear condition for equality in three variables.* Any condition that can be put in the form $ax + by + cz + d = 0$ is a linear condition for equality in three variables.

linear condition for equality in three variables. A condition that is of the form $ax + by + cz + d = 0$, where a, b, or c is not zero.

$$\text{A}\quad \begin{aligned} x + y + z - 9 &= 0 \\ 2x - y + z - 8 &= 0 \\ x + 3y - 2z - 1 &= 0. \end{aligned}$$

$$\text{B}\quad \begin{aligned} x + y + z - 9 &= 0 \\ -x + 2y - 1 &= 0 \\ -11x + 33 &= 0. \end{aligned}$$

D1

B How do you know that each solution of system A must be an ordered triple?

In lesson 285 you observed that a system of two linear conditions in two variables could have exactly one solution, infinitely many solutions, or no solutions. Likewise, a system of three linear conditions in three variables can have exactly one solution, infinitely many solutions, or no solutions.

Later in your study of mathematics, you will learn that the locus of a linear condition in three variables is a plane in space. You will also learn that the number of solutions of a system of three linear conditions in three variables is determined by the way in which three planes intersect.

System A, expressed in D1, has exactly one ordered triple as its solution. All the systems considered in this lesson will be of the kind that has exactly one solution.

C Look again at D1. Replace x by 3, y by 2, and z by 4 in system A. Tabulate the set of (x, y, z) that is the solution set of A.

D Study system B given in D1. What x satisfies $-11x + 33 = 0$? What is the first component of each (x, y, z) that satisfies system B?

E If you replace x by 3 in $-x + 2y - 1 = 0$, what y satisfies the condition that you obtain? What is the second component of each (x, y, z) that satisfies system B?

F Now replace x by 3 and y by 2 in the condition $x + y + z - 9 = 0$. What z satisfies the condition that you obtain? What is the third component of each (x, y, z) that satisfies system B?

G ? Tabulate the solution set of system B. How do you know that system B is equivalent to system A?

You were able to determine the solution set of B quite easily because one condition in B involves only the variable x and a second con-

C $m(x+y+z-9)+n(2x-y+z-8)+p(x+3y-2z-1)=0.$
D $1(x+y+z-9)+(-1)(2x-y+z-8)+0(x+3y-2z-1)=0.$
E $0(x+y+z-9)+2(2x-y+z-8)+1(x+3y-2z-1)=0.$

D2

dition involves only two variables, x and y. This suggests that it would be helpful to derive an equivalent system like B whenever you need to determine the solution set of a system like A. In the exercises that follow, you will see how system B can be derived from system A.

H ? Study condition C, expressed in D2. How is the left side of C formed from the left sides of the conditions in system A?

I ? Suppose that you replace m, n, and p in condition C by any three real numbers. How do you know that any (x, y, z) that satisfies system A also satisfies the condition that you obtain?

J What replacements were made for m, n, and p in condition C to obtain condition D, expressed in D2? Show the steps that you can use to obtain $-x+2y-1=0$ from D.

K What replacements were made for m, n, and p in condition C to obtain condition E? How can you obtain $5x+y-17=0$ from E?

Conditions F and G, expressed in D3, are the conditions that you obtained for exercises J and K. From exercise I, you know that any (x, y, z) that satisfies system A also satisfies both F and G.

L Study condition H. How is the left side of H formed from the left sides of F and G?

M ? Suppose that you replace r and s in condition H by any two real numbers. Does any (x, y, z) that satisfies both F and G also satisfy the condition that you obtain? Why does this mean that any solution of system A will satisfy the condition that you obtain?

F $-x+2y-1=0.$
G $5x+y-17=0.$
H $r(-x+2y-1)+s(5x+y-17)=0.$
I $1(-x+2y-1)+(-2)(5x+y-17)=0.$

D3

N What replacements were made for r and s in condition H to obtain condition I? How can you obtain $-11x+33=0$ from I?

Think again about systems A and B, expressed in D1. Notice that the first condition in B is the same as one of the conditions in system A. The second condition in B is the condition that you derived for exercise J. The third condition in B is the condition that you derived for exercise N.

O ? Without replacing x, y, and z in the condition $x+y+z-9=0$, how do you know that any (x, y, z) that satisfies system A must satisfy the first condition in system B?

P ? Without replacing x, y, and z in the condition $-x+2y-1=0$, how do you know that any (x, y, z) that satisfies system A must satisfy the second condition in system B?

Q ? Without replacing x, y, and z in the condition $-11x+33=0$, how do you know that any (x, y, z) that satisfies system A must satisfy the third condition in system B?

R Use your answers to exercises O, P, and Q to explain why any solution of system A is also a solution of system B.

Now you can use the method that you have just studied to derive a system that will help you determine the solution set of a given system.

A ? Compare systems J and K, expressed in D4. Is each condition in K a standard form of a condition in J? How do you know that any solution of system J is also a solution of system K?

Since systems J and K have the same solution set, we can work with system K to determine the solution set of system J. To determine the solution set of K, we will develop a system that is equivalent to K and that involves a condition in three variables, a condition in two variables, and a condition in one variable. First we will use system K to derive two conditions involving only two variables. That is, we will eliminate one of the variables. Then we will use these two conditions to derive a condition involving only one variable.

B ? Now study condition L, expressed in D5. How were the left sides of the conditions in K used to form the left side of L?

C Suppose that you replace m, n, and p in condition L by any three real numbers. How do you know that any solution of system K also satisfies the condition that you obtain?

Now we must choose two different sets of replacements for m, n, and p in condition L. Each set of replacements should produce a condition that involves only two variables. We can, for example, choose to eliminate y.

D ? To eliminate y, suppose that you begin by replacing m by 0 in condition L. Why must you then replace n and p in such a way that $n(-2y)+p(y)=0$? If you replace n by 1 and p by 2 in $n(-2y)+p(y)$, what do you obtain?

E Look again at D5. Replace m by 0, n by 1, and p by 2 in condition L. Then show how the condition that you obtain can be put in the form of condition M.

F How do you know that the solution set of $-x-12z+5=0$ contains the solution of system K?

Since condition M involves only two variables and is satisfied by the solution of system K, we can use M as one of the conditions in the equivalent system that we are deriving. First, however, we must derive another condition like M, that involves only x and z. Then we can use the two conditions in x and z to derive a third condition that involves only one variable.

G To develop another condition involving x and z, suppose that you begin by replacing n by 0 in condition L. Why should you then replace m and p so that $m(y)+p(y)=0$? If you replace m by -1, what replacement should you choose for p?

J
$$2x+y=2z+2$$
$$3x+2y=4z+5$$
$$x+y=8z.$$

K
$$2x+y-2z-2=0$$
$$-3x-2y+4z+5=0$$
$$x+y-8z=0.$$

D4

L $m(2x+y-2z-2)+n(-3x-2y+4z+5)+p(x+y-8z)=0.$

M $-x-12z+5=0.$

N $-x-6z+2=0.$

D5

H Make the replacements in L that are suggested in exercise G. Then show how the condition that you obtain can be put in the form of condition N expressed in D5.

I How do you know that the solution set of $-x-6z+2=0$ contains the solution of system K?

Exercises F and I point out that the solution of system K satisfies both M and N. Now we can use M and N to derive a condition that involves only one variable.

J Look at D6. How is the left side of condition O related to the left sides of conditions M and N?

K Suppose that you make replacements for r and s in condition O. How do you know that any (x, y, z) that satisfies both M and N will be a solution of the condition that you obtain? Why does this mean that the solution of system K will satisfy the condition that you obtain?

L You can replace r and s in condition O so that you eliminate x. Why should you choose replacements so that $r(-x)+s(-x)=0$? If you replace r by -1, what replacement should you make for s?

M Obtain a condition from condition O by making the replacements suggested in exercise L. Then show how the condition that you obtain can be put in the form of condition P.

N How do you know that the solution set of $6z-3=0$ contains the solution of system K?

System K is expressed again in D7. System Q, expressed in D7, is the system that we have just derived to help find the solution set of K. Notice that the first condition in Q is the same as one of the conditions in K. (We could have chosen any condition in K for this first condition.) The second condition in Q is one of the conditions involving two variables, which we derived in exercises B through I. (We could have chosen either of the conditions that involve two variables for this second condition.) The third condition in Q is the condition involving only one variable, which we derived in exercises J through N.

O $r(-x-12z+5)+s(-x-6z+2)=0.$

P $6z-3=0.$

D6

K
$$2x+y-2z-2=0$$
$$-3x-2y+4z+5=0$$
$$x+y-8z=0.$$

Q
$$x+y-8z=0$$
$$-x-12z+5=0$$
$$6z-3=0.$$

D7

O How do you know that the solution of system K is a member of the solution set of Q?

P What (x, y, z) satisfies system Q?

Q ? Show that the solution of Q also satisfies system K. Is the solution of Q the only solution of system K?

R Tabulate the solution set of system K. Is system Q equivalent to system K?

In this lesson you learned to find the solution set of a system of three conditions in three variables by obtaining an equivalent system whose solution set is more easily determined.

On your own

For each of exercises 1 through 11, tabulate the set of (x, y, z) that is the solution set of the given system.

1
$$2x+4y-z+7=0$$
$$y+z-3=0$$
$$2y+4=0.$$

$x + y - z + 3 = 0$
2 $3x - y + 2z - 18 = 0$
$x + y + z - 11 = 0.$

$2x - y - z + 2 = 0$
3 $x + y - 3z + 1 = 0$
$-x + 2y - 2z - 1 = 0.$

$2x - y + 7z - 30 = 0$
4 $x + 2y + z + 10 = 0$
$-5x - y - z + 27 = 0.$

$4x + 3y + 2z - 3 = 0$
5 $2x - 6y - z + 2 = 0$
$x + 3y + z - 1\frac{3}{4} = 0.$

$4x + y - 6z + 4 = 0$
6 $3x - y + 9z - 1\frac{1}{2} = 0$
$2x - 2y + 12z + 3 = 0.$

$.3x + .1y + .5z - 32 = 0$
7 $x - y + .02z - 11 = 0$
$.05x + y + .04z - 13 = 0.$

$x + z = 5y$
8 $z + 2 = 3x - 2y$
$2x + y + z + 15 = 0.$

$\frac{5}{6}y - \frac{3}{8}z = 17 - \frac{1}{4}x$
9 $y - \frac{1}{2}z = \frac{2}{3}x - 4$
$x + y = z + 24.$

$3(x - 2) - 8 = y - 2(z + 5)$
10 $2y - 107 = 7(x + 1) - 2z$
$3(x + 7) + y = z + 39.$

$4(z + 2y) - 7 = 2(6y - 3x) + 30$
11 $2y - 5(x - 4z) = 3(8z - x) - 10$
$3x - 5(7y + 2z) - 5 = x - 2y.$

Problems involving systems of conditions in three variables

In this lesson you will apply what you have learned about systems of linear conditions in three variables. You will see how compound conditions for equality in three variables can help you find the answers to problems.

Read the problem in D1.

A Let x, y, and z represent the measures of $\overline{AB}$, $\overline{BC}$, and $\overline{CA}$, respectively. How can you represent the perimeter of $\triangle ABC$? What is the perimeter of $\triangle ABC$? Is $x + y + z = 226$ one of the simple conditions for the problem in D1?

B How can you represent the sum of the measures of $\overline{BC}$ and $\overline{CA}$? What does $6x - (y + z)$ represent? Explain why $6x - (y + z) = 12$ is another simple condition for the problem.

C Does $(x + y) - z$ represent the difference of the sum of the measures of $\overline{AB}$ and $\overline{BC}$ and the measure of $\overline{CA}$? How do you know that $(x + y) - z = 30$ is another simple condition for the problem?

The perimeter of $\triangle ABC$ is 226 in. The sum of the measures of sides BC and CA is 12 less than 6 times the measure of side AB. The measure of $\overline{CA}$ is 30 less than the sum of the measures of $\overline{AB}$ and $\overline{BC}$. What is the length of each side of $\triangle ABC$ in inches?

D1

The system expressed below in color can be used to solve the problem in D1.

$$x + y + z = 226$$
$$6x - (y + z) = 12$$
$$(x + y) - z = 30.$$

D Tabulate the set of (x, y, z) that satisfy the system for the problem in D1.

E What is the length of each side of $\triangle ABC$ in inches?

Read the problem in D2.

F Let h represent the hundreds' digit; let t represent the tens' digit; and let u represent the units' digit. How can you represent the sum of the digits? Is $h + t + u = 17$ a simple condition for the problem?

G ? Explain why $100h + 10t + u$ represents the given number in the problem.

H ? You know that $100h + 10t + u$ represents the given number in the problem. If the units' digit and the hundreds' digit are interchanged, how can you represent the new number? Does $(100u + 10t + h) - (100h + 10t + u)$ represent the difference of the new number and the given number?

I What is another simple condition for the problem?

J What does $100t + 10h + u$ represent? Why is $(100t + 10h + u) - (100h + 10t + u) = 540$ another simple condition for the problem?

The system expressed below in color can be used to solve the problem in D2.

$$h + t + u = 17$$
$$(100u + 10t + h) - (100h + 10t + u) = 198$$
$$(100t + 10h + u) - (100h + 10t + u) = 540.$$

K Tabulate the set of (h, t, u) that satisfy the system for the problem in D2.

L What is the answer to the problem in D2?

The numeral for a given number has three digits. The sum of the digits is 17. If the units' digit and the hundreds' digit are interchanged, the new number is 198 greater than the given number. If the tens' digit and the hundreds' digit are interchanged, the new number is 540 greater than the given number. What is the given number?

D2

Mr. Edwards invested \$2400 in three stocks. For one year, the dividend rate on the first stock was 5%; the dividend rate on the second stock was 4%; and the dividend rate on the third stock was 6%. For that year, the dividend Mr. Edwards received from the third stock was \$2 less than the sum of the dividends from the first and the second stocks. The dividend from the second stock was \$68 less than the sum of the dividends from the first and the third stocks. How much money had he invested in each of the three stocks?

D3

Now read the problem in D3.

M Let x, y, and z represent the amounts of money that Mr. Edwards invested in the first, the second, and the third stocks, respectively. What does $x + y + z$ represent? How much did Mr. Edwards invest altogether? Explain why $x + y + z = 2400$ is one of the simple conditions for the problem.

N Use the interest formula, $i = prt$, to help explain what $.05x$, $.04y$, and $.06z$ represent.

O Explain why $.05x + .04y - .06z = 2$ is another simple condition for the problem.

P How can you represent the sum of the dividends from the first and third stocks? What is another simple condition for the problem?

The system expressed below in color can be used to solve the problem in D3.

$$x + y + z = 2400$$
$$.05x + .04y - .06z = 2$$
$$.05x + .06z - .04y = 68.$$

Q Tabulate the set of (x, y, z) that satisfy the condition for the problem in D3. Then give the answer to the problem.

You used the interest formula to develop a system of conditions for the problem in D3. Now you will use the cost formula to develop a system of conditions.

Read the problem in D4.

A Let x represent the number of pounds of \$.40 nuts; let y represent the number of pounds of \$.50 nuts; and let z represent the number of pounds of \$.80 nuts. What does $x + y + z$ represent?

B What is one of the simple conditions for the problem?

C Use the formula $c = np$ to help explain what $.40x$ represents. What does $.50y$ represent? What does $.80z$ represent? To what does $.60(100)$ refer?

D What is another simple condition for the problem?

E In exercise A we agreed to use x to represent the number of pounds of \$.40 nuts and z to represent the number of pounds of \$.80 nuts. Why is $z = 3x$ another simple condition for the problem?

You can use the system expressed below in color to solve the problem in D4.

$$x + y + z = 100$$
$$.40x + .50y + .80z = .60(100)$$
$$z = 3x.$$

Mr. Edwards invested \$2400 in three stocks. For one year, the dividend rate on the first stock was 5%; the dividend rate on the second stock was 4%; and the dividend rate on the third stock was 6%. For that year, the dividend Mr. Edwards received from the third stock was \$2 less than the sum of the dividends from the first and the second stocks. The dividend from the second stock was \$68 less than the sum of the dividends from the first and the third stocks. How much money had he invested in each of the three stocks?

D3

A merchant wishes to mix three kinds of nuts, one selling at \$.40 per pound, another selling at \$.50 per pound, and a third selling at \$.80 per pound. He wants the mixture to sell for \$.60 per pound and to contain 3 times as many pounds of \$.80 nuts as of \$.40 nuts. For 100 pounds of the mixture, how many pounds of each kind of nut must he use?

D4

F Tabulate the set of (x, y, z) that satisfy the system for the problem.

G What is the answer to the problem in D4?

Now read the problem in D5.

H Let x, y, and z represent the first, the second, and the third integers, respectively. How can you represent 2 times the first integer? The sum of the second and the third integers?

I Is $y + z - 2x = 27$ one of the simple conditions for the problem?

J What does $7z - 2y$ represent? What does $7z - 2y - 3x$ represent? Explain why $7z - 2y - 3x = 17$ is another simple condition for the problem.

K How can you represent the sum of 4 times **?** the first integer and 3 times the second integer? What is another simple condition for the problem?

The system expressed below in color can be used to solve the problem in D5.

$$y + z - 2x = 27$$
$$7z - 2y - 3x = 17$$
$$10z - (4x + 3y) = 17.$$

L Tabulate the set of (x, y, z) that satisfy the system of conditions for the problem.

M What is the answer to the problem in D5?

Read the problem in D6.

N Let a represent the measure of ∠A; let b represent the measure of ∠B; and let c represent the measure of ∠C. How can you represent 2 times the measure of ∠A? Why is $c = 2a$ one of the simple conditions for the problem?

O How can you represent the sum of the measures of ∠B and ∠C? Explain why $b + c - 3a = 24$ is another simple condition for the problem.

P Can you determine the answer to the prob- **?** lem in D6 from the two simple conditions expressed in exercises N and O? Explain your answer.

Notice that the problem does not give any information that enables you to develop another simple condition. However, you can use a property concerning triangles to develop another condition.

Q Explain why $a + b + c = 180$ is a simple **?** condition for the problem.

R What is a system of conditions for the prob- **?** lem in D6?

Two times a first integer is 27 less than the sum of a second and a third integer. The difference of 7 times the third integer and 2 times the second integer is 17 more than 3 times the first integer. The sum of 4 times the first integer and 3 times the second is 17 less than 10 times the third. What are the three integers?

D5

In △ABC, the measure of ∠C in degrees is 2 times the measure of ∠A. The sum of the measures of ∠B and ∠C is 24 greater than 3 times the measure of ∠A. What is the measure of each angle of △ABC in degrees?

D6

S Find the set of (a, b, c) that is the solution set of the system for the problem in D6. Then give the answer to the problem.

In this lesson you solved problems that involved compound conditions in three variables.

On your own

For each problem, first develop a system of conditions in three variables. Then tabulate the solution set of the system and give the answer to the problem.

1 Martha had 93 coins in her piggy bank. The coins were pennies, nickels, and dimes, and there were 3 more pennies than nickels. The total value of the coins was \$5.39. How many coins of each kind did Martha have in her bank?

2 Three rectangles, each of which is 9 ft. long, have a total area of 171 sq. ft. The width of the first rectangle is $\frac{1}{2}$ the width of the third rectangle. The sum of the widths of the second and third rectangles is 1 less than 4 times the width of the first rectangle. What is the width of each rectangle in feet?

3 Mr. and Mrs. Anderson flew to Florida and took their dog with them. Mrs. Anderson's airline ticket was $\frac{1}{2}$ the price of Mr. Anderson's ticket because they traveled on the family plan. The dog had to ride in the pressurized baggage compartment, and his fare was $\frac{1}{6}$ of Mr. and Mrs. Anderson's combined fare. The total cost of all three tickets was \$144.20. What was the price of each ticket?

4 Mr. Dean invested \$1800 in three kinds of bonds. The yearly interest rates were 2%, 3%, and $4\frac{1}{2}$%, respectively. The total yearly interest that he received from the three bonds was \$51. The interest on the 3% bond was the same amount as the combined interest on the 2% and the $4\frac{1}{2}$% bonds. How much money had he invested at each rate?

5 The sum of a first number and a second number is 12 less than 4 times a third number. The difference of the first number and the second number is 2 times the third number. The sum of 2 times the second number and 3 times the third number is 18 greater than 2 times the first number. What are the three numbers?

6 The sum of the ages of three sisters, Mary, Helen, and Ann, is 22. In 2 years, the sum of the ages of Mary and Ann will be the same as Helen's age. Two years ago the difference of Helen's age and Mary's age was 2 times Ann's age. How old is each girl now?

7 In $\triangle DEF$, 2 times the measure of $\angle D$ in degrees is 24 less than the sum of the measures of $\angle E$ and $\angle F$ in degrees. If $\angle D^\circ$ is subtracted from 2 times $\angle F^\circ$, the difference is equal to $\angle E^\circ$. What is the measure in degrees of each angle of $\triangle DEF$?

8 For a certain china pattern, the cost of 4 dinner plates, 2 luncheon plates, and 5 salad plates is \$37.50. The cost of 5 dinner plates, 8 luncheon plates, and 6 salad plates is \$67.40. The cost of 10 dinner plates, 4 luncheon plates, and 3 salad plates is \$66.70. What is the price of each kind of plate?

9 Three women sold tickets to a charity luncheon. Mrs. Adams sold 13 more tickets than the average number of tickets sold per woman. The difference of the number of tickets that Mrs. Adams sold and the number of tickets that Mrs. Rossetti sold was 45 less than the number of tickets that Mrs. Clark sold. Mrs. Clark sold $\frac{3}{4}$ as many tickets as Mrs. Adams sold. How many tickets did each woman sell?

10 The perimeter of $\triangle ABC$ is 6 in. greater than 5 times the length of side AC. Twice the length of side BC is 4 less than the sum of twice the length of side AB and twice the length of side AC. The sum of the length of side AC and $\frac{1}{3}$ the length of side BC is 2 greater than the length of side AB. What is the length of each side of the triangle in inches?

11 A mixture consisting of 50 lb. of coffee A, 30 lb. of coffee B, and 40 lb. of coffee C sells for \$.60 per pound. The price per pound of coffee A added to the price per pound of coffee B is \$.07 more than the price per pound of coffee C. The price per pound of coffee A added to the price per pound of coffee C is \$.97 more than the price per pound of coffee B. What is the price per pound of each kind of coffee?

12 At a soda fountain, 5 milkshakes, 9 sodas, and 4 sundaes cost \$6.35. The cost of 3 milkshakes, 8 sodas, and 7 sundaes is \$6.10. The cost of 12 milkshakes, 5 sodas, and 11 sundaes is \$9.85. What is the price of a milkshake, of a soda, and of a sundae?

SPECIAL CHALLENGE

An ordered pair such as $(2, -3)$ may be thought of as a vector. We have considered two operations on these vectors: scalar multiplication and vector addition.

A What vector is equal to $4 \odot (-\frac{1}{2}, 7)$? What vector is equal to $(4, -2\frac{1}{3}) \oplus (1, \frac{5}{6})$?

Look at D1. Vectors can be either *row vectors* or *column vectors.* Vector A is a row vector. Vector B is a column vector. For convenience, we sometimes use brackets to indicate a column vector. For example, vector B may be expressed by the symbol $[-\frac{1}{2}, 5]$.

Now consider the expression $5x + 3y$. The constant coefficients in $5x + 3y$ can be used to form the row vector $(5, 3)$. The variables in $5x + 3y$ can be used to form the column vector $[x, y]$. $5x + 3y$ is the *inner product* of $(5, 3)$ and $[x, y]$. The sentence in D2 expresses this idea. To find the inner product, multiply each component of the row vector by the corresponding component of the column vector and then add these products.

Find the inner products expressed below.

B $(-2, 6)\begin{pmatrix} m \\ n \end{pmatrix}$ **D** $(a, b)\begin{pmatrix} c \\ d \end{pmatrix}$

C $(\frac{1}{3}, -5)\begin{pmatrix} 2 \\ -1 \end{pmatrix}$ **E** $(2, h)\begin{pmatrix} h \\ -3 \end{pmatrix}$

F What is $(5, \frac{3}{4})[-2, 8]$? Remember that the symbol $[-2, 8]$ indicates a column vector.

You can find the inner product of a row vector and a column vector only if the two vectors have the same number of components. Thus, $(5, 8)[6, -2, 1]$ and $(-7, 4, \frac{1}{2})[2, 3]$ are not defined.

G What is $(5, -\frac{1}{2}, 3)[2, \frac{5}{6}, -\frac{2}{3}]$?

H What is $(3, -4, 2)[x, y, 1]$?

I What condition is expressed by the sentence $(2, 1, -3)[x, y, 1] = 0$?

A $(4, -3)$ **B** $\begin{pmatrix} -\frac{1}{2} \\ 5 \end{pmatrix}$

D1

$$(5, 3)\begin{pmatrix} x \\ y \end{pmatrix} = 5x + 3y.$$

D2

C
$$2x - 3y + 5 = 0$$
$$3x + y - 2 = 0.$$

D
$$\begin{matrix} (2, -3, 5) \\ (3, 1, -2) \end{matrix}\begin{pmatrix} x \\ y \\ 1 \end{pmatrix} = \begin{pmatrix} 0 \\ 0 \end{pmatrix}.$$

E
$$\begin{pmatrix} 2 & -3 & 5 \\ 3 & 1 & -2 \end{pmatrix}\begin{pmatrix} x \\ y \\ 1 \end{pmatrix} = \begin{pmatrix} 0 \\ 0 \end{pmatrix}.$$

D3

J Consider system C expressed in D3. How can you express each condition in this system by using symbols for row and column vectors?

Statement D shows how system C can be expressed with symbols for row and column vectors. In statement E, the two row vectors have been combined to form a *matrix* (mā′-triks). Each number in the matrix is an element of the matrix. Notice that a matrix is expressed by a rectangular arrangement of numerals.

K What is the matrix representation of the system of conditions expressed below?

$$5x - 2y + 3z + 4 = 0$$
$$x + 3y - 2z - 6 = 0$$
$$3x - y + 2z + 1 = 0.$$

L Find the solution of the following system:

$$\begin{pmatrix} 1 & 0 & 5 \\ 0 & 1 & -2 \end{pmatrix}\begin{pmatrix} x \\ y \\ 1 \end{pmatrix} = \begin{pmatrix} 0 \\ 0 \end{pmatrix}.$$

APPLYING MATHEMATICS

For each problem, first develop a system of conditions. Next, tabulate the solution set of the system. Then give the answer to the problem.

1 The cost of 12 lb. of nuts and 18 lb. of candy is \$23.22. The cost of 18 lb. of nuts and 12 lb. of candy is \$23.88. What is the cost per pound of nuts and of candy?

2 There are 3 digits in the numeral for a given number. The sum of the digits is equal to 4 times the units' digit. The sum of the units' digit and the tens' digit is 2 less than the hundreds' digit. The sum of the hundreds' digit and the units' digit is 1 greater than 4 times the tens' digit. What is the number?

3 Mr. Miller has three investments. The first investment pays 5% interest, the second pays 4% interest, and the third pays $3\frac{1}{2}$% interest. The sum of the amount invested at 5% and the amount invested at 4% is \$25 less than the amount invested at $3\frac{1}{2}$%. The sum of the income from the 5% investment and the income from the 4% investment is \$6.35 greater than the income from the $3\frac{1}{2}$% investment. Three times the income from the 5% investment is \$.45 less than the sum of the incomes from the 4% investment and the $3\frac{1}{2}$% investment. What is the total amount of Mr. Miller's investments?

4 A chemist has two acid solutions. One of the solutions is 55% acid and the other solution is 85% acid. From these two solutions, he wants to make a mixture of 60 pints that is 63% acid. How many pints of each solution should he use in the mixture?

5 A motorboat went 5 mi. downstream in $\frac{1}{2}$ hr. The boat made the return trip upstream in $\frac{2}{3}$ hr. What was the rate of the current in miles per hour?

THINK If x represents the rate of the motorboat and y represents the rate of the current, what does $\frac{1}{2}(x+y)$ represent? What does $\frac{2}{3}(x-y)$ represent?

6 A carpenter and his helper built a cabinet and charged \$27.45 for their services. The carpenter received \$2.70 per hour. His helper received \$1.90 per hour. The carpenter worked $2\frac{1}{2}$ hours longer than his helper worked. How many hours did each man work?

7 In $\triangle ABC$, the sum of the measures of $\angle B$ and $\angle C$ in degrees is 30 less than 4 times the measure of $\angle A$ in degrees. The sum of 2 times the measure of $\angle A$ and 2 times the measure of $\angle B$ is 40 greater than 2 times the measure of $\angle C$. What is the measure in degrees of each angle of $\triangle ABC$?

8 Two trains left a station at the same time, traveling in opposite directions. After $3\frac{1}{2}$ hr., the trains were 280 mi. apart. One train traveled 10 miles per hour faster than the other train. How many miles per hour did each train travel?

9 One day a bellboy received a total of 49 coins in tips. The coins were nickels, dimes, and quarters. The value of the dimes was the same as the value of the nickels. The number of quarters was 4 greater than the number of nickels. How many coins of each kind did the bellboy receive in tips?

10 The sum of 4 times a first number and 2 times a second number is 5 times a third number. The third number is the difference of the second number and the first number. The sum of 2 times the first number, 3 times the second number, and $\frac{1}{2}$ the third number is 816. What are the three numbers?

11 Two years ago Helen was 9 times as old as her sister Martha was. In 4 years Helen will be only 3 times as old as Martha will be. What is the present age of each girl?

CHECKING UP

If you have trouble with this test, you can find help in lessons 285 through 290.

Test 265

1 What is the y-intercept of the locus of $x+y+4=0$?

2 Put the condition $3(2x-5)=4y+7$ in the form $ax+by+c=0$.

3 By what numbers can you replace m and n in $m(2x-y-7)+n(4x+3y+1)=0$ to obtain a condition that does not involve x?

4 Let x represent the length of a rectangle and let y represent the width of the rectangle. What is an expression involving x and y that represents the perimeter of the rectangle?

5 Which (x, y) that satisfies $2x-7=3y$ has 0 as a first component?

6 How is the locus of $x=5$ located with respect to the y-axis?

7 Put $2(3x-y+8)+(-3)(2x+5y-23)=0$ in the form $ax+by+c=0$.

8 What is the slope of the locus of $y=\frac{3}{4}x-2$?

9 The numeral for an integer has two digits. x represents the tens' digit and y represents the units' digit. What is an expression that involves x and y and that represents 3 less than 5 times the integer?

10 Suppose that the slope of ℓ_1 is -2 and its y-intercept is point (0, 3). Give a condition of the form $ax+by+c=0$ that has ℓ_1 for its locus.

11 Tabulate the set of (x, y) that satisfies the system of conditions expressed below.

$2x+y=0$
$3x-2y+7=0.$

12 What (x, y, z) satisfies the system of conditions expressed below?

$2x+3y+4z=1$
$3x+4y=0$
$6z=3.$

24 291 Exploring ideas

Systems of conditions for equality and inequality

In this lesson you will study systems of conditions for inequality as well as for equality. First you will study simple conditions for inequality.

A If x is replaced by 0 and y is replaced by 3 in $y>x-1$, you obtain $3>0-1$. Since it is true that 3 is greater than $0-1$, (0, 3) is a member of $\{(x, y) \mid y>x-1\}$. Which ordered pairs named below are also members of $\{(x, y) \mid y>x-1\}$?

(3, 0) (5, 6) (6, 5) (−2, 1) (−19, −15)

B If 4 is the first component of a solution of $y>x-1$, then the second component must satisfy $y>4-1$, or $y>3$. Describe the set of integers that satisfy $y>3$. Describe the set of real numbers that satisfy $y>3$. Which ordered pairs named below are members of the solution set of $y>x-1$?

(4, −7.5) (4, 0) $(4, 1\frac{2}{3})$ (4, 3.26) (4, 725)

C Name three solutions of $y>x-1$ that have first components of −7.8. Name three solutions of $y>x-1$ that have first components of 1. Name three solutions of $y>x-1$ that have first components of $95\frac{3}{4}$.

Now you will consider a graph of $y=x-1$ to determine how the locus of $y>x-1$ is related to the locus of $y=x-1$.

D When you make a graph of $y=x-1$, why is it necessary to know the coördinates of only two points in the locus? What point in the locus has 0 as its first coördinate? What point has 3 as its first coördinate?

E The line determined by point $(0, -1)$ and point $(3, 2)$ is represented in D1. How do you know that this line is the locus of $y = x - 1$?

F Which points named below are in the locus of $y = x - 1$?

$(-2, -3)$ $(2, -3)$ $(1, 0)$ $(3, 1)$

You have learned that a line separates a plane into two sets of points that have no members in common. For example, all the points above the locus of $y = x - 1$ form one set, and all the points below the locus of $y = x - 1$ form another set. Each of these sets of points is a half-plane. From now on we will refer to a half-plane as an *open half-plane* to remind you that the boundary is not included in the half-plane. Thus, the locus of $y = x - 1$ separates the plane into two open half-planes and is itself the boundary of each open half-plane.

G Look again at D1. Consider the open half-planes that have the locus of $y = x - 1$ as their boundary. Name a point in each axis that is in the same open half-plane as point $(-3, -2)$. Name a point in each axis that is in the same open half-plane as point $(3, 1)$.

H Show that $(-1, 0)$, $(0, 4)$, and $(1, 2)$ are solutions of $y > x - 1$. Are point $(-1, 0)$, point $(0, 4)$, and point $(1, 2)$ in the locus of $y > x - 1$? Are these points in the same open half-plane as point $(-3, -2)$?

I Name three other points in the locus of $y > x - 1$. Are these points also in the open half-plane whose boundary is $y = x - 1$ and that contains point $(-3, -2)$?

The set of points above the locus of $y = x - 1$ is the locus of $y > x - 1$. This means that the locus of $y > x - 1$ is an open half-plane that is determined by the locus of $y = x - 1$.

J Show that $(4, 1)$, $(3, -2)$, and $(-2, -4)$ are solutions of $y < x - 1$. How do you know that point $(4, 1)$, point $(3, -2)$, and point $(-2, -4)$ are in the locus of $y < x - 1$? Are these points in the same open half-plane as point $(3, 1)$, represented in D1?

K Name three other points in the locus of $y < x - 1$. Are these points also in the open

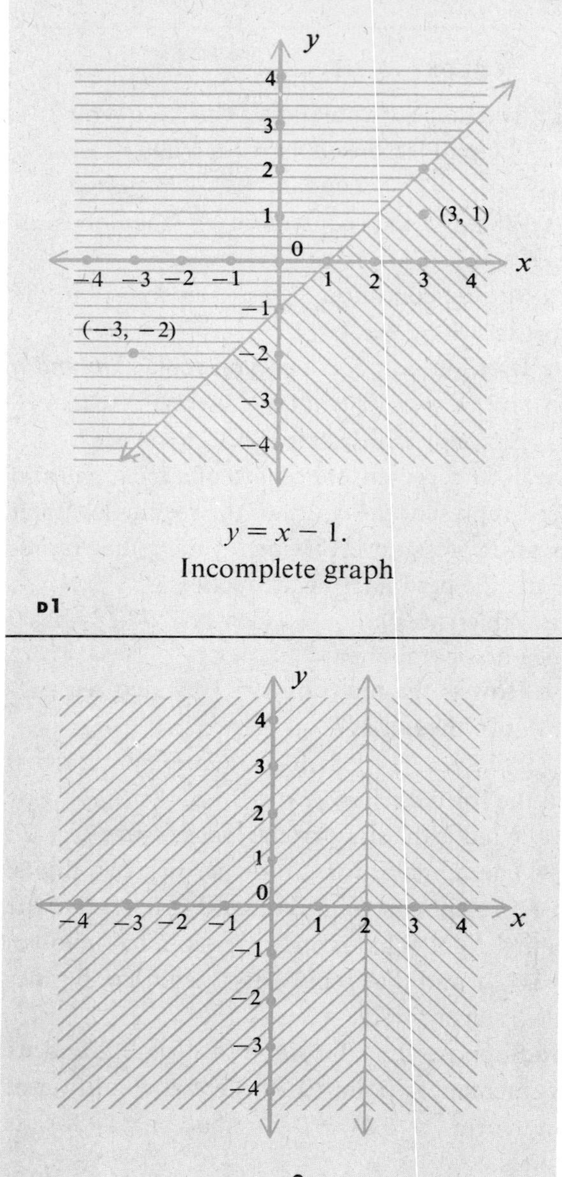

$y = x - 1$.
Incomplete graph

D1

$x = 2$.
Incomplete graph

D2

half-plane whose boundary is $y = x - 1$ and that contains point (3, 1)?

The set of points below the locus of $y = x - 1$ is the locus of $y < x - 1$. This means that the locus of $y < x - 1$ is the other open half-plane that is determined by the locus of $y = x - 1$.

L Now look at D2. The line represented in D2 is the locus of $x = 2$. What is the first coördinate of every point in the locus of $x = 2$?

M The set of points to the right of the locus of $x = 2$ is an open half-plane. What is the boundary of this open half-plane? The first coördinate of each point in this open half-plane is greater than what number? This open half-plane is the locus of $x > 2$.

N The set of points to the left of the locus of $x = 2$ also is an open half-plane. What is the boundary of this open half-plane? This open half-plane is the locus of what condition?

O Make a graph of the locus of $y = x$. The open half-plane above this locus is the locus of what condition? The open half-plane below this locus is the locus of what condition?

P Make a graph of the line that is the boundary of the locus of $y < x + 3$. The line represented in your graph is also the boundary of the locus of what other condition?

For each of exercises Q through T, make a graph of the locus of the given condition.

Q $x > y - 3$.

R $x + y < 4$.

S $x > 1$.

T $y < -2$.

Now you will make graphs of systems that involve conditions for inequality as well as conditions for equality.

A The locus of $x + y = 4 \wedge y = 1$ is represented in D3. How many members are in the solution set of this system?

B What (x, y) satisfies the system whose locus is represented in D3?

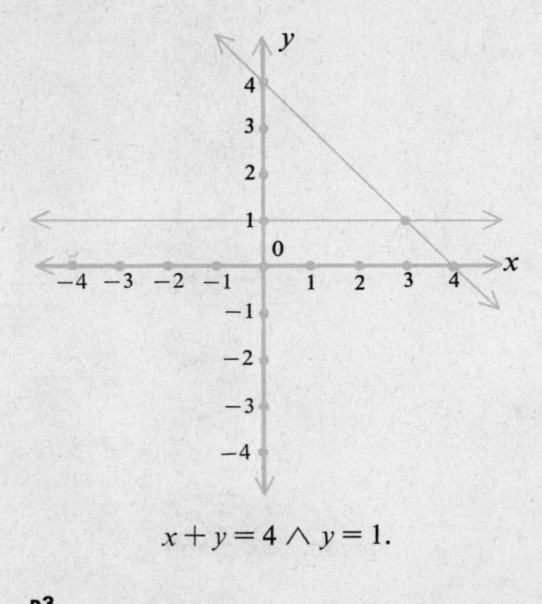

$x + y = 4 \wedge y = 1.$

D3

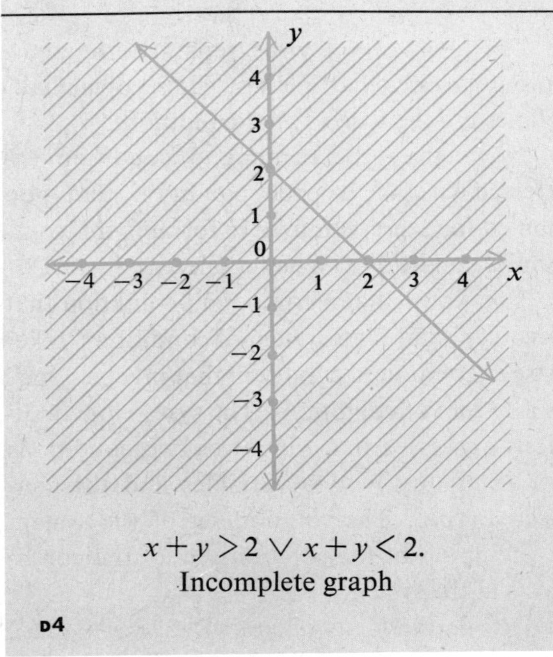

$x + y > 2 \vee x + y < 2.$

Incomplete graph

D4

C Make a graph of the locus of the system $y = x \wedge x + y = -4$. Then use the graph to help tabulate the set of (x, y) that satisfy this system.

D Now look at D4. The line represented in D4 is the locus of what condition?

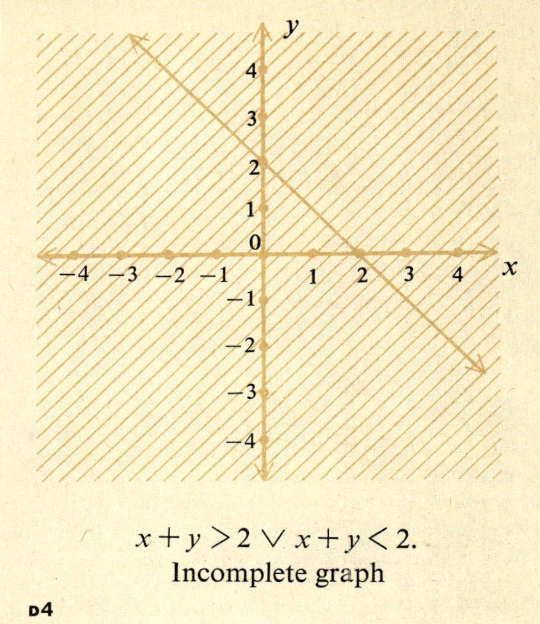

$x+y>2 \vee x+y<2.$
Incomplete graph

D4

E The locus of $x+y=2$ separates the plane into two open half-planes. These open half-planes are the loci of what conditions?

F Now study the compound condition expressed in D4. Is each condition that you named for exercise E used in forming this compound condition? What connective is used?

You know that a compound condition that involves "and" is a system of conditions. Likewise, a compound condition that involves "or" is a system of conditions. The system of conditions expressed in D4 involves two conditions for inequality in two variables and the connective "or." The solution set of the system is the union of the solution sets of the conditions in the system.

G How is the locus of $x+y>2 \vee x+y<2$ represented in D4?

H Why is the locus of $x+y>2 \vee x+y<2$ the same as the locus of $x+y \neq 2$? The locus of $x+y \neq 2$ is the union of what two sets of points?

I Make a graph of $y=-x$. Then use vertical shading to represent the locus of the system $y>-x \vee y<-x$. The locus of this system is the union of what two sets of points?

J What simple condition involving the idea of "not equal to" has the same locus as the system $y>-x \vee y<-x$?

For each of exercises K through N, make a graph of the system of conditions expressed.

K $y=x+1 \wedge 3x=6$.

L $y<1 \vee y>1$.

M $x-2=y \wedge 2x+1=y$.

N $x-y<3 \vee 3<x-y$.

O Look at D5. What geometric figure is the locus of $y>-x+1$? Of $y=-x+1$?

The union of an open half-plane and the line that is its boundary is a *closed half-plane*. The union of the locus of $y>-x+1$ and the locus of $y=-x+1$ is a closed half-plane. Since $y>-x+1 \vee y=-x+1$ is the same as $y \geqq -x+1$, the closed half-plane represented in D5 is the locus of $y \geqq -x+1$.

P Why are point (1, 0) and point (2, −1) in the closed half-plane that is the locus of

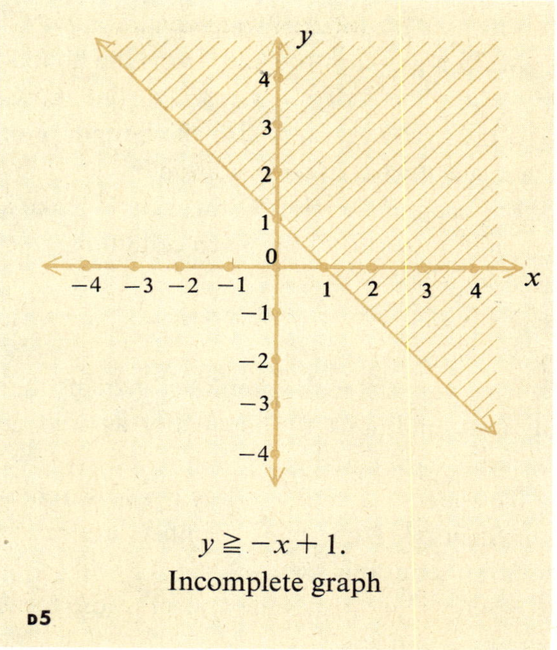

$y \geqq -x+1.$
Incomplete graph

D5

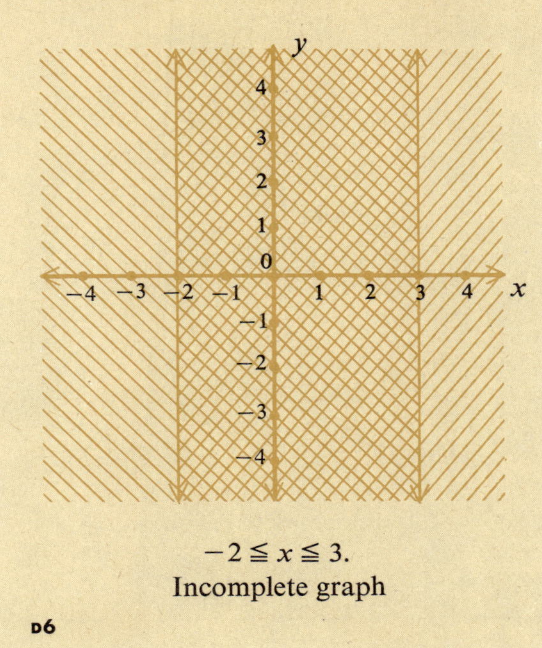

$-2 \leqq x \leqq 3.$
Incomplete graph

D6

$y \geqq -x + 1$? Why are point (1, 3) and point (−1, 3) also in this closed half-plane?

Q Now consider the locus of $y \leqq -x + 1$. The locus of $y \leqq -x + 1$ is the union of the loci of what two simple conditions? The locus of $y \leqq -x + 1$ is the union of what two geometric figures? How do you know that the locus of $y \leqq -x + 1$ is a closed half-plane?

R Make a graph of $y \leqq -x + 1$.

For each of exercises S through V, make a graph of the system expressed.

S $y \geqq x.$

T $y > -2 \vee y = -2.$

U $y + x \leqq 3.$

V $y \geqq -2x.$

W Now look at D6. How is the locus of $-2 \leqq x$ indicated in D6? Is the locus of $-2 = x$ included in the locus of $-2 \leqq x$? The locus of $-2 \leqq x$ is what geometric figure?

X How is the locus of $x \leqq 3$ indicated? Is the locus of $x = 3$ included in the locus of $x \leqq 3$? The locus of $x \leqq 3$ is what geometric figure?

Y Is the locus of $-2 \leqq x \leqq 3$ the intersection of two closed half-planes? How is the locus of this system indicated in D6?

Z Consider the system $-1 \leqq y \leqq 2$. The locus of $-1 \leqq y \leqq 2$ is the intersection of two closed half-planes. These two closed half-planes are the loci of what conditions? Make a graph of the system $-1 \leqq y \leqq 2$.

In this lesson you made graphs of systems including conditions for equality and conditions for inequality. The loci of some of the systems were open half-planes and the loci of other systems were closed half-planes.

On your own

For each of exercises 1 through 14, make a graph of the system expressed.

1 $x = 2 \wedge y = 4.$

2 $x - y = 3 \wedge x = 2.$

3 $2x + y < 0 \vee 2x + y < -2.$

4 $x + 2y = 0 \wedge x - 2y = 4.$

5 $3x + y \neq 3.$

6 $x - 2y \leqq 0.$

7 $-4 \leqq x \leqq -1.$

8 $-2 < x < 0.$

9 $-3x \leqq x + y \wedge x + y \leqq 0.$

10 $x < y \wedge -x < y.$

11 $2x + y < 1 \wedge y > -1.$

12 $2x + y \leqq 1 \wedge y \geqq -1.$

13 $x \leqq 3 \wedge y \geqq -2.$

14 $(0 \leqq x \leqq 4) \wedge (0 \leqq y \leqq 4).$

Exercises 15 through 21 refer to the loci of the systems expressed in exercises 1 through 14.

15 Which loci contain only one point?

16 Which locus is an open half-plane?

17 Which locus is a closed half-plane?

18 Which loci are the intersection of two closed half-planes?

19 Which loci are the intersection of two open half-planes?

20 Which locus is the union of two open half-planes that are disjoint sets?

21 Which locus is the union of a square and its interior?

24 292 Exploring ideas

Convex sets

In this lesson you will use what you have learned about open and closed half-planes to examine the idea of a polygonal convex set.

A Study D1. The line ℓ_1 is the locus of what condition?

B The points below ℓ_1 form the locus of what condition? What kind of geometric figure do these points form?

C The points above ℓ_1 form the locus of what condition? What kind of geometric figure do these points form?

D The line ℓ_1 is the boundary of how many open half-planes? Is every line in a plane the boundary of exactly two open half-planes?

E How do you know that the locus of $y = x - 2$, the locus of $y < x - 2$, and the locus of $y > x - 2$ are disjoint sets? What geometric figure is the union of these three loci?

F The two open half-planes that have the locus of $y = 3x + 2$ as their boundary are the loci of what conditions? What is the locus of $(y = 3x + 2) \vee (y < 3x + 2) \vee (y > 3x + 2)$?

G Now look at D2. Line ℓ_2 is the locus of what condition? The region of the plane that is indicated by shading is the locus of what condition?

H Describe the location of the points whose coördinates satisfy $y = 2x - 3 \vee y > 2x - 3$. What kind of geometric figure is the locus of $y = 2x - 3 \vee y > 2x - 3$?

I The locus of $y \leqq 0$ contains the points in the x-axis. What other points does this locus contain?

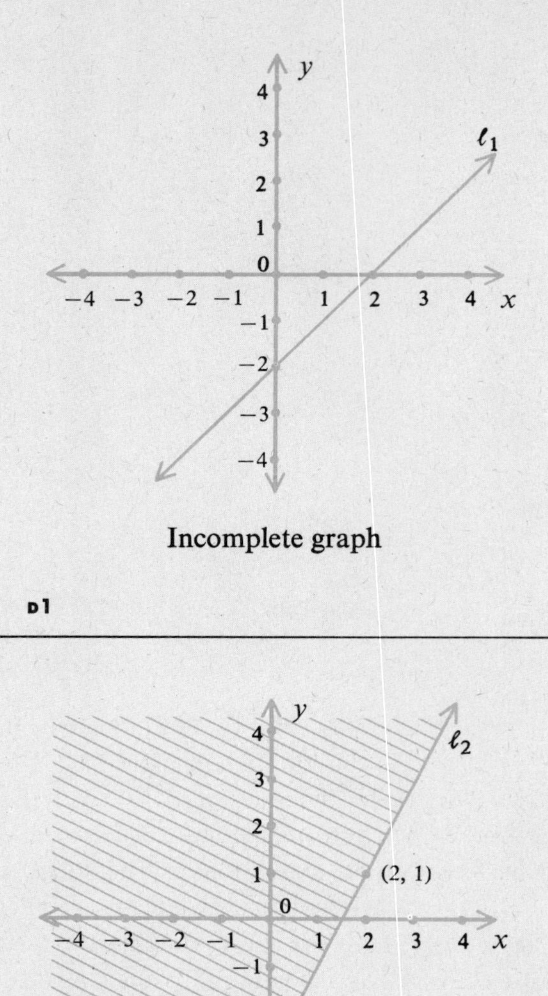

J Make a graph of $y \leqq 0$. What kind of geometric figure is the locus of $y \leqq 0$?

K The locus of $x \geqq 0$ contains the points in the y-axis and what other points?

L Make a graph of $x \geqq 0$. What kind of geometric figure is the locus of $x \geqq 0$?

M Now look at D3. How is the closed half-plane that is the locus of $y \leqq 0$ indicated? How is the locus of $x \geqq 0$ indicated?

N How do you know that the locus of system A is the intersection of two closed half-planes? How is this locus indicated in D3?

The intersection of two or more closed half-planes is a *polygonal convex set*. Since the locus of the system $y \leqq 0 \wedge x \geqq 0$ is the intersection of two closed half-planes, the locus is a polygonal convex set.

O Make a graph of the system $x \leqq 0 \wedge y \geqq 0$. How do you know that the locus of this system is a polygonal convex set?

P Now look at D4. How is the locus of $y \geqq x$ indicated? How is the locus of $y \leqq 2$ indi-

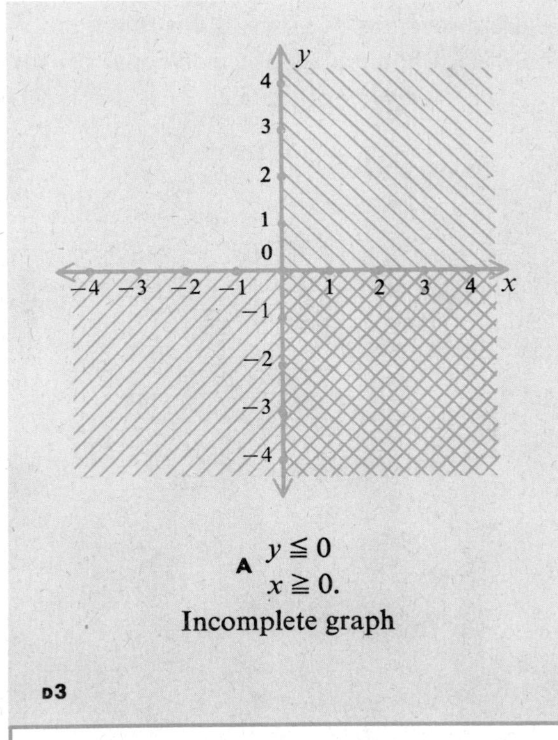

A $y \leqq 0$
$x \geqq 0.$
Incomplete graph

D3

polygonal con vex set (kon veks′ or kon′-veks). A set of points that is the intersection of two or more closed half-planes.

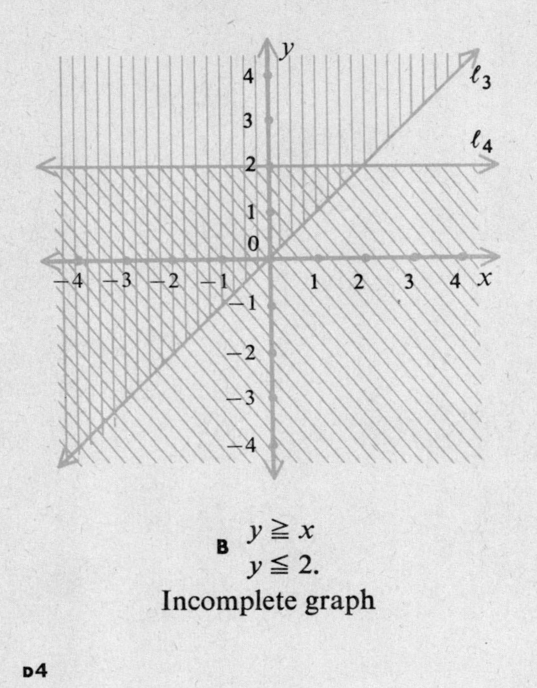

B $y \geqq x$
$y \leqq 2.$
Incomplete graph

D4

cated? What kind of geometric figure is each of these loci?

Q How do you know that the locus of system B is a polygonal convex set? Name three points that are in the locus of this system.

Each of the boundaries of the closed half-planes that determine a polygonal convex set includes a *boundary* of the polygonal convex set. For example, the locus of $y = x$, represented in D4, is the boundary of the closed half-plane that is the locus of $y \geqq x$. Therefore, the locus of $y = x$ includes a boundary of the polygonal convex set represented in D4.

R Explain why the locus of $y = 2$ also includes a boundary of the polygonal convex set represented in D4.

S ? Does the polygonal convex set represented in D4 contain every point that is in a boundary of the set? Explain your answer.

T Make a graph of $y \leqq x \wedge y \leqq 1$. Is the locus of this system a polygonal convex set?

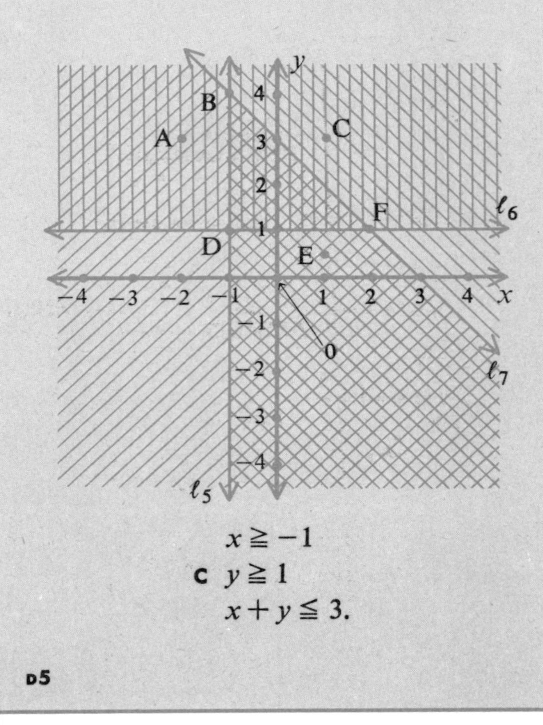

$$\text{C} \quad \begin{matrix} x \geqq -1 \\ y \geqq 1 \\ x + y \leqq 3. \end{matrix}$$

D5

corner point of a polygonal convex set. The point of intersection of two boundaries of a polygonal convex set.

U What lines include the boundaries of the polygonal convex set that you represented for exercise T?

V Make a graph of $y \leqq x + 1 \wedge x \geqq 1$. How do you know that the locus of this system is a polygonal convex set?

W Two lines include the boundaries of the polygonal convex set that you represented for exercise V. These lines are the loci of what conditions?

Since the only convex sets that are mentioned in this book are polygonal convex sets, we will often refer to these geometric figures simply as convex sets. Next you will study convex sets that are the intersection of three or more closed half-planes.

A Look at D5. Which line, ℓ_5, ℓ_6, or ℓ_7, is the locus of $x = -1$? Which of points A through F are in the locus of $x \geqq -1$?

B Which line represented in D5 is the locus of $y = 1$? The locus of $x + y = 3$?

C Which of points A through F are in the locus of $y \geqq 1$? In the locus of $x + y \leqq 3$?

D Which of points A through F are in the locus of system C, expressed in D5? Is each point that you named in the triangular region that is determined by points B, D, and F?

E Do points B, D, and F determine a triangular region that is the intersection of three closed half-planes? Is this region a convex set? Explain your answers.

Notice that point B is the point of intersection of two boundaries of the convex set that we are discussing. A point that is the intersection of two boundaries of a polygonal convex set is a *corner point* of the set.

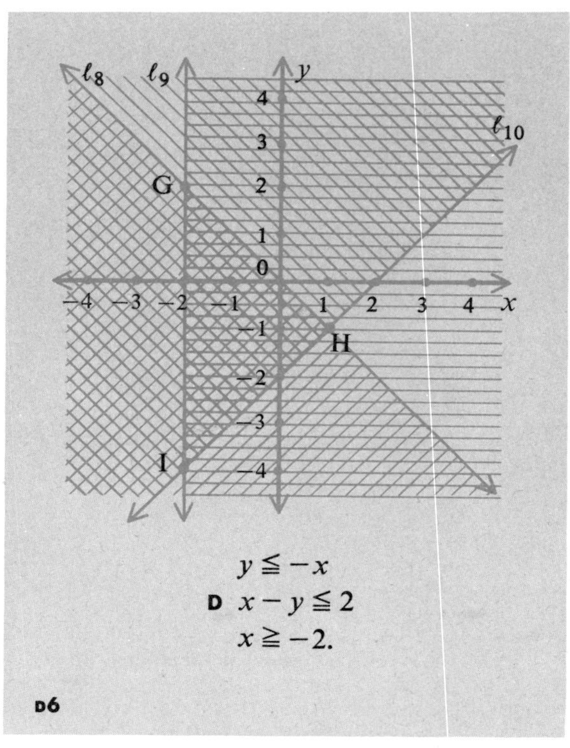

$$\text{D} \quad \begin{matrix} y \leqq -x \\ x - y \leqq 2 \\ x \geqq -2. \end{matrix}$$

D6

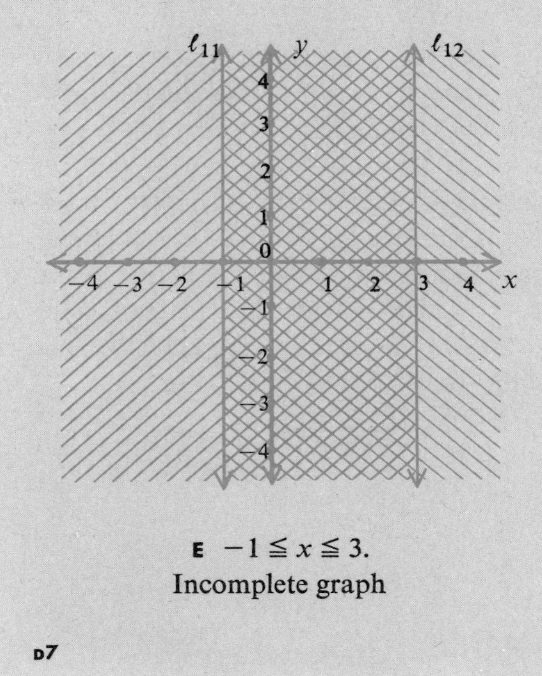

E $-1 \leqq x \leqq 3$.
Incomplete graph

D7

F How do you know that each of points B, D, and F is a corner point of a convex set?

G How do you know that the coördinates of point B satisfy $x=-1 \wedge x+y=3$? What point has coördinates that satisfy the condition $x=-1 \wedge y=1$? The condition $y=1 \wedge x+y=3$?

H Now look at D6. Which line is the locus of $y=-x$? The locus of $x-y=2$? The locus of $x=-2$?

I How do you know that the triangular region determined by points G, H, and I is a polygonal convex set?

J Explain why the convex set that we are discussing is the locus of system D, given in D6. Name the corner points of this convex set.

K Which corner point has coördinates that satisfy the condition $y=-x \wedge x-y=2$? The condition $y=-x \wedge x=-2$? Give a compound condition for equality that is satisfied by the coördinates of the third corner point.

L Make a graph of the convex set associated with $(x+y \geqq 2) \wedge (x-2y \geqq -4) \wedge (x \leqq 4)$. Then give the coördinates of each corner point of the set.

M For each corner point that you named for exercise L, give a compound condition for equality that is satisfied by its coördinates.

N ? Point $(-1, 0)$ is in a polygonal convex set whose boundaries are subsets of the loci of $x=-2$, $y=1$, and $y=2x$. The convex set is the locus of what system of conditions? Name the corner points of the convex set.

Now you will consider a polygonal convex set that is the intersection of four closed half-planes.

O Look at D7. One closed half-plane is the locus of $-1 \leqq x$. The other closed half-plane is the locus of what condition? How is the locus of system E indicated?

P Now look at D8. One closed half-plane is the locus of $-2 \leqq y$. The other closed half-

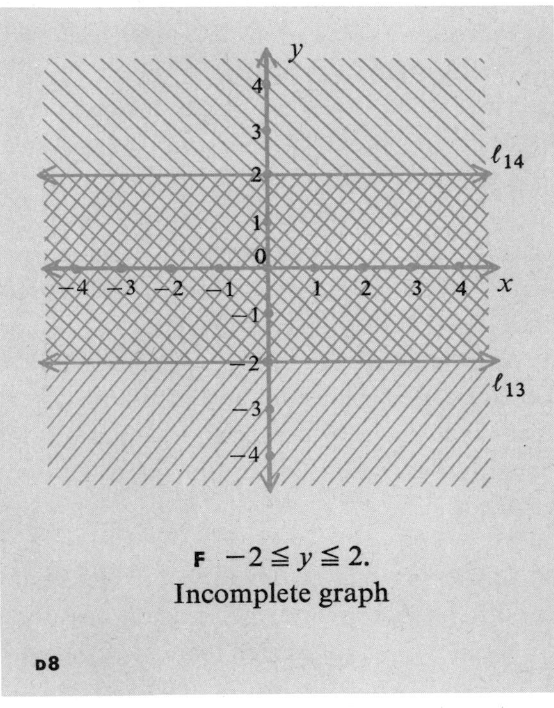

F $-2 \leqq y \leqq 2$.
Incomplete graph

D8

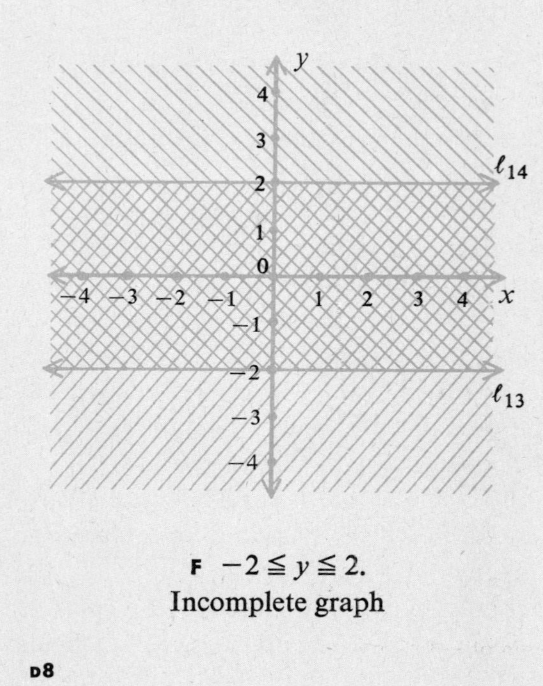

F $-2 \leqq y \leqq 2.$
Incomplete graph

D8

plane is the locus of what condition? How is the locus of system F indicated?

Q The loci of systems E and F are represented again in D9. Have systems E and F been used to form system G, expressed in D9?

R How is the locus of system G indicated? How do you know that the locus of this system is a polygonal convex set?

S Name the corner points of the convex set that is the locus of system G. For each corner point, give a compound condition for equality that is satisfied by its coördinates.

T Make a graph of $(-2 \leqq x \leqq 3) \wedge (y \leqq 4) \wedge (x \leqq y)$. Then name the corner points of the locus and give a compound condition for equality that is satisfied by the coördinates of each corner point.

In this lesson you made graphs of systems of conditions that involve the ideas of "less than or equal to" and "greater than or equal to." You learned that the loci of such systems are polygonal convex sets, and you learned how to determine the corner points and the lines that include the boundaries of these sets.

On your own

Make a graph of the polygonal convex set that is the locus of each system of conditions expressed below. Name any corner points of the polygonal convex set and the conditions for equality whose loci include the boundaries of the set.

1 $x \geqq 0$
$y \geqq 3x.$

2 $x \geqq 0$
$x + y \leqq 3$
$y \geqq 0.$

3 $x \geqq 0$
$y \geqq 0$
$y \geqq -x + 2.$

4 $-3 \leqq x \leqq 0$
$-2 \leqq y \leqq 3.$

5 $y \geqq 0$
$x + y \leqq 2$
$x + y \geqq -2.$

6 $x \geqq 0$
$y \geqq 0$
$x + 2y \leqq 3.$

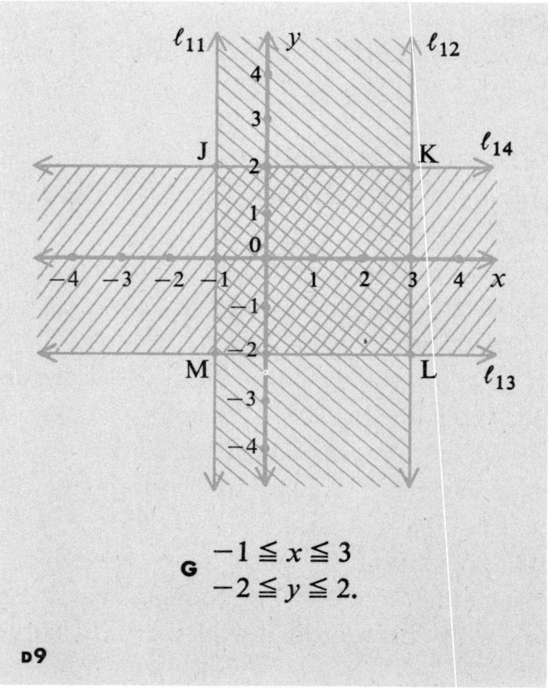

G $-1 \leqq x \leqq 3$
$-2 \leqq y \leqq 2.$

D9

7 $-4 \leqq x \leqq 1.$

$x \leqq 2$

8 $y \geqq -3$

$x \geqq y.$

$x \geqq 0$

9 $y \geqq 0$

$2x + 3y \leqq 6.$

10 If the loci of $2x - y = 10$ and $5x + 2y = 7$ include the boundaries of a polygonal convex set, give the coördinates of a corner point of the set.

11 Give the coördinates of the corner points of the polygonal convex set whose boundaries are subsets of the loci of $3x - 7y = 5$, $2x + y = 9$, and $x = y$.

12 The corner points of a polygonal convex set are point (0, 0), point (0, −2), and point (−2, 0). Give the three conditions for equality whose loci include the boundaries of the convex set.

KEEPING SKILLFUL

For each of exercises 1 through 6, find the sum.

1 $(x^2 + 5x + 3) + (x^2 - 2) + (x^2 - 10)$

2 $(y^3 + y^2) + (y^2 - 10y) + (y^3 - 5y)$

3 $(12x^2 + 4) + (x^2 + 1) + (x^2 + 4x)$

4 $(x^4 + 3x) + (2x^3 + 4x) + (6x^3 - 4x)$

5 $\frac{7}{3x} + \frac{5}{4x} + \frac{1}{12x}$

6 $\frac{2}{y-4} + \frac{3}{y+4} + \frac{10}{y^2 - 16}$

For each of exercises 7 through 12, find the difference.

7 $(8x^2 + 3x + 15) - (2x^2 + 6x - 11)$

8 $(12y^2 - 10) - (3y^2 + 10y - 4)$

9 $\frac{4}{8x^2} - \frac{3}{16x^2}$

10 $\frac{3}{y-2} - \frac{2}{y+2}$

11 $\frac{16}{x-3} - \frac{25}{x+4}$

12 $\frac{4}{x} - \frac{12}{25x^2}$

24 293 Exploring ideas

Maximum and minimum values of linear functions

The functions that you will consider in this lesson contain ordered pairs whose first components are also ordered pairs. The first components of the members of such functions are associated with points in a convex set.

Set A, tabulated in D1, is a set of ordered pairs of numbers. Set B is a set of numbers. The diagram in D1 represents one way in which each element of A can be mapped onto an element of B.

A Has (5, 3) been mapped onto 2?

The symbol at the right below expresses the ordered pair whose first component is (5, 3) and whose second component is 2. The ordered pair ((5, 3), 2) represents the mapping of (5, 3) onto 2.

((5, 3), 2)

B What ordered pairs represent the other mappings indicated in D1?

The set of ordered pairs that represent the mappings given in D1 is a relation. Each member of the relation represents a mapping of an element of the domain onto an element of the range. Because each element of the domain of

$A = \{(5, 3), (-1, 4), (0, 6), (-2, -10)\}.$

$B = \{\ 2,\quad 8,\quad 14\}.$

D1

the relation is paired with exactly one element of the range, the relation is a function. The function is tabulated in D2.

C Which set tabulated in D1 is the domain of function f? Which set is the range?

D Let (x, y) represent each element of the domain of function f. Does each (x, y) have exactly one image in the range of function f?

You can use the symbol $f(x, y)$ to express the element of the range of function f that is the image of (x, y) in the domain. If (x, y) is replaced by (5, 3), then its image is f(5, 3), or 2.

E Explain why $f(-1, 4) = 14$. Which element in the range of function f is f(0, 6)? Which element in the range is $f(-2, -10)$?

F Now you will use set C, tabulated in D3, as the domain of a function g. Let (x, y) represent each member of the domain of function g. What does $g(x, y)$ represent?

The condition expressed in D4 determines function g. The condition requires that $g(x, y)$, the image of (x, y), be the sum of $2x$ and y. If (x, y) is replaced by (4, 6), then g(4, 6) is equal to $2(4) + 6$. Therefore, $\big((4, 6), 14\big)$ is an element of function g.

G What statement do you obtain if you replace (x, y) by $(-2, 7)$ in $g(x, y) = 2x + y$? What is $g(-2, 7)$? How do you know that $\big((-2, 7), 3\big)$ is an element of function g?

H Use $(0, -5)$ and then (3, 2) as replacements for (x, y) in $g(x, y) = 2x + y$. Name the elements of function g whose first components are $(0, -5)$ and (3, 2).

I Tabulate the function that is determined by $g(x, y) = 2x + y$. Tabulate the range of function g.

J The set tabulated in D5 is the domain of the function determined by $h(x, y) = x - 2y + 3$. What statements do you obtain if you use each element of the domain as a replacement for (x, y) in $h(x, y) = x - 2y + 3$?

$$A = \{(5, 3),\ (-1, 4),\ (0, 6),\ (-2, -10)\}.$$

$$B = \{\ 2,\quad 8,\quad 14\}.$$

D1

$$f = \{\big((5, 3), 2\big),\ \big((-1, 4), 14\big),\ \big((0, 6), 8\big),\ \big((-2, -10), 14\big)\}.$$

D2

$$C = \{(4, 6),\ (-2, 7),\ (0, -5),\ (3, 2)\}.$$

D3

$$g(x, y) = 2x + y.$$

D4

$$\{(1, 5),\ (2, 0),\ (4, 1),\ (-1, 4)\}$$

$$h(x, y) = x - 2y + 3.$$

D5

K Tabulate function h.

L Now use the set tabulated in D5 as the domain of the function that is determined by the condition $f(x, y) = 2x - y - 4$. Tabulate function f.

The domain elements of the functions that you have considered so far in this lesson have been ordered pairs, and the range elements have been determined by first-degree polynomials. These functions are linear, or first-degree, functions in two variables. The standard form of a condition that determines such a function is $f(x, y) = ax + by + c$, where $a \neq 0$ or $b \neq 0$, and where a, b, and c are parameters.

M Does $f(x, y) = 2x - y - 4$ determine a linear function in two variables?

Now you will study a linear function in two variables that has an infinite set of ordered pairs as its domain.

A Look at D6. $D \times D$ is the domain of the function determined by $f(x, y) = x - y + 2$. Replace (x, y) by $(10, 3)$. What is $f(10, 3)$? Is $((10, 3), 9)$ an element of function f?

B Each ordered pair named below is an element of the domain of function f. For each ordered pair, find its image.

$(3, 10)$ $(-2, 6)$ $(6, -2)$ $(0, 8)$ $(-4, -4)$

C Explain why function f is an infinite set.

D Suppose that function g is determined by $g(x, y) = 2y - 3x + 1$. If the domain of function g is $D \times D$, how do you know that $((2, 3), 1)$ is an element of the function?

E Each ordered pair named below is an element of the domain of the function determined by $g(x, y) = 2y - 3x + 1$. For each ordered pair, find its image.

$(1, 1)$ $(3, -2)$ $(0, -3)$ $(-1, -1)$ $(2, 0)$

Next you will study linear functions where the elements of the domain are associated with the points in a polygonal convex set.

F Look at D7. How is the locus of each condition in system A indicated? Each of these loci is what kind of geometric figure?

G How do you know that the locus of system A is a convex set? This convex set is the union of what simple polygon and its interior?

H Which ordered pairs named below are associated with points in the locus of system A?

$(1, 1)$ $(-2, 3)$ $(1, 4)$ $(3, 0)$ $(1, 2)$ $(0, 0)$

Next you will use the solution set of system A as the domain of the function determined by the condition expressed in D8.

I Why can you use $(1, 0)$, but not $(-1, 0)$, as a replacement for (x, y) in $f(x, y) = 2x - y$? Explain why $f(1, 0) = 2$. How do you know that $((1, 0), 2)$ is an element of function f?

$$f(x, y) = x - y + 2.$$

D6

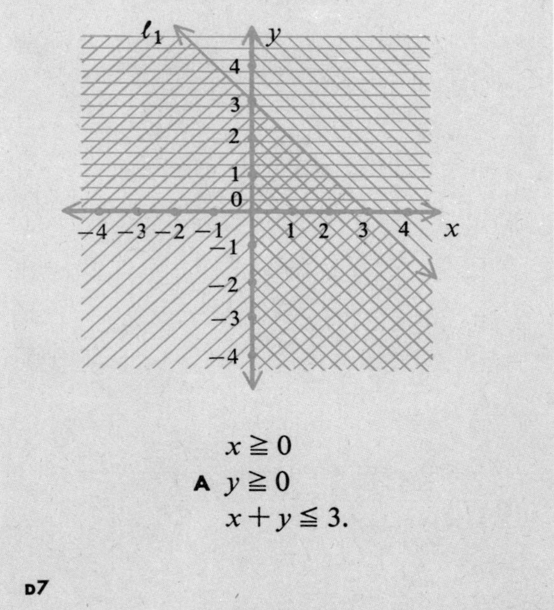

$$x \geqq 0$$
$$\textbf{A} \quad y \geqq 0$$
$$x + y \leqq 3.$$

D7

$$f(x, y) = 2x - y.$$

D8

J Why can you use both $(2, 1)$ and $(1, 2)$ as replacements for (x, y) in $f(x, y) = 2x - y$? What is $f(2, 1)$? What is $f(1, 2)$?

K Which ordered pairs named below are in the domain of function f? For each ordered pair that is in the domain, find its image.

$(1, -4)$ $(0, 1)$ $(0, 2)$ $(\frac{1}{2}, 1)$ $(2\frac{1}{2}, 3)$

L From exercise K, you know that $f(0, 1)$ is -1 and $f(0, 2)$ is -2. Because $-1 > -2$, $f(0, 1) > f(0, 2)$. Show that $f(0, 0) > f(0, 1)$. Show that $f(2, 1) > f(1, 1)$.

M Four elements of the range of function f are named below. Which of these elements is the greatest? Which element is the least?

$f(1, \frac{1}{2})$ $f(3, 0)$ $f(0, \frac{1}{4})$ $f(0, 3)$

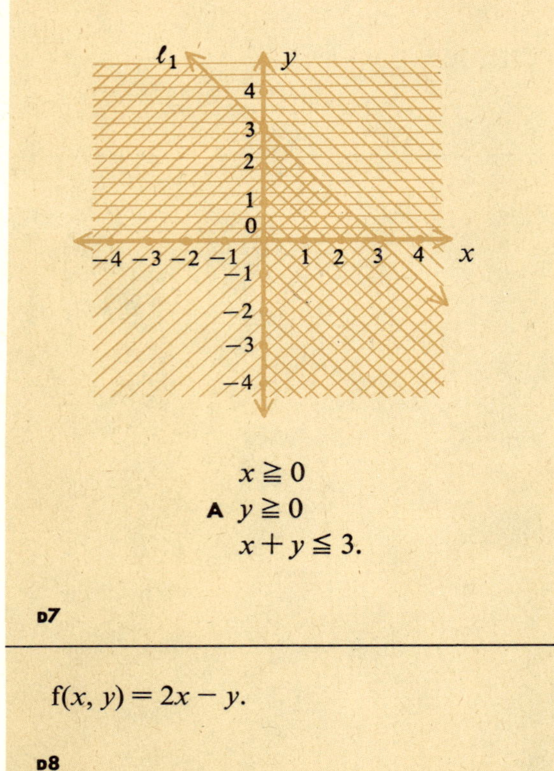

N Four range elements of function f are named below. First show that f(3, 0), or 6, is greater than each of these range elements. Then show that f(0, 3), or -3, is less than each of these range elements.

f(1, 1) f(0, 1) $f(1\frac{1}{2}, 2\frac{1}{2})$ $f(\frac{1}{4}, 2)$

Now you will study a property that will tell you that f(3, 0), or 6, is the greatest element of the range of function f and that f(0, 3), or -3, is the least element of the range.

Look again at D7. You will recall that the triangular closed region represented in the display is the convex set that is the locus of the domain of function f. The vertices of the triangle that determines the closed region, namely, points (3, 0), (0, 0), and (0, 3), are the corner points of the polygonal convex set.

O Point (3, 0) is a corner point of the locus of the domain, and f(3, 0) = 6. Name the other range elements that are determined by corner points.

The greatest element in the range of a function is the *maximum* (mak′sə məm) *value* of the function. The least element in the range of a function is the *minimum* (min′ə məm) *value* of the function. We will accept without proof a property concerning the maximum value and the minimum value of a linear function in two variables. The property is expressed below.

Function f is a linear function in two variables, and the locus of the domain is a polygonal convex set that is a closed region determined by a polygon. The maximum value and the minimum value of function f are determined by corner points of the polygonal convex set.

P You know that 6, 0, and -3 are the range elements of function f that are determined by the corner points of the locus of the domain. Explain why 6 is the maximum value of the function determined by $f(x, y) = 2x - y$. What is the minimum value of function f?

Now consider the function determined by $g(x, y) = 2x + 3y + 1$. The domain of function g is the set of ordered pairs associated with the closed region represented in D7.

Q What are the corner points in the locus of the domain of function g? Show that g(3, 0) = 7. What is g(0, 0)? What is g(0, 3)?

R Why is 10 the maximum value of function g? Why is 1 its minimum value?

S Function h is determined by the condition $h(x, y) = 10x - 5y - 15$. The domain of function h is the same as the domain of function g. What is h(3, 0)? What is h(0, 0)? What is h(0, 3)? Which of these elements is the maximum value of function h? The minimum value?

T Now look at D9. The convex set represented in the display is the locus of the solution set of system B. This convex set is a closed region determined by what kind of polygon?

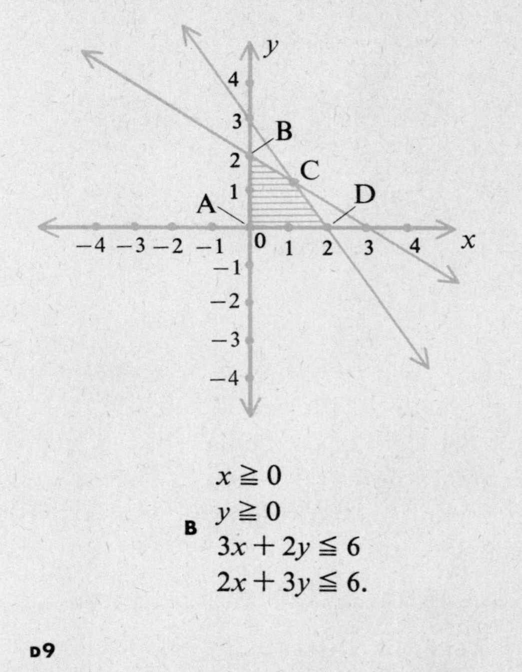

$x \geqq 0$
$y \geqq 0$
B $3x + 2y \leqq 6$
$2x + 3y \leqq 6.$

D9

$f(x, y) = 4x + 3y.$
$g(x, y) = 7x + 5y - 10.$
$h(x, y) = .5x - .2y.$

D10

U Name the corner points of the convex set represented in D9. Which corner point has coördinates that satisfy $x = 0 \wedge y = 0$? That satisfy $2x + 3y = 6 \wedge x = 0$? What compound condition for equality is satisfied by the coördinates of point C? By the coördinates of point D?

V Use your answers to exercise U to help you find the coördinates of the corner points of the convex set represented in D9.

The domain of each function expressed in D10 is the set of ordered pairs associated with the points in the convex set represented in D9.

W For each (x, y) associated with a corner point in the locus of the domain, find $f(x, y)$. Explain why $8\frac{2}{5}$ is the maximum value of function f. What is the minimum value of function f?

X For each (x, y) associated with a corner point in the locus of the domain, find $g(x, y)$. What is the maximum value of function g? What is the minimum value of this function?

Y How can you determine the maximum value and the minimum value of function h? What are these values?

Z The domain of the function determined by $f(x, y) = x - y$ is the solution set of the system expressed below.

$$-1 \leqq x \leqq 3$$
$$0 \leqq y \leqq 3.$$

Make a graph of the domain of function f. Next give the coördinates of the corner points of the locus of the domain. Then give the maximum and minimum values of function f.

In this lesson you studied linear functions in two variables where the ordered pairs in the domain are associated with points in a polygonal convex set. You learned that the maximum and minimum values of such functions are determined by the corner points of the locus of the domain.

On your own

For each of exercises 1 through 4, tabulate the domain and the range of the relation named. Then tell whether the relation is a function. For each function, find its maximum and minimum values.

1 $\{((7, 6), 2),\ ((-1, 3), 4),\ ((7, 6), 3)\}$

2 $\{((7, 6), 2),\ ((-1, 3), 4),\ ((-1, 3), 2)\}$

3 $\{((7, 6), 2),\ ((2, 6), 2),\ ((6, 2), 2)\}$

4 $\{((7, 6), 2),\ ((6, 7), 2),\ ((-1, 3), 4)\}$

5 A system of conditions is expressed below. What (x, y) satisfy the system?

$$|x| = 2$$
$$|y| = 3.$$

Each condition expressed in exercises 6 through 10 determines a function. The domain of each function is the set that you tabulated for exercise 5. Tabulate each function. Then give its maximum and minimum values.

6 $f(x, y) = 5x + 3y$.

7 $f(x, y) = x - y + 6$.

8 $f(x, y) = 3x + 2y - 12$.

9 $f(x, y) = 20x - 15y + 30$.

10 $f(x, y) = 4(x + y) - 6(x - y + 2)$.

11 Make a graph of the convex set that is the locus of the system of conditions expressed below. Then give the coördinates of the corner points of this locus.

$$x \geqq 0$$
$$y \geqq 0$$
$$2x + y \leqq 4.$$

Each condition expressed below determines a function. The domain of each function is the solution set of the system given in exercise 11. Find the maximum and minimum values of each function.

12 $f(x, y) = x + 3y - 2$.

13 $f(x, y) = .5x - 3.5y + 7$.

14 $f(x, y) = x - y - 20$.

Each of exercises 15 through 18 gives a condition that determines a function and a system of conditions whose solution set is the domain of the function. For each function, make a graph of the convex set that is the locus of the domain. Then give the coördinates of the corner points and find the maximum and minimum values of the function.

15 $f(x, y) = 3x - 5y + 9$.

$y \leqq x + 2$
$x \leqq 3$
$y \geqq 2$.

16 $f(x, y) = -10x + 3y + 25$.

$y \leqq 3x + 4$
$y \leqq 4 - x$
$y \geqq -1$.

17 $f(x, y) = 6x + 4y - 8$.

$3 \leqq x \leqq 5$
$y \geqq 0$
$2x - y \geqq 4$.

18 $f(x, y) = 12x - 4y + 2$.

$2y - 3x \geqq 6$
$y \leqq 3$
$2x + y \leqq 7$
$\frac{1}{4}x - y \leqq 2$.

19 The corner points of a polygonal convex set are points (0, 0), (0, 10), and (10, 10). This set is the locus of the domain of the function determined by $f(x, y) = 100x - 75y + 30$. Find the maximum and minimum values of the function.

KEEPING SKILLFUL

Tabulate the solution set of each of the conditions expressed below. Then, for each irrational solution, give a rational approximation to the nearer thousandth.

1 $x^2 + x - 42 = 0$.

2 $x^2 - 10x = 24$.

3 $(x - 4)^2 - 16 = 0$.

4 $9x^2 = 91 - 18x$.

5 $\frac{1}{4}x^2 + x = 8$.

6 $2x^2 - 10x - 20 = 0$.

7 $x^2 + 27 = -12x$.

8 $3x^2 + 2 = 245$.

9 $25x^2 + 30x = 0$.

10 $x^2 = 16x - 55$.

11 $4x^2 + 10x = 3$.

12 $2x^2 = 48x - 288$.

13 $\frac{1}{9}x^2 + 1\frac{1}{3}x = 5$.

14 $6x^2 - 5 = 15$.

15 $6x^2 + 7x + 12 = 10$.

16 $\frac{1}{16}x^2 + 9 = 1\frac{1}{2}x$.

17 $4x^2 + 20x = 75$.

18 $-10x^2 + 15x - 3 = 0$.

19 $(x + 5)(4x + 2) = 0$.

24 **294** **Exploring problems**

Linear programming

The problems that you will study in this lesson can be solved by a method that is called *linear programming.* Such problems involve finding the maximum or the minimum value of a linear function.

Read the problem in D1. You are asked to find how many minutes Mr. Harris should use each machine if he wants to make the copies at the minimum cost. Let x represent the number of minutes that machine A should be used. Let y represent the number of minutes that machine B should be used.

A In x minutes, will machine A make $2x$ copies? Each of the $2x$ copies costs how many cents? What does $2(2x)$, or $4x$, represent?

B In y minutes, will machine B make $3y$ copies? Each of the $3y$ copies costs how many cents? What does $6(3y)$, or $18y$, represent?

C If machine A is used for x minutes and machine B is used for y minutes, does $4x + 18y$ represent the total cost of making the copies? Explain your answer.

D If c also represents the total cost in cents of using machine A for x minutes and machine B for y minutes, explain why the sentence below in color expresses a condition for the problem in D1.

$$c = 4x + 18y.$$

E The condition expressed above determines a linear function in two variables. This means that $f(x, y) = 4x + 18y$ is the same condition as $c = 4x + 18y$. Explain why $f(x, y)$ represents the total cost of using machine A for x minutes and machine B for y minutes.

Mr. Harris wants at least 240 copies of a certain document. He has two copying machines in his office. Machine A can make 2 copies per minute at a cost of 2 cents per copy. Machine B can make 3 copies per minute at a cost of 6 cents per copy. The machines will be available for his use for a total of at most 100 minutes. If Mr. Harris wants to make the copies at the minimum cost, for how many minutes should he use each machine?

D1

Now you will learn how the function determined by $f(x, y) = 4x + 18y$ can help solve the problem in D1.

F Suppose that you replace (x, y) by $(-2, -3)$ in $f(x, y) = 4x + 18y$. What is $f(-2, -3)$?

G ? Can you use $((-2, -3), -48)$ to get a sensible answer to the problem in D1? If you use negative numbers as replacements for x and y in $f(x, y) = 4x + 18y$, will you get a sensible answer to the problem?

From your answers to exercise G, you know that you cannot use every member of $D \times D$ as a replacement for (x, y) in $f(x, y) = 4x + 18y$ because some members do not provide a sensible answer. In other words, the problem includes certain requirements concerning the set of (x, y) that is the domain of the function determined by $f(x, y) = 4x + 18y$. For example, since the number of minutes that each machine can be used is non-negative, each replacement for (x, y) in $f(x, y) = 4x + 18y$ must satisfy $x \geqq 0$, as well as $y \geqq 0$.

H Does $x + y$ represent the total number of minutes that the two copy machines are used?

Mr. Harris wants at least 240 copies of a certain document. He has two copying machines in his office. Machine A can make 2 copies per minute at a cost of 2 cents per copy. Machine B can make 3 copies per minute at a cost of 6 cents per copy. The machines will be available for his use for a total of at most 100 minutes. If Mr. Harris wants to make the copies at the minimum cost, for how many minutes should he use each machine?

D1

$$f(x, y) = 4x + 18y.$$

$$x \geqq 0$$
$$y \geqq 0$$
$$x + y \leqq 100$$
$$2x + 3y \geqq 240.$$

D2

Explain why each replacement for (x, y) in $f(x, y) = 4x + 18y$ must satisfy $x + y \leqq 100$.

I Does $2x + 3y$ represent the total number of copies that Mr. Harris can make if he uses machine A for x minutes and machine B for y minutes? Explain why each replacement for (x, y) in $f(x, y) = 4x + 18y$ must also satisfy $2x + 3y \geqq 240$.

Now look at D2. The basic condition for the problem in D1 is $f(x, y) = 4x + 18y$ because the condition contains $f(x, y)$, which represents the cost that the problem asks you to minimize. The basic condition also contains the variables that represent the numbers of minutes that the machines should be used. The solution set of the system of conditions expressed in D2 is the domain of the function determined by $f(x, y) = 4x + 18y$.

J Is (10, 85) in the domain of function f?

From $f(x, y) = 4x + 18y$, you know that $f(10, 85) = 4(10) + 18(85)$, or 1570.

K Is f(10, 85), or 1570, the number of cents that it will cost to use machine A for 10 minutes and machine B for 85 minutes?

L How do you know that (46, 50) is an element of the domain of function f? What is f(46, 50)? How many cents will it cost to use machine A for 46 minutes and machine B for 50 minutes?

M Read the problem in D1 again. You know that for each (x, y) in the domain of function f, $f(x, y)$ represents the number of cents that it will cost to use machine A for x minutes and machine B for y minutes. How do you know that the minimum value of function f is the minimum cost of using the machines?

Now you will find the minimum value of function f. Look at D3.

N The polygonal convex set that is the locus of the domain of function f is represented in D3. Name the coördinates of the corner points. What property tells you that the minimum value of function f is the image of one of the ordered pairs associated with a corner point?

O Find f(0, 80), f(0, 100), and f(60, 40). Which of these numbers is the minimum value of the function determined by $f(x) = 4x + 18y$?

P The second component of $\big((60, 40), 960\big)$ is the least number of cents that it will cost to use the two machines. What does the first component of this ordered pair represent?

Now you can use the first component of $\big((60, 40), 960\big)$ to get the answer to the problem in D1.

If Mr. Harris wants to make the copies at the minimum cost, he should use machine A for 60 minutes and machine B for 40 minutes.

Q ? Now suppose that machine B makes copies at a cost of 4 cents per copy, instead of 6

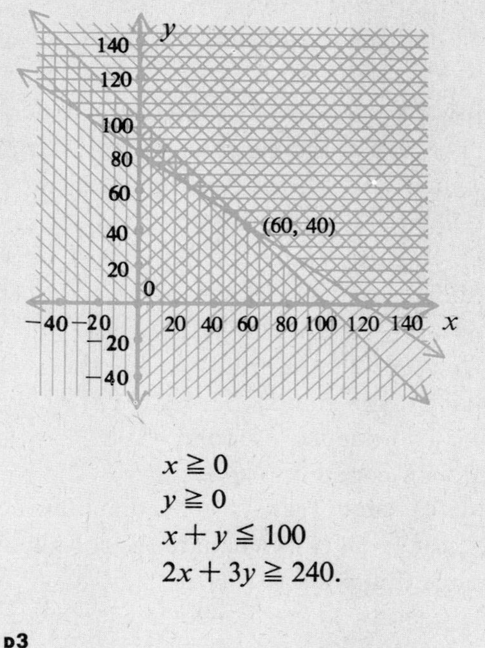

$x \geqq 0$
$y \geqq 0$
$x + y \leqq 100$
$2x + 3y \geqq 240.$

D3

Mr. Flynn sells the shirts he makes at a profit of \$2 each. He sells the slacks that he makes at a profit of \$3 each. The manpower and machinery that Mr. Flynn has available limit his production. If he could triple his production of shirts, he would still make at most 90 shirts and pairs of slacks per day. If he could double his production of slacks, he would still make at most 60 shirts and pairs of slacks per day. How many shirts and how many pairs of slacks should Mr. Flynn make per day to receive a maximum profit?

D4

cents per copy. Why is $f(x, y) = 4x + 12y$ the basic condition for the problem? The domain of function f is the solution set of what system of conditions? To minimize the cost, why should Mr. Harris use machine A for 60 minutes and machine B for 40 minutes?

Next you will see how the maximum value of a function can be used to get the answer to a problem.

Read the problem in D4.

A If Mr. Flynn makes x shirts per day, he will make $2x$ dollars of profit. If he makes y pairs of slacks per day, what does $3y$ represent? What does $2x + 3y$ represent?

B Let p represent the quantity that you are to maximize. In other words, let p represent the number of dollars of profit that Mr. Flynn will make from the production of x shirts and y pairs of slacks. Why is the condition expressed below in color the basic condition for the problem in D4?

$$p = 2x + 3y.$$

C The condition expressed above determines a linear function in two variables. This means that $g(x, y) = 2x + 3y$ is the same condition as $p = 2x + 3y$. What does $g(x, y)$ represent in the problem?

D Suppose that you replace (x, y) by $(-1, -\frac{1}{3})$ in $g(x, y) = 2x + 3y$. What is $g(-1, -\frac{1}{3})$?

E ? Can you use $((-1, -\frac{1}{3}), -3)$ to get a sensible answer to the problem in D4? How do you know that each (x, y) that satisfies $g(x, y) = 2x + 3y$ must satisfy $x \geqq 0$? Must satisfy $y \geqq 0$?

F If Mr. Flynn could triple his production of x shirts, what would $3x + y$ represent? Explain why each (x, y) that satisfies the basic condition for the problem must also satisfy $3x + y \leqq 90$.

G If Mr. Flynn could double his production of y slacks, what would $x + 2y$ represent? What is another condition that must be satisfied by each (x, y) that satisfies $g(x, y) = 2x + 3y$?

Mr. Flynn sells the shirts he makes at a profit of \$2 each. He sells the slacks that he makes at a profit of \$3 each. The manpower and machinery that Mr. Flynn has available limit his production. If he could triple his production of shirts, he would still make at most 90 shirts and pairs of slacks per day. If he could double his production of slacks, he would still make at most 60 shirts and pairs of slacks per day. How many shirts and how many pairs of slacks should Mr. Flynn make per day to receive a maximum profit?

D4

$x \geqq 0$
$y \geqq 0$
$3x + y \leqq 90$
$x + 2y \leqq 60.$

D5

The system of conditions expressed in D5 involves each condition that you have considered in exercises E, F, and G. The solution set of this system is the domain of the function determined by the basic condition for the problem in D4, the condition $g(x, y) = 2x + 3y$.

H Is (10, 20) in the domain of function g?

I From $g(x, y) = 2x + 3y$ you know that $g(10, 20) = 2(10) + 3(20)$. Find g(10, 20).

J What is the number of dollars of profit that Mr. Flynn will receive if he makes 10 shirts and 20 pairs of slacks per day?

K Explain why the maximum value of the function determined by $g(x, y) = 2x + 3y$ is the maximum profit that Mr. Flynn will receive if he makes x shirts and y pairs of slacks per day.

The polygonal convex set that is the locus of the domain of function g is represented in D6.

L How do you know that the maximum value of function g is the image of the ordered pair associated with a corner point in the locus of the domain?

M Which corner point of the convex set has coördinates that satisfy $x = 0 \wedge y = 0$? That satisfy $x = 0 \wedge x + 2y = 60$?

N What are the coördinates of the corner points that you named for exercise M?

O The coördinates of point C satisfy what compound condition for equality? The coördinates of point D satisfy what compound condition for equality? What are the coördinates of points C and D?

P For each (x, y) that is associated with a corner point, find $g(x, y)$.

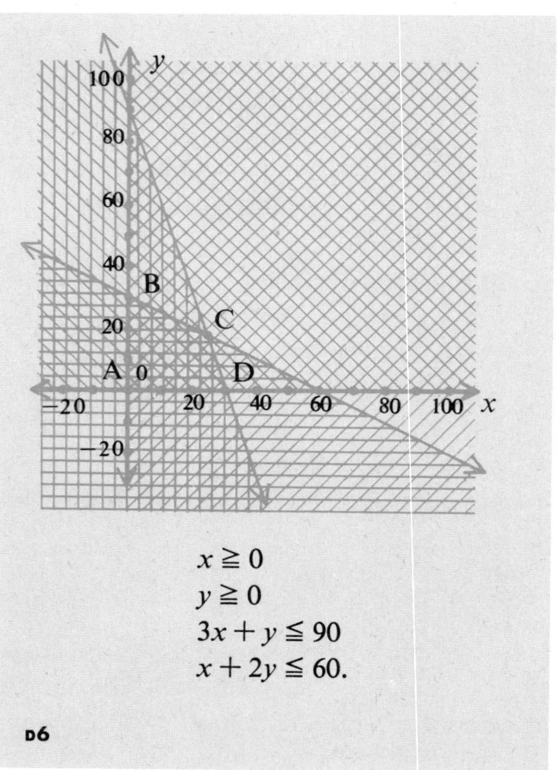

D6

Q Explain why $((24, 18), 102)$ is the element of function g whose second component is the maximum value of function g.

R What is the maximum profit that Mr. Flynn can receive per day?

S To what does the first component of $((24, 18), 102)$ refer? Give the answer to the problem in D4.

In this lesson you learned how to solve certain problems by the method known as linear programming. The problems involved the minimum value or the maximum value of a linear function in two variables where the locus of the domain was a polygonal convex set.

On your own

Use the problem in D7 in connection with exercises 1 through 8.

1 Suppose that x pairs of model A and y pairs of model B are made per day, and that they are sold for a profit of p dollars. Express a condition involving x, y, and p that is the basic condition for the problem.

2 The basic condition for the problem determines a linear function in two variables. Call this function f. Use functional notation to express the condition that determines function f.

3 The domain of function f is the set of (x, y) that satisfy a certain system of conditions. What is the system of conditions?

4 Make a graph of the domain of function f. Then name the coördinates of the corner points of the locus of the domain.

5 What member of function f has a second component that is the maximum value of the function?

6 Give the answer to the problem.

7 Assume that the manufacturer decides to make at most 4 pairs of model B. What changes should you make in your answers to exercises 1 through 6?

A manufacturer wants to produce two kinds of book ends: model A, which he will sell at a profit of $2 per pair, and model B, which he will sell at a profit of $3 per pair. Each model requires work on a drill press and a jigsaw. Each of these tools, however, is available for at most 120 min. per day. Model A requires 10 min. of work on the jigsaw and 5 min. on the drill press; model B requires 5 min. of work on the jigsaw and 10 min. on the drill press. How many pairs of each model should the manufacturer make to maximize his profit?

D7

A farmer has 20 chickens and 60 ducks. He wants to buy at least 100 more chickens and ducks, and he has space for at most 140 ducks on his farm. He wants to have at least as many ducks as chickens. He can buy the chickens at a cost of 15 cents each, and he can buy the ducks at a cost of 20 cents each. How many chickens and how many ducks should the farmer buy to minimize his cost?

D8

8 Assume that the profit per pair of model A is $1 instead of $2. What changes should you make in your answers to exercises 1 through 6?

Use the problem in D8 in connection with exercises 9 through 16.

9 Suppose that the farmer buys x chickens and y ducks, and that the total cost of the chickens and ducks is c dollars. What condi-

A farmer has 20 chickens and 60 ducks. He wants to buy at least 100 more chickens and ducks, and he has space for at most 140 ducks on his farm. He wants to have at least as many ducks as chickens. He can buy the chickens at a cost of 15 cents each, and he can buy the ducks at a cost of 20 cents each. How many chickens and how many ducks should the farmer buy to minimize his cost?

D8

tion involving x, y, and c is the basic condition for the problem?

10 Suppose that function g is the function determined by the basic condition for the problem. Use functional notation to express the basic condition.

11 The solution set of what system of conditions is the domain of function g?

12 Make a graph of the domain of function g. Then name the coördinates of the corner points of the locus of the domain.

13 What member of function g has a second component that is the minimum value of the function?

14 Give the answer to the problem.

15 For the problem in D8, suppose that the farmer paid 15 cents for each chicken, and that he paid $7\frac{1}{2}$ cents, instead of 20 cents, for each duck. In this case, how many chickens and how many ducks should the farmer buy to minimize his cost?

16 After the farmer raises all the chickens and ducks to maturity, he can sell each chicken at a profit of 25 cents and each duck at a profit of 40 cents. How many chickens and how many ducks should he buy to maximize his profit when he sells them?

SPECIAL CHALLENGE

In the Special Challenge on page 423, we discussed the matrix representation of a system of linear conditions. A matrix representation can be used in finding the solution set of a system of conditions.

A Look at D1. What are the conditions in system A?

Consider a system of linear conditions in which each condition is in standard form. In solving such a system by deriving an equivalent system of conditions, we change only the constants on the left sides of the conditions. For this reason, we can use the matrix of system A to derive equivalent systems.

B Look at D2. We will refer to the matrix of system A as "matrix A." Matrix B was obtained by multiplying each element in row 1 of matrix A by $\frac{1}{2}$. What are the conditions in system B?

Multiplying row 1 of matrix A by $\frac{1}{2}$ is the same as multiplying each side of the condition $2x + 5y - 7 = 0$ by $\frac{1}{2}$. Since the conditions $2x + 5y - 7 = 0$ and $x + \frac{5}{2}y - \frac{7}{2} = 0$ are equivalent, system B is equivalent to system A.

C Row 1 of matrix C is the same as row 1 of matrix B. Multiply row 1 of matrix B by -4. What three numbers do you get?

D If you add the numbers you obtained for exercise C to the corresponding elements of row 2 of matrix B, you will obtain row 2 of matrix C. What are the conditions in system C?

E If $(-4)(x + \frac{5}{2}y - \frac{7}{2}) + (4x + y + 3) = 0$ is simplified, do you obtain the second condition in system C?

You know that you can use the condition $m(ax + by + c) + n(dx + ey + f) = 0$ to derive equivalent systems of conditions. Thus, since system C can be derived from system B in this way, system C is equivalent to system B.

$$\text{A} \quad \begin{pmatrix} 2 & 5 & -7 \\ 4 & 1 & 3 \end{pmatrix}\begin{pmatrix} x \\ y \\ 1 \end{pmatrix} = \begin{pmatrix} 0 \\ 0 \end{pmatrix}.$$

D1

$$\text{A} \quad \begin{pmatrix} 2 & 5 & -7 \\ 4 & 1 & 3 \end{pmatrix}$$

$$\text{B} \quad \begin{pmatrix} 1 & \frac{5}{2} & -\frac{7}{2} \\ 4 & 1 & 3 \end{pmatrix}$$

$$\text{C} \quad \begin{pmatrix} 1 & \frac{5}{2} & -\frac{7}{2} \\ 0 & -9 & 17 \end{pmatrix}$$

$$\text{D} \quad \begin{pmatrix} 1 & \frac{5}{2} & -\frac{7}{2} \\ 0 & 1 & -\frac{17}{9} \end{pmatrix}$$

$$\text{E} \quad \begin{pmatrix} 1 & 0 & \frac{11}{9} \\ 0 & 1 & -\frac{17}{9} \end{pmatrix}$$

D2

F $3x - 4y + 3 = 0$
$-5x + 3y - 4 = 0.$

G $x + \frac{7}{11} = 0$
$y - \frac{3}{11} = 0.$

D3

F Explain how matrix D was obtained from matrix C. What are the conditions in system D? Why are systems D and C equivalent?

Row 2 of matrix E is the same as row 2 of matrix D. Row 1 of matrix E was obtained in the following way: Row 2 of matrix D was multiplied by $-\frac{5}{2}$. The products obtained were added to the corresponding elements of row 1 of matrix D.

G What conditions are in system E? Which of these conditions is the simplified form of $(-\frac{5}{2})(y - \frac{17}{9}) + (x + \frac{5}{2}y - \frac{7}{2}) = 0$?

H System E is equivalent to system D and, consequently, is equivalent to system A. What (x, y) satisfies system E? What is the solution of system A?

Now think of the procedure that we followed to arrive at matrix E. Matrix B resulted when we obtained 1 in row 1, column 1. Matrix C resulted when we obtained 0 in row 2, column 1. Matrix D resulted when we obtained 1 in row 2, column 2. Matrix E resulted when we obtained 0 in row 1, column 2. Matrix E is in a form that makes the solution of the system obvious.

I Look at D3. What is the matrix representation of system F? What is the matrix representation of system G?

J Show the steps that you can use to obtain the matrix for system G from the matrix for system F. What is the (x, y) that satisfies system F?

KEEPING SKILLFUL

Tabulate the solution set of each of the conditions expressed below, if possible. Otherwise, give a standard description of the solution set.

1 $\frac{x^2 + x - 2}{x} = 0.$

2 $\frac{5}{x} = \frac{10}{3x + 7}.$

3 $x(x + 3) > -2.$

4 $\sqrt{x^2 + 144} = 5\sqrt{x}.$

5 $x(x + 3) < 10.$

6 $\frac{x + 6}{1 - x} = \frac{4 - x}{1 + x}.$

7 $\frac{5}{x + 10} = 12.$

8 $10x^2 + 3x < 1.$

9 $3\sqrt{x + 7} - 1 = 74.$

10 $x^2 + 12x + 27 > 0.$

11 $7\sqrt{4x + 1} = 14 + 5\sqrt{4x + 1}.$

12 $\sqrt{x - 6} + \sqrt{x + 7} = 13.$

13 $\sqrt{x + 6} - 6 = x - 12.$

14 $18 + \frac{4(x + 1)}{x - 8} = 16.$

APPLYING MATHEMATICS

For each problem, first write a sentence that expresses a condition. Then give the answer to the problem. The problems involve physical measures. Remember to use the rules for computing with approximations that you studied in lesson 163, *Book 2*. Use 3.14 as an approximation of π.

1 During June, Southport had 3.26 in. of precipitation; during July the city had 1.2 in. of precipitation; and during August the city had 1.04 in. of precipitation. What was the average number of inches of precipitation in Southport during the three months?

2 The length of a radius of a circular hooked rug is 5.2 ft. What is the area of the rug in square feet?

3 A machine lifted a 3000-lb. steel beam a distance of 48.6 ft. How many foot-pounds of work did the machine do?

4 A windowpane is in the shape of a square. The perimeter of the windowpane is 41.1 in. What is the length of a side of the windowpane in inches?

5 A 70-lb. piece of a certain kind of metal contains 16.45 lb. of copper. What per cent of this piece of metal is copper?

6 The elevation of Park City is 3480 ft. $\pm$ 5. The elevation of Bloomfield is 10,300 ft. $\pm$ 50. The elevation of the city of Bloomfield is how many feet greater than the elevation of Park City?

7 A garden is in the shape of a trapezoid. The length of an altitude of the trapezoid is 75 in. The lengths of the bases are 90 in. and 105 in. What is the area of the garden in square inches?

8 A swimming pool is in the shape of a rectangular right prism. The depth of the pool is 4.5 ft., the length is 22.5 ft., and the width is 16 ft. What is the volume of the swimming pool in cubic feet?

9 The Carter family traveled by automobile to a resort 825 mi. from their home. Their total travel time for the trip was 20.2 hr. At what average speed in miles per hour did the Carter family travel?

10 The thickness of a sheet of a certain kind of paper is 7.2×10^{-3} cm. What is the thickness in centimeters of 245 sheets of the same kind of paper?

11 A 52-foot ladder is placed against a wall so that the bottom of the ladder is 16.6 ft. from the base of the wall. What is the measure of the angle that is formed by the ground and the ladder?

12 Water weighs about 62.5 lb. per cubic foot. What is the volume in cubic feet of 28,540 lb. of water?

13 A motorboat and a sailboat left a dock at the same time. The motorboat traveled directly north at a rate of 35 miles per hour. The sailboat traveled directly south at a rate of 13 miles per hour. How many miles apart were the motorboat and the sailboat after 1.3 hours?

14 A patio is in the shape of a rectangle whose perimeter is 70.6 ft. The length of the patio is 24.25 ft. What is the width of the patio?

15 One hydrogen atom weighs 1.67×10^{-24} g. What is the weight in grams of 5 hydrogen atoms?

16 The living room in the Harrisons' new home is in the shape of a square whose side is 14.3 ft. long. What is the area of the living room in square feet?

17 Mrs. Campbell bought a utility cabinet in the shape of a rectangular right prism. The length of a base of the cabinet is 2.5 ft. and the width is 1.5 ft. The height of the cabinet is 6 ft. What is the capacity of the cabinet in cubic feet?

CHECKING UP

The small numerals within parentheses tell what pages to turn to for help if you need it.

Test 266

1 Name the (x, y) that satisfies the condition $2x - 3y - 1 = 0 \wedge y - 3 = 0$. (405)

2 What is the y-intercept of the locus of $y = 5x - 6$? (398)

3 The locus of $y \leqq -3x + 2$ is the union of the loci of what two simple conditions? (428)

4 What is the slope of the locus of $y = \frac{2}{3}x + 5$? (398)

5 Which (x, y) that satisfies $2x - 3 = 5y$ has 0 as a first component? (397)

6 In the real plane, what is the first coördinate of every point in the locus of $3x = 20$? (427)

7 The locus of $\{(x, y) \mid y = -5\}$ is what geometric figure? (398)

8 How many members are in the solution set of $3x + 4y = 7 \wedge y = 2$? (408)

9 Give a condition involving x and y whose locus is a line with a slope of -2 and whose y-intercept is point $(0, 5)$. (398)

10 Suppose that ℓ is a line that is parallel to the x-axis. Point $(0, -3)$ is the y-intercept. Give a condition of the form $ax + by + c = 0$ that has ℓ as its locus. (398)

11 Make a graph of the boundary of the locus of $y < 2x + 3$. (426)

12 Make a graph of the convex set that is the locus of $(x \geqq 0) \wedge (y \geqq 0) \wedge (x + 2y \leqq 6) \wedge (3x + y \leqq 6)$. (431)

13 Give the coördinates of the corner points of the polygonal convex set that you represented for exercise 12. (432)

Test 267

Tell what words or symbols best complete exercises 14 through 26.

14 When you put $2y - x = 5$ in the form $ax + by + c = 0$, you obtain ~~~~~. (397)

15 The union of an open half-plane and the line that is its boundary is a ~~~~~ half-plane. (428)

16 A system of three linear conditions in three variables can have exactly one solution, infinitely many solutions, or ~~~~~. (414)

17 If you replace m by 3 and n by ~~~~~ in $m(5x - 2y - 14) + n(3x - 4y) = 0$, you eliminate the variable x. (406)

18 If $f(x, y) = 3x - y$, then $f(4, -3) =$ ~~~~~. (436)

19 The set of points below the locus of $y = 2x - 5$ is the locus of ~~~~~. (426)

20 The locus of $y > x + 2$ is an open half-plane whose boundary is the locus of ~~~~~. (426)

21 A polygonal convex set is a set of points that is the intersection of two or more ~~~~~. (431)

22 ~~~~~ is the (x, y, z) that satisfies the system $(y = 5) \wedge (z + y = 2) \wedge (x + y + z = 0)$. (414)

23 A condition of the form $f(x, y) =$ ~~~~~ determines a linear function. (436)

24 The locus of $\{(x, y) \mid x = -3\}$ is parallel to the ~~~~~. (406)

25 If $f(x, y) = x + 3y$, then $f(5, 2)$ is ~~~~~ than $f(3, 3)$. (437)

26 Any condition that can be put in the form $ax + by + cz + d = 0$ is a ~~~~~ condition for equality in three variables. (414)

Test 268

For each of problems 27 through 30, first give a system of conditions. Then give the answer to the problem.

27 Beth purchased 3 pads of scratch paper and 5 pads of notebook paper for \$1.71. Alice purchased 4 pads of scratch paper and 2 pads of notebook paper for \$1.02. What was the price of each kind of paper? (410)

28 Jim had 50 coins consisting of pennies and nickels. Their value was \$1.22. How many of each kind of coin did Jim have? (410)

29 Roger, Dan, and Steve share a paper route. The three boys can deliver 142 papers when Roger works for 15 minutes, Dan for 20 minutes, and Steve for 16 minutes. In 20 minutes, Roger and Dan working together can deliver 120 papers. The three boys can finish delivering the 152 papers on their route if each boy works 19 minutes. How many minutes would it take each boy to complete the route by himself? (418)

30 In a right triangle, the measure of one acute angle is $\frac{1}{2}$ the sum of 6 and the measure of the other acute angle. What is the measure in degrees of each acute angle of the right triangle? (410)

For problem 31, first determine the basic condition. Next, express the system of conditions whose solution set is the domain of the function determined by the basic condition. Finally, make a graph of the locus of the domain of the function and give the answer to the problem.

31 Susan, Carol, and Diane have formed a corporation to manufacture doll clothes. A local department store has agreed to furnish the material and to pay \$.30 for each completed item. Susan can work at most 200 min. per week, Carol can work at most 224 min. per week, and Diane can work at most 160 min. per week. In making the doll clothes, Susan cuts out the garment, Carol does the machine work, and Diane the handwork. One week they decided to make one style of playsuit and one style of dress. It takes 3 min. of cutting, 6 min. of machine work, and 7 min. of handwork to make a playsuit. A dress takes 8 min. of cutting, 8 min. of machine work, and 4 min. of handwork. How many playsuits and how many dresses should the girls have planned to make during the week to receive a maximum profit? (441)

CHECKING UP

The small numerals within parentheses tell what pages to turn to for help if you need it.

Test 269

1 What is the base of $(\sqrt{5}xy)^4$? (169)

2 What is the sum of $3x^2 - 2x + 7$ and $2x^2 + 5x - 8$? (185)

3 Give the absolute value of $\sqrt[3]{-27}$. (273)

4 What polynomial is the additive inverse of $x^2 - 5x + 3$? (213)

5 Name the binomial factors of $9x^2 - 49$. (199)

6 Find the expression that is the difference of $(5x^2 - 2)$ and $(x - 3x^2 + 8)$. (189)

7 Find the product of $3x - 2y$ and $5x + 4y$. (196)

8 Put $3(x + 2) - 3 > 1$ in a standard form. (262)

9 What number satisfies $\frac{x-2}{4+x} = 0$? (373)

10 What compound condition involving "or" is equivalent to $|7 - x| = 6$? (275)

11 What (x, y) is a solution of the condition $3x + y = 3 \wedge 2x - 5y = 19$? (401)

Test 270

Tell what words or symbols best complete exercises 12 through 22.

12 A single force that has the same effect as two forces is called a ~~~ force. (26)

13 The ~~~ property can be used to obtain $15x^3 - 10x^2$ from $5x(3x^2 - 2x)$. (193)

14 The solution set of $2 - 3x^2 = 0$ is ~~~. (369)

15 The product of $6xy$ and $2x + 3xy - 5y + 10$ is ~~~. (193)

16 A quotient is in lowest terms if and only if the only common factors of the dividend and the divisor are ~~~. (221)

17 The locus of any linear function is a ~~~. (339)

18 For any function, the first component of any member whose second component is 0 is a ~~~ of the function. (339)

19 The least common multiple of the divisors of $\frac{5(x^2+4x+4)}{6x^2y(x^2-1)}$ and $\frac{10(x-1)}{9xy^2(x^2+2x+1)}$ is the expression ~~~. (231)

20 The ordered pair ~~~ is the member of the function determined by $f(x) = \frac{3}{4}x^2 + 5$ for which $f(x) = 5$. (349)

21 The solution set of $3 > t \vee t > 7$ is the ~~~ of the solution sets of $3 > t$ and $t > 7$. (120)

22 The function h is determined by the condition $h(x) = \frac{3}{4}x - 5$. The member of function h that has a second component of 1 is ~~~. (338)

Test 271

From the list below each exercise, choose the correct answer for the exercise.

23 x^6 is not equal to ~~~. (169)

a $(x^2)^3$ c $x^2 \cdot x^3$

b $\frac{(x^2)^4}{x^2}$ d $\frac{x^3 \cdot x^3 \cdot x^3}{x^3}$

24 If quadrilateral JKLM is a parallelogram, with sides JK, JM, KL, and LM, then ~~~. (22)

a $\overrightarrow{JK} \oplus \overrightarrow{JM} = \overrightarrow{JL}$ c $\overrightarrow{JL} \oplus \overrightarrow{JM} = \overrightarrow{KL}$

b $\overrightarrow{JK} \oplus \overrightarrow{KL} = \overrightarrow{ML}$ d $\overrightarrow{KM} \oplus \overrightarrow{LM} = \overrightarrow{KL}$

25 The trinomial ~~~ is not the square of a binomial. (199)

a $4y^2 + 14y + 49$ c $25 - 30x + 9x^2$

b $x^2 + 8xy + 16y^2$ d $9x^2 - 48x + 64$

26 The statement ~~~ is a conditional. (122)

a "Tom is foolish or Tom is young"

b "If he runs, then he is guilty"

c "It is not the case that the dog bites"

d "The night was dark and cold"

27 The ordered pair ~~~ is a member of $\{(x, y) \mid 3y = 5x - 7\}$. (293)

a (2, 1) b (−4, −1) c (−4, 9) d (5, 18)

28 If $f(x) = -3x^2$ determines the function f, then ~~~. (306)

a $f(5) < f(-25)$ c $f(10) < f(5)$

b $f(2) < f(20)$ d $f(-1) < f(-3)$

29 A factor of $8x^2 - 18x - 45$ is the binomial ~~~. (207)

a $2x - 3$ c $4x + 5$

b $4x - 15$ d $x + 9$

30 The solution set of the compound condition $5 + 2x < 3(x + 1) \wedge 3x < 2(x + 4) - 3$ is ~~~. (267)

a $\{x \mid -5 < x < -1\}$ c $\{x \mid -1 < x < 8\}$

b $\{x \mid 4 < x < 7\}$ d $\{x \mid 2 < x < 5\}$

31 The locus of $f(x) = \frac{k}{x}$, where $k \neq 0$, is a ~~~. (317)

a line c hyperbola

b parabola d half-plane

32 The product of the solutions of the quadratic condition $2x^2 - 13x - 7 = 0$ is the number ~~~. (367)

a 14 b $-3\frac{1}{2}$ c $1\frac{6}{7}$ d $-6\frac{1}{2}$

33 For each $x < 0$, the points in the locus of $f(x) = \frac{1}{2}x^2$ are contained in the ~~~ quadrant. (314)

a first c third

b second d fourth

34 The slope of the line that contains points (3, −2) and (−8, 5) is ~~~. (343)

a $\frac{3-(-8)}{-2-5}$ c $\frac{-2-5}{-8-3}$

b $\frac{3-8}{5-2}$ d $\frac{5-(-2)}{-8-3}$

35 The solution set of $x^2 + 2x - 15 = 0$ is ~~~. (369)

a {1, −13} c {0, 15}

b {−2, 5} d {−5, 3}

36 The binomial ~~~ is not a factor of $4x^2 - 36y^2$. (199)

a $2x + 6y$ c $x^2 - 9y^2$

b $4x - 36y$ d $x - 3y$

Unit 25

Permutations, combinations, and probability

25 295 Exploring ideas

Subsets of a finite set

In this unit you will first study some ideas concerning the subsets of a given set. Then you will see how these ideas are important in the study of probability.

A What does the symbol in D1 represent?

B You will recall that the empty set is a subset of every set and that every set is a subset of itself. What is the only set that is a subset of ∅ and that also contains every member of ∅?

C ? How do you know that ∅ is the only subset of ∅?

D Look at D2. How do you know that ∅ is a subset of A? That {Ohio} is a subset of A?

E ? Are ∅ and {Ohio} the only subsets of A? Which of these two subsets is a proper subset of A?

F Look again at D2. Name the subset of B that has no members. Tabulate two subsets of B, each of which has exactly one member.

G Is {Ohio, Oklahoma} the same set as {Oklahoma, Ohio}? How many different subsets of B contain every member of B?

H How many subsets does B have?

I Tabulate the subset of C that has no members. Tabulate three subsets of C, each of which has exactly one member.

J Is {Ohio, Oklahoma} a subset of C? Tabulate two other subsets of C, each of which has exactly two members.

K Tabulate the subset of C that has exactly three members.

L How many subsets does C have? How many of these subsets are proper subsets?

$\emptyset$

D1

A = {Ohio}.
B = {Ohio, Oklahoma}.
C = {Ohio, Oklahoma, Oregon}.

D2

SET	SUBSETS
$\emptyset$	$\emptyset$
{Ohio}	$\emptyset$ {Ohio}
{Ohio, Oklahoma}	$\emptyset$ {Ohio} {Oklahoma} {Ohio, Oklahoma}
{Ohio, Oklahoma, Oregon}	$\emptyset$ {Ohio} {Oklahoma} {Oregon} {Ohio, Oklahoma} {Ohio, Oregon} {Oklahoma, Oregon} {Ohio, Oklahoma, Oregon}

D3

The sets given in D1 and D2 are given again in D3, along with their subsets. Notice that the number of members in {Ohio} is one greater than the number of members in $\emptyset$. Notice also that {Ohio} has twice as many subsets as $\emptyset$.

M How is the number of members contained in {Ohio, Oklahoma} related to the number of members in {Ohio}? How does the number of subsets of {Ohio, Oklahoma} compare with the number of subsets of {Ohio}?

N How is the number of members contained in {Ohio, Oklahoma, Oregon} related to the number of members in {Ohio, Oklahoma}? Does {Ohio, Oklahoma, Oregon} have twice as many subsets as {Ohio, Oklahoma}?

So far, you have worked only with subsets of sets that have at most three members. Next, you will learn a convenient way of selecting all possible subsets of any given finite set and of determining how many subsets the given set has.

A Set R is tabulated in D4. The diagram in the display will help you select all possible subsets of R. Does every subset of R contain Ala-

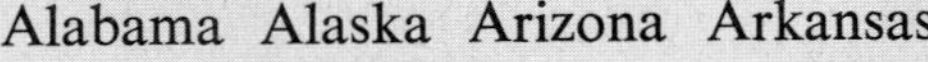

Alabama Alaska Arizona Arkansas

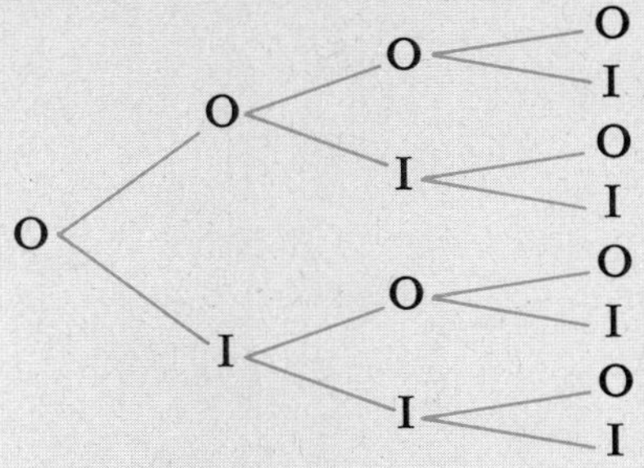

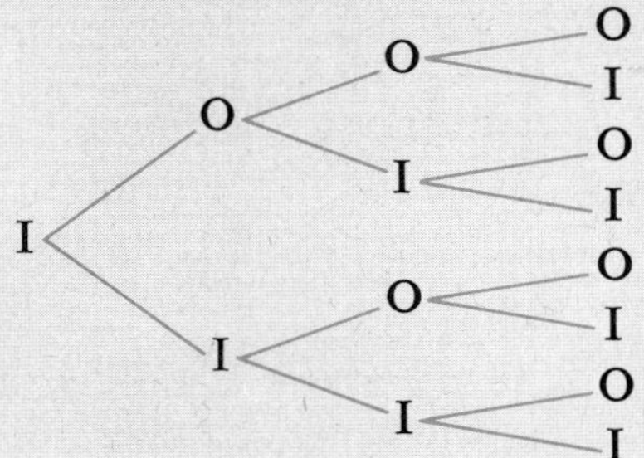

D4

R = {Alabama, Alaska, Arizona, Arkansas}.

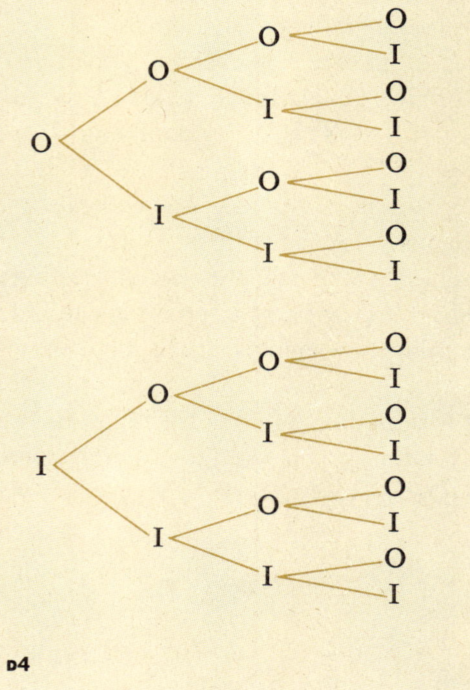

D4

bama? Name a subset of R to explain your answer.

Because a subset of R either contains Alabama or does not contain Alabama, you have exactly two choices regarding Alabama when you are selecting a subset of R. Let O represent the choice that Alabama is not in the subset. Let I represent the choice that Alabama is in the subset.

B Suppose that Alabama is not selected to be a member of a subset. In other words, O is the choice for Alabama. What two choices are there for Alaska?

C If O is the choice for Alabama and for Alaska, what choices are there for Arizona?

D Suppose that the choice is O for Alabama, O for Alaska, and O for Arizona. What two choices are there for Arkansas?

E If the choice is O for each member of R, what subset have you selected?

F Suppose that the choice is O for Alabama, O for Alaska, O for Arizona, and I for Arkansas. What subset of R have you selected?

G How many subsets of R can you select that do not contain Alabama? Use the diagram in D4 to obtain your answer.

H Now suppose that the choice for Alabama is I and that the choice for each of the other members of set R is O. What subset of R have you selected?

I How many subsets of R have Alabama as a member? How many different sets are subsets of R?

J How many subsets of R contain every member of R? How many subsets are proper subsets of R?

You can find the number of subsets of a finite set, such as R, without listing all the choices and counting them. Instead of making a diagram like the one in D4, you can use the fundamental counting property.

> REMINDER
>
> The universe for r and s is I_p. If a first event can occur in r ways, and if, after the first event has occurred, a second event can occur in s ways, then the two successive events can occur in rs ways.
>
> *See lesson 193, page 416, Book 2.*

From the diagram in D4, you know that O and I are the two choices for each of the four members of R. Therefore, $2 \times 2 \times 2 \times 2$ is the number of ways in which you can select a subset of R. This means that there are 2^4 subsets of R.

$M = \{$Maine, Maryland, Michigan, Minnesota, Missouri$\}$.

D5

K How does the exponent of 2^4 compare with the number of members in set R?

The property of finite sets that you have just developed is expressed below.

The universe for n *is the set of non-negative integers. If the number of members in a given finite set is* n, *then there are* 2^n *subsets of the given set.*

L Now look at D5. When you select a subset of set M, how many choices are there for Maine? How many choices are there for each of the other members of M?

M How can you find the number of subsets of M? What is this number?

In this lesson you learned how to find all the subsets of a finite set. You also studied a property of finite sets that enables you to find the number of subsets of a given finite set.

On your own

Use set S, tabulated below, in connection with exercises 1 through 9.

$$S = \{1, 2, 3\}.$$

1 Use the letters O and I to make a diagram that shows all the possible ways of selecting a subset of S.

2 How many sets are subsets of S?

3 Tabulate each proper subset of S.

4 Tabulate the subset of S that contains every element of S.

5 Tabulate each subset of S that contains exactly one element.

6 Tabulate each subset of S that contains exactly two elements.

7 How many subsets of S contain the element 1?

8 How many subsets contain the element 2?

9 How many subsets of S have 3 as a member?

For each of exercises 10 through 14, first tabulate the set described. Then tell how many subsets the given set has.

10 The set of Great Lakes

11 The set of United States coins, each of which is less than twenty cents in value

12 The set of integers between 3 and 4

13 The set of days of the week

14 The set of positive integers that are less than 5

15 What set is a subset of each set described in exercises 10 through 14?

KEEPING SKILLFUL

Put each condition expressed below in the form $y = mx + b$. Then give the slope and the y-intercept of the locus of the condition.

1 $x + y = 20.$

2 $3x + y = 5.$

3 $2x + 2y = 10.$

4 $y - 2x = x + 4.$

5 $6x + 2y + 3 = 9.$

6 $x = 6y.$

For each of exercises 7 through 10, make a graph of the locus of the set of (x, y) that is the solution set of the condition expressed.

7 $2x + y = 10.$

8 $x - y = 8.$

9 $4x + y = 3.$

10 $4x = y.$

In each of exercises 11 and 12, two systems, A and B, are expressed. For each exercise, first make one graph in which you represent the loci of the conditions in each system. Next, tabulate the solution set of each system. Then tell whether or not systems A and B are equivalent.

11 A $3x + y = 14$, $4x - 8y = 0.$ B $x - y = 2$, $x + 2y = 8.$

12 A $5x + y = 0$, $2x - y = 7.$ B $5x - y = 11$, $4x = 3y.$

25 | 296 | Exploring ideas

Permutations and combinations

In the last lesson you were concerned with all the subsets of a given set. Now you will work with specific subsets of finite sets. For example, you will be interested in the number of 2-element subsets of a given finite set.

A Set L is tabulated in D1. How many elements are in L? How many sets are subsets of L?

B For the diagram in D1, we have used the letters I and O to indicate whether or not a member of set L is contained in a subset. Tabulate a 2-element subset of L that does not contain A. Tabulate each of the other 2-element subsets of L.

C How do you know that each 2-element subset of L is a combination of the elements of {A, B, C} taken 2 at a time?

> REMINDER
> A combination is a set that is a subset of a given set and that contains a given number of elements.
> *See lesson 196, page 427, Book 2.*

D The combinations that you tabulated for exercise B are given in the column at the left in D2. Can you form any other combinations of the elements of {A, B, C} taken 2 at a time?

In *Book 2* you learned how to find the number of specific combinations of a given set. Before you found the number of combinations, you first studied the idea of a permutation of a set. You will recall that a permutation is an ordered arrangement of some or all of the members of a set. For example, since (C, A) is an ordered pair formed from 2 of the elements of {A, B, C}, we say that (C, A) is a permutation of the elements of {A, B, C} taken 2 at a time.

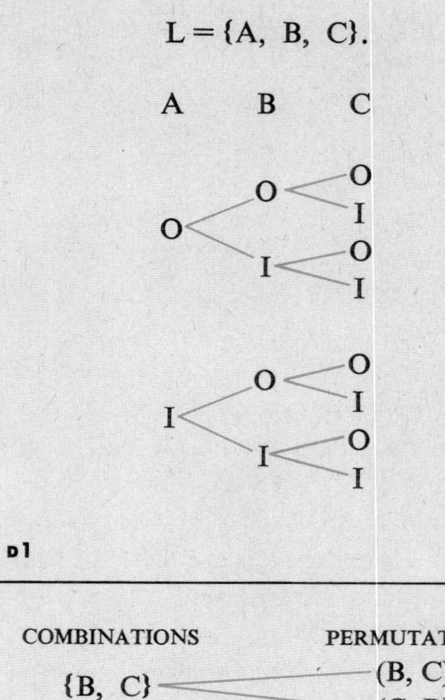

D1

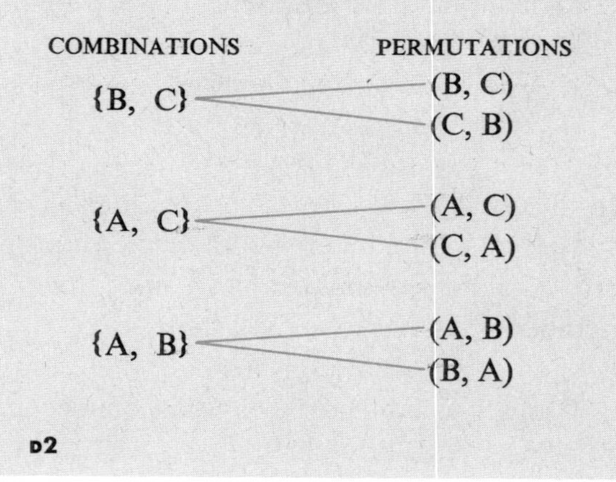

D2

E ? Study the column at the right in D2. (B, C) is one permutation of {B, C} taken 2 at a time. Is {B, C} the same combination as {C, B}? Is (B, C) the same permutation as (C, B)? Explain your answers.

F Which ordered pairs expressed in the column at the right in D2 are permutations of {A, C}? Which ordered pairs are permutations of {A, B}?

G For each 2-element combination named in D2, how do you know that there are 2 permutations of the elements taken 2 at a time? Use the fundamental counting property to explain your answer.

H How do you know that there are 3×2, or 6, permutations of the elements of {A, B, C} taken 2 at a time? Is each of these permutations expressed at the right in D2?

From exercises D through H, you can see that the product of the number of 2-element combinations of {A, B, C} and the number of permutations of each combination is the same as the total number of permutations of {A, B, C} taken 2 at a time.

The idea developed in the preceding exercises can be used to find the number of specific combinations of any finite set. For example, you can find the number of 3-element combinations, or 3-element subsets, of a set containing 7 elements.

A Now look at D3. Notice that set T is a combination of the 7 elements of S taken 3 at a time. How do you know that $3 \times 2 \times 1$ is the number of permutations of set T taken 3 at a time?

You will recall that a product whose factors are a given positive integer and every positive integer less than the given integer is called a factorial and can be expressed by a symbol such as 4! or 3!. Therefore, the number of permutations of T taken 3 at a time, which is $3 \times 2 \times 1$, can be expressed by the symbol 3!.

B Look again at D3. Are all the ordered triples that are permutations of {D, E, F} expressed in the display?

S = {D, E, F, G, H, I, J}.
T = {D, E, F}.

(D, E, F)	(E, D, F)	(F, D, E)
(D, F, E)	(E, F, D)	(F, E, D)

D3

A $C(7, 3) \times P(3, 3) = P(7, 3)$.

B $C(7, 3) = \dfrac{P(7, 3)}{P(3, 3)}$.

C $C(7, 3) = \dfrac{7 \times 6 \times 5}{3!}$.

D4

C Is $7 \times 6 \times 5$ the number of permutations of the 7 elements of S taken 3 at a time? Use the fundamental counting property to explain your answer.

Now look at sentence A in D4. You will recall that we can use the symbol C(7, 3) to refer to the number of combinations of the 7 elements of set S taken 3 at a time; we can use the symbol P(3, 3) to refer to the number of permutations of each 3-element combination of S taken 3 at a time; and we can use the symbol P(7, 3) to refer to the number of permutations of the 7 elements of set S taken 3 at a time.

D How do you know that statement A is true? How was B obtained from A?

E From exercise C, you know that P(7, 3) is equal to $7 \times 6 \times 5$. From exercise A, you know that P(3, 3) is equal to 3!. How was statement C obtained from B?

F How can you obtain $C(7, 3) = 35$ from statement C?

G How many 3-element combinations can be formed from set S, expressed in D3?

H Now look at D5. You can use statement D to find the number of 4-element combinations that can be formed from a set of 6 elements. Explain how each of statements E and F was obtained.

I How many 4-element combinations can be formed from a set that contains 6 elements? A set that has 6 elements has how many 4-element subsets?

Now you will develop formulas for finding the number of combinations and the number of permutations of a given set.

Condition G, expressed in D6, is the permutation formula that you used in *Book 2*. The universe for each variable is I_p. $P(n, m)$ represents the number of permutations of n different objects taken m at a time. n represents the number of different objects. m represents the number of objects in each permutation. From the formula, you know that $P(n, m)$ is the product of exactly m factors. Each factor is one less than the preceding factor. The number of factors is less than or equal to n.

A To find the number of permutations of 8 different objects taken 5 at a time, what replacement do you make for n in formula G? What replacement do you make for m? Do you then obtain statement H, expressed in D6?

B What is a standard name of P(8, 5)?

Think again about the permutation formula expressed in D6. Suppose that there are two factors involved. Then 1 is the number that is subtracted from n to obtain the least factor. Suppose that there are 3 factors involved. Then 2 is the number that is subtracted from n to obtain the least factor.

If you continue the procedure described above, you will note that, in each case, the least factor is obtained by subtracting 1 less than the number of factors from n. Thus, in

D $C(6, 4) \times P(4, 4) = P(6, 4)$.

E $C(6, 4) = \frac{P(6, 4)}{P(4, 4)}$.

F $C(6, 4) = \frac{6 \times 5 \times 4 \times 3}{4!}$.

D5

G $P(n, m) = n(n-1)(n-2)\ldots(m \text{ factors})$.

H $P(8, 5) = 8 \times 7 \times 6 \times 5 \times 4$.

D6

I $P(n, m) = n(n-1)(n-2)\ldots(n-m+1)$.

J $(n-m)! = (n-m)(n-m-1)(n-m-2)\ldots(3)(2)(1)$.

K $P(n, m) = \frac{[n(n-1)(n-2)\ldots(n-m+1)](n-m)!}{(n-m)!}$.

L $P(n, m) = \frac{n!}{(n-m)!}$.

D7

each case, $n-(m-1)$, or $n-m+1$, represents the least factor. Therefore, condition I, expressed in D7, is the same formula as condition G.

C Think about condition I. Does $n-m$ represent the positive integer that is one less than $n-m+1$? Is $(n-m)-1$ one less than $n-m$? Is $(n-m)-2$ one less than $(n-m)-1$?

Now read sentence J in D7. For the moment, suppose that $(n-m)!$ represents the factorial of any $n-m$ where $n>m$. The factors in the right side of the condition are all the positive integers that are less than or equal to $n-m$.

D ? How was condition K obtained from I? What property of quotients justifies K?

Study the expression that is the dividend in the right side of condition K. Notice that $[n(n-1)(n-2)\ldots(n-m+1)]$ is the product of n and every positive integer that is less than n but greater than $n-m$. Notice also that $(n-m)!$ is the product of $n-m$ and every positive integer less than $n-m$. Therefore, the dividend is the product of n and every positive integer less than n.

E ? How was condition L obtained from condition K?

You can use condition L in place of condition I as a formula for finding the number of permutations of n different objects taken m at a time.

F To find the number of permutations of 8 different objects taken 3 at a time, what replacements do you make for n and m in formula L? Show how you can obtain 336 for P(8, 3).

G Formula L can also be used when $m=n$. For example, suppose that you want to find the number of permutations of 5 different objects taken 5 at a time. Look at D8. How can you obtain statement M from formula L?

H How was statement N obtained from M?

M $$\mathrm{P}(5, 5)=\frac{5!}{(5-5)!}.$$

N $$\mathrm{P}(5, 5)=\frac{5!}{0!}.$$

D8

L $$P(n, m)=\frac{n!}{(n-m)!}.$$

D9

> **zero factorial.** Zero factorial is equal to 1.

Before you can understand statement N, you must know the meaning of the symbol expressed at the right. You can read this symbol "zero factorial."

0!

We want to define 0! in such a way that formula L, expressed in D7, can be used when $m=n$.

Look again at sentence N in D8. From your work earlier in this lesson, you know that the number of permutations of 5 different objects taken 5 at a time is 5!. This suggests that we should define 0! in such a way that $\frac{5!}{0!}=5!$.

We know that, if a is a non-zero number, then 1 is the only number by which we can divide a to obtain a. Therefore, if we want $\frac{5!}{0!}=5!$ to be a true statement, then 0! must be equal to 1.

I ? Formula L is repeated in D9. If $m=n$, how can $P(n, m)=n!$ be obtained from formula L?

J How many permutations can be formed from 4 different objects taken 4 at a time?

O $C(n, m) = \dfrac{P(n, m)}{P(m, m)}.$

P $C(n, m) = \dfrac{n!}{(n-m)!\,m!}.$

D10

Condition O, expressed in D10, is the combination formula that you used in *Book 2.* Notice that this formula is the idea concerning combinations that you developed in the first part of this lesson. $C(n, m)$ represents the number of m-element combinations that can be formed from a set of n elements. $P(n, m)$ represents the number of permutations of n elements taken m at a time. $P(m, m)$ represents the number of permutations of each m-element combination taken m at a time. The universe for n and m is I_p.

K To obtain condition P from O, why can you replace $P(n, m)$ by $\dfrac{n!}{(n-m)!}$? Why can you replace $P(m, m)$ by $m!$?

Condition P is also a formula for finding the number of m-element combinations of the n elements in a given set.

L Suppose that you want to find the number of 3-element combinations of a set of 5 elements. What replacements do you make for n and m in formula P?

M Is $C(5, 3) = \dfrac{5!}{(2!)3!}$? How many 3-element combinations can be formed from a set of 5 elements?

N ? Think again about formula P. If $m = n$, how do you obtain $C(m, m) = \dfrac{m!}{(m-m)!\,m!}$ from formula P? For each m, is $C(m, m) = 1$?

Now that 0! has been defined, it is possible to extend the universe for the variables in formula P. Until now, we have restricted this universe to the set of positive integers. If we extend the universe to include zero, we can consider such combinations as C(5, 0) and C(0, 0).

O ? To find C(5, 0), what replacements do you make for n and m in formula P? How can you obtain $C(5, 0) = 1$? A 5-element set has how many empty subsets?

P ? To find C(0, 0), what replacements do you make for n and m in formula P? How can you obtain $C(0, 0) = 1$? The empty set has how many empty subsets?

In this lesson you used permutations and combinations to find the number of specific subsets, or combinations, that can be formed from a given set. You also studied permutation and combination formulas.

On your own

For each of exercises 1 through 9, give a standard name of the number expressed.

1 6!	**4** C(3, 3)	**7** 4!
2 P(4, 2)	**5** 7!	**8** C(5, 1)
3 C(8, 4)	**6** P(7, 2)	**9** P(6, 6)

Use set V, tabulated below, in connection with exercises 10 through 15.

$$V = \{A, B, C, D, E, F\}.$$

10 Set V has how many subsets?

11 Find the number of permutations of the elements of V taken 5 at a time.

12 Find the number of permutations of V taken 2 at a time.

13 Find the number of permutations of V taken 4 at a time.

14 Find the number of 5-element combinations of V.

15 Find the number of 6-element combinations of V.

A set is described in each of exercises 16 through 19. For each exercise, first tabulate the set. Next tell how many subsets it has. Then find the number of 3-element subsets of the set.

16 The set of integers that are greater than -11 and less than -5

17 The set of all positive integers that are factors of 10

18 The set of odd numbers each of which is greater than 20 and less than 26

19 The set of perfect squares each of which is less than 40

KEEPING SKILLFUL

For each of exercises 1 through 10, find the sum of the numbers named.

1 $-41.6, -85.3$

2 $-25\frac{1}{2}, 17\frac{9}{10}$

3 $12\frac{5}{8}, -3\frac{3}{10}$

4 $630, 450, -850$

5 $17\frac{2}{3}, 19\frac{4}{5}, 20\frac{1}{4}$

6 $-18\frac{1}{3}, 8\frac{3}{4}, -10\frac{1}{3}$

7 $\frac{1}{8}, \frac{1}{5}, -\frac{3}{10}, -\frac{17}{20}$

8 $.16, .625, .175$

9 $24.6, 29.99, -200$

10 $-750, -.85, -62$

Find the difference of the numbers named in each of exercises 11 through 18. The first number named is the minuend.

11 $8.5, 19.7$

12 $-6000, 24\frac{1}{3}$

13 $200.6, 78.99$

14 $12\frac{1}{2}, -9\frac{3}{4}$

15 $-24\frac{3}{8}, 162\frac{1}{3}$

16 $75.99, -24.5$

17 $-\frac{4}{17}, \frac{5}{34}$

18 $-\frac{1}{20}, -1\frac{4}{5}$

Find the product of the numbers named in each of exercises 19 through 26.

19 $75.9, -.94$

20 $1\frac{4}{5}, 5$

21 $-.625, -.9$

22 $-250, 65.2$

23 $10\frac{2}{3}, 20\frac{1}{4}, 1\frac{1}{2}$

24 $-25\frac{1}{2}, -3\frac{1}{17}, 4$

25 $.95, .6, .9$

26 $-17\frac{1}{3}, -6\frac{7}{13}, -1\frac{1}{4}$

Find the quotient of the numbers named in each of exercises 27 through 34. The first number named is the dividend.

27 $-60, -\frac{5}{13}$

28 $-12\frac{4}{5}, 5\frac{1}{3}$

29 $4\frac{15}{16}, \frac{13}{20}$

30 $666, -18$

31 $3120, 130$

32 $-620, 5.4$ (Tenths)

33 $75.2, -.07$ (Tenths)

34 $-20.46, -.95$ (Hundredths)

25 | **297** Exploring ideas

Pascal's triangle

In the last lesson you studied combination and permutation formulas. In this lesson you will observe a pattern obtained from the use of the formula for $C(n, m)$.

A Set S is tabulated in D1. Tabulate each 1-element subset of S.

B How many 1-element subsets of S are there? For each selection of 1 element from S, how many elements are left?

If 1 element has been selected from 5 elements, then a selection of 4 elements has also been made. Therefore, each time that you selected 1 element from S, you actually made 2 selections: the 1 element and the remaining 4 elements. This suggests that C(5, 1) should be equal to C(5, 4).

C Now use the formula $C(n, m) = \frac{n!}{(n-m)!\,m!}$ to find C(5, 1) and C(5, 4). How does the number of combinations of 5 elements taken 1 at a time compare with the number of combinations of 5 elements taken 4 at a time?

D Use the combination formula to find the number of 2-element subsets of S.

E ? Explain why, for each 2-element selection, you also made a 3-element selection.

F Find the number of 3-element subsets of S. How does C(5, 2) compare with C(5, 3)?

$$S = \{A, B, C, D, E\}.$$

D1

The preceding exercises indicate that the number of combinations of n elements taken m at a time is the same as the number of combinations of n elements taken $n - m$ at a time. This idea is expressed below as a theorem.

The universe for each variable is the set of non-negative integers. For each m *and* n, C(n, m) = C(n, n − m).

A proof of this theorem is given in D2. Step 1 can be obtained from the combination formula that you developed in lesson 296. The second step is justified by the fact that $n - (n - m) = m$. The commutative property of multiplication can be used to obtain the third step. The fourth step is the formula for $C(n, m)$. From steps 1 through 4 and the transitive property of equality, step 5 is obtained.

1 $C(n, n-m) = \dfrac{n!}{(n-(n-m))!\,(n-m)!}$.

2 $\dfrac{n!}{(n-(n-m))!\,(n-m)!} = \dfrac{n!}{m!\,(n-m)!}$.

3 $\dfrac{n!}{m!\,(n-m)!} = \dfrac{n!}{(n-m)!\,m!}$.

4 $\dfrac{n!}{(n-m)!\,m!} = C(n, m)$.

5 $C(n, m) = C(n, n-m)$.

D2

If you find $C(n, m)$ for various replacements of n and m and arrange the results in a table, you can discover an interesting pattern. The table in D3 gives the values of $C(n, m)$ that you obtain when you replace n and m by members of {0, 1, 2, 3, 4, 5}. For example, C(3, 1) is named by the second entry in the fourth row, and C(5, 0) is named by the first entry in the sixth row.

n \ m	0	1	2	3	4	5
0	1					
1	1	1				
2	1	2	1			
3	1	3	3	1		
4	1	4	6	4	1	
5	1	5	10	10	5	1

D3

Since each row in the table contains one more entry than the row above it, the table is a triangular arrangement. This arrangement is called *Pascal's triangle*. Blaise Pascal (blez pas kal′) was a seventeenth-century French mathematician who did some of the earliest work in probability theory.

A If $n = m$, what is $C(n, m)$? What is the last entry in each row of Pascal's triangle?

B For each n, what number is $C(n, 0)$? How is this shown in Pascal's triangle?

C Which entry in the sixth row names C(5, 1)? Which entry names C(5, 4)? Use the theorem that was developed earlier in this lesson to explain why the second and fifth entries in the sixth row are the same.

D Name two other entries that illustrate the theorem $C(n, m) = C(n, n-m)$.

E Locate the entries for C(2, 0) and C(2, 1). Which entry is directly below the entry for C(2, 1)? How is C(3, 1) related to the sum of C(2, 0) and C(2, 1)?

F Locate the entries for C(4, 1) and C(4, 2). Which entry is directly below the entry for C(4, 2)? How is C(5, 2) related to the sum of C(4, 1) and C(4, 2)?

G If the pattern suggested in exercises E and F holds for all the entries in Pascal's triangle, where should you find the entry that names the sum of C(3, 2) and C(3, 3)? Which entry is this?

From your answers to exercises E, F, and G, you know that the statements expressed in D4 are true.

H Study statement A. Suppose that $C(n, m)$ represents C(2, 1). Does $C(n, m-1)$ represent C(2, 0)? How can you represent C(3, 1)?

I Study statement B. If $C(n, m)$ represents C(4, 2), which combination is represented by $C(n, m-1)$? By $C(n+1, m)$?

J How can statement C be represented if C(3, 3) is represented by $C(n, m)$?

Exercises E through J suggest the theorem that is expressed below.

The universe for each variable is the set of non-negative integers. For each m *and* n, C(n, m − *1*) + C(n, m) = C(n + *1*, m).

This theorem can help you form Pascal's triangle. Notice that $C(n, m-1)$ and $C(n, m)$ can represent the numbers named by any two adjacent entries in a row of the triangle. The entry for $C(n+1, m)$, which is directly below the second of the two adjacent entries, can be found by adding the numbers named by the two adjacent entries.

The theorem just expressed can be developed in another way. Notice that it concerns combinations of a set containing n elements and combinations of a set containing $n+1$ elements.

If you think of set W, tabulated in D5, as a set containing n elements, then set T, which contains the extra element D, is a set containing $n+1$ elements. In this case, $n=3$.

K How do you know that all the 2-element subsets of T are tabulated in D5? Use C(4, 2) to explain your answer.

A C(2, 0) + C(2, 1) = C(3, 1).
B C(4, 1) + C(4, 2) = C(5, 2).
C C(3, 2) + C(3, 3) = C(4, 3).

D4

W = {A, B, C}. T = {A, B, C, D}.

{A, D}	{B, D}	{C, D}
{A, B}	{A, C}	{B, C}

D5

Notice that the 2-element subsets of T can be divided into two groups. Three of the subsets contain D; the other three subsets do not contain D. Now you will see that the subsets that contain D correspond to the 1-element subsets of set W. The subsets that do not contain D correspond to the 2-element subsets of set W.

L How do you know that {A}, {B}, and {C} are all the 1-element subsets of W? Which subset tabulated in D5 is {A} ∪ {D}? Which is {B} ∪ {D}? Which is {C} ∪ {D}?

M Is each 2-element subset of T that contains D the same as the union of {D} and a 1-element subset of W?

N Tabulate all the 2-element subsets of W. These subsets are the same as which 2-element subsets of T?

Exercises K through N show that there are six 2-element subsets of T. Three of these subsets are the 1-element subsets of W "with D attached." The other three are the 2-element subsets of W. Hence, C(3, 1) + C(3, 2) is equal to C(4, 2). Notice that this agrees with the theorem $C(n, m-1) + C(n, m) = C(n+1, m)$.

Now you can use the theorems developed in this lesson to extend Pascal's triangle. Notice

n \ m	0	1	2	3	4	5	6	7
0	1							
1	1	1						
2	1	2	1					
3	1	3	3	1				
4	1	4	6	4	1			
5	1	5	10	10	5	1		
6								
7								

D6

that the triangle given in D6 includes 6 and 7 as replacements for n and m in $C(n, m)$. The following exercises will help you complete this triangle.

A Copy the triangle given in D6. What should be the first entry in the seventh row of Pascal's triangle? How many entries should be in this row?

B What are the first two entries in the sixth row? What sum can you use to obtain the second entry in the seventh row?

C What two entries in the sixth row can be used to find the third entry in the seventh row? What is the third entry in the seventh row?

D What two entries can be used to find the fourth entry in the seventh row? What is the fourth entry in the seventh row?

E The fifth entry in the seventh row is the entry for C(6, 4). What entry did you make for C(6, 2)?

You know that C(6, 4) = C(6, 2) by the theorem which states that $C(n, m)$ is equal to $C(n, n - m)$. Thus, since you have already found that C(6, 2) = 15 by adding the numbers named by the entries for C(5, 1) and C(5, 2), it is not necessary to add C(5, 3) and C(5, 4) to find the entry for C(6, 4). When you have found each $C(n, m)$ entry, you have also found each $C(n, n - m)$ entry in Pascal's triangle.

F The sixth entry in the seventh row of Pascal's triangle names C(6, 5). This entry is the same as which other entry in the same row?

G How many entries should be in the eighth row of Pascal's triangle?

H What is the first entry in the eighth row? How do you know that the first and eighth entries are the same?

I What entries in the seventh row will help you find the second entry in the eighth row? What is the second entry in the eighth row? How do you know that the seventh entry is the same as the second entry?

J What two entries can be used to find the entry for C(7, 2)? What is this entry? What other entry in the eighth row is the same as the entry for C(7, 2)?

K What is the entry for C(7, 3)? Explain why the entry for C(7, 4) is the same as the entry for C(7, 3).

You know that the set of permissible replacements for n and m in $C(n, m)$ is the set of non-negative integers. You also know that the set of non-negative integers is an infinite set. Therefore, Pascal's triangle has infinitely many entries.

In this lesson you studied two theorems that help you understand the pattern of Pascal's triangle.

On your own

1 Make a Pascal's triangle. Use the members of {0, 1, 2, . . . , 12} as replacements for n and m in $C(n, m)$.

For each of exercises 2 through 13, use the triangle that you made for exercise 1 to determine the value of $C(n, m)$.

2 C(3, 2)	**6** C(12, 4)	**10** C(7, 2)
3 C(10, 6)	**7** C(9, 6)	**11** C(10, 7)
4 C(8, 3)	**8** C(11, 8)	**12** C(6, 4)
5 C(5, 3)	**9** C(4, 2)	**13** C(12, 10)

14 For each row of the triangle that you made for exercise 1, find the sum of the numbers named by the entries. How is the sum of the numbers named in each row related to the sum of the numbers named in the preceding row?

15 Give a proof of the theorem that states that $C(n, m-1) + C(n, m) = C(n+1, m)$. The universe for each variable is the set of nonnegative integers. First use the combination formula to find an expression for $C(n+1, m)$, for $C(n, m-1)$, and for $C(n, m)$.

KEEPING SKILLFUL

For each of exercises 1 through 9, first derive an equivalent system that will help you determine the solution set of the system expressed. Then tabulate the set of (x, y) that is the solution set of the given system.

1 $2x + 3y = 16$
$x + y + 10 = 17.$

2 $x + 3y = 0$
$x - y = 8.$

3 $2x + \frac{1}{2}y = 3$
$y = 4x.$

4 $\frac{1}{2}x + \frac{1}{2}y = 11$
$x - y = -2.$

5 $.2x + .4y = 0$
$10x + .5y - 78 = 0.$

6 $15x = 10y$
$12x - 6y = 1.$

7 $\frac{1}{5}x - \frac{1}{5}y = 2$
$\frac{1}{8}x + \frac{1}{3}y = 15.$

8 $x = -.5y$
$y - x + 50 = -250.$

9 $5(x + 3) = 10y$
$10(x - 1) = 16 + 4(y - 2).$

The binomial theorem

In lesson 247 you learned how to find the product of $a + b$ and $a + b$. In other words, you learned how to find the second power of a binomial. In this lesson you will use Pascal's triangle to develop a convenient method of finding such powers as $(a+b)^3$ and $(a+b)^7$.

A We will assume that $a + b \neq 0$. What is $(a+b)^0$? What is $(a+b)^1$? What is $(a+b)^2$?

B Is $(a+b)^3 = (a+b)(a^2 + 2ab + b^2)$? What is the product of $a + b$ and $a^2 + 2ab + b^2$?

C In $(a+b)^{17}$, how many times is $a + b$ used as a factor? How could you find $(a+b)^{17}$?

To obtain $(a+b)^n$, where n is a positive integer greater than 2, you can use repeated multiplication. If you know $(a+b)^{n-1}$, you can also find $(a+b)^n$ by multiplying $(a+b)^{n-1}$ by $a + b$. However, this process soon becomes tedious. Now you will learn a much easier method.

The process of finding a power of a binomial is sometimes called *expanding the binomial*. We refer to $a^2 + 2ab + b^2$ as the *expansion* of $(a+b)^2$. Each expansion of $(a+b)^n$, where n is a member of {0, 1, 2, 3, 4}, is given in D1.

A $(a+b)^0 = 1.$
B $(a+b)^1 = a + b.$
C $(a+b)^2 = a^2 + 2ab + b^2.$
D $(a+b)^3 = a^3 + 3a^2b + 3ab^2 + b^3.$
E $(a+b)^4 = a^4 + 4a^3b + 6a^2b^2 + 4ab^3 + b^4.$

D1

D Study D1. The expansion of $(a+b)^1$ contains how many more terms than the expansion of $(a+b)^0$? Compare the number of terms in the expansion of $(a+b)^2$ with the number of terms in the expansion of $(a+b)^1$.

E For each expansion given in D1, does the expansion of $(a+b)^n$ contain $n+1$ terms?

Notice that 4 and a^3b are factors of the second term of the expansion of $(a+b)^4$. In such a term as $4a^3b$, the factor that is a number is often referred to as the *numerical coefficient*. Thus, in $4a^3b$, 4 is the numerical coefficient of a^3b. In such a term as a^4, since $a^4 = 1a^4$, the number 1 is considered to be the numerical coefficient. We will simply say "coefficient" when we mean "numerical coefficient."

F Look again at D1. What is the coefficient in the first term of the expansion of $(a+b)^3$? What is the coefficient in the last term?

G What are the coefficients in the first and last terms of each expansion given in D1?

Now you will see that the coefficients in the expansion of $(a+b)^n$ are related to the numbers named in Pascal's triangle. The first five rows of the triangle are given in D2.

H Notice that the coefficients of the terms in the expansion of $(a+b)^4$ are 1, 4, 6, 4, and 1, in that order. These same numbers are expressed in which row of Pascal's triangle?

I In the expansion of $(a+b)^4$, is C(4, 0) the coefficient of a^4? Is C(4, 1) the coefficient of a^3b? What entry in Pascal's triangle names the coefficient of a^2b^2 in the expansion of $(a+b)^4$?

J ? Is expression F, given in D3, the expansion of $(a+b)^4$? Explain your answer.

K To see the pattern of the terms in the expansion of $(a+b)^4$, it is helpful to obtain expression G from expression F. Why is expression G also the expansion of $(a+b)^4$?

Notice the following features of expression G. In each term, the sum of the exponents of a and b is 4. The exponent of a in the first term is 4; in each of the remaining terms, the exponent of a is 1 less than in the preceding term. The exponent of b in the first term is 0;

A $(a+b)^0 = 1.$

B $(a+b)^1 = a+b.$

C $(a+b)^2 = a^2 + 2ab + b^2.$

D $(a+b)^3 = a^3 + 3a^2b + 3ab^2 + b^3.$

E $(a+b)^4 = a^4 + 4a^3b + 6a^2b^2 + 4ab^3 + b^4.$

D1

n \ m	0	1	2	3	4
0	1				
1	1	1			
2	1	2	1		
3	1	3	3	1	
4	1	4	6	4	1

D2

F $C(4, 0)a^4 + C(4, 1)a^3b + C(4, 2)a^2b^2 + C(4, 3)ab^3 + C(4, 4)b^4$

G $C(4, 0)a^4b^0 + C(4, 1)a^3b^1 + C(4, 2)a^2b^2 + C(4, 3)a^1b^3 + C(4, 4)a^0b^4$

D3

H $C(3, 0)a^3b^0 + C(3, 1)a^2b^1 + C(3, 2)ab^2 + C(3, 3)a^0b^3$

D4

$(a+b)(a+b)(a+b)$

a	a	a	aaa
		b	aab
	b	a	aba
		b	abb
b	a	a	baa
		b	bab
	b	a	bba
		b	bbb

D5

in each of the remaining terms, the exponent of b is 1 greater than in the preceding term.

Notice that the exponent of b in each term is the same as the replacement for m in $C(n, m)$. Notice also that the replacement for n in each term is 4.

From the observations just made, and from studying expression G, you can develop a general term for the expansion of $(a+b)^4$. That is, you can develop a term that will represent any term in the expansion. The coefficient of each term can be represented by $C(4, m)$, where the replacement for m is 1 less than the number of the term. For each term, the exponent of b is also 1 less than the number of the term. Therefore, m can represent the exponent of b. Since 4 is the sum of the exponents of a and b in each term, the exponent of a can be represented by $4-m$.

The general term for the expansion of $(a+b)^4$ is $C(4, m)a^{4-m}b^m$. To obtain all the terms in the expansion of $(a+b)^4$, you can replace m in $C(4, m)a^{4-m}b^m$ by each member of $\{0, 1, 2, 3, 4\}$.

L ? To obtain the third term in the expansion of $(a+b)^4$, which member of $\{0, 1, 2, 3, 4\}$ would you use as a replacement for m in the general term? Explain your answer.

M Look at D1 and D2 again. How do the coefficients in the expansion of $(a+b)^3$ compare with $C(3, 0)$, $C(3, 1)$, $C(3, 2)$, and $C(3, 3)$?

N ? Expression H, given in D4, is the expansion of $(a+b)^n$ for what replacement of n?

O ? What is the general term for the expansion of $(a+b)^3$?

Now you will see why the coefficients in the expansion of a binomial are related to the combinations named in Pascal's triangle.

To find $(a+b)^2$, you can first use the distributive property to obtain the expression $a(a+b)+b(a+b)$ from $(a+b)(a+b)$. You can then obtain $aa+ab+ba+bb$. Notice that you obtain the four terms in the product of $a+b$ and $a+b$ by multiplying each term of the first $a+b$ by each term of the second $a+b$.

A To find $(a+b)^3$, why can you multiply each term in $aa+ab+ba+bb$ by each term in $a+b$? Name the eight terms that you obtain.

The diagram in D5 shows how the eight terms that you just named are obtained from the three factors of $(a+b)(a+b)(a+b)$. The diagram shows, for example, that the term aaa is obtained by multiplying an a from the first $a+b$ by an a from the second $a+b$. This product is then multiplied by an a from the third $a+b$.

B Explain how the term baa is obtained from the three factors of $(a+b)(a+b)(a+b)$.

C How many of the eight terms named in D5 contain three a's? How many contain three

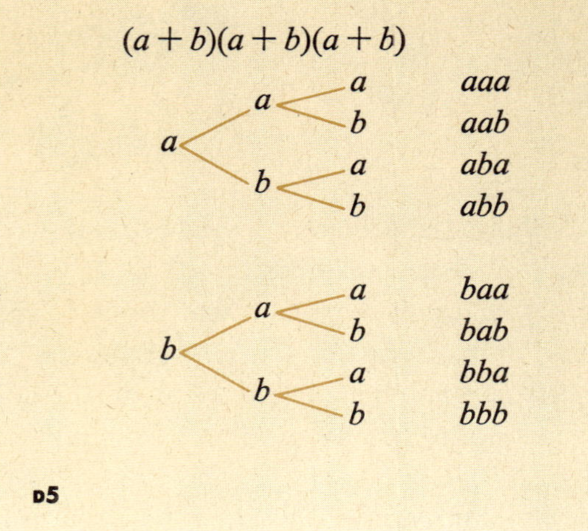

b's? Is 1 the coefficient of a^3 and of b^3 in the expansion of $(a+b)^3$?

D How many terms contain two a's and one b? Why does a product of two a's and one b occur in C(3, 1) ways? Why is 3 the coefficient of a^2b in the expansion of $(a+b)^3$?

E How many terms named in D5 contain one a and two b's? Why does a product of one a and two b's occur in C(3, 2) ways?

F Is C(3, 2) = C(3, 1)? Explain why the coefficient of ab^2 is the same as the coefficient of a^2b in the expansion of $(a+b)^3$.

You have just seen why the coefficients in the expansion of $(a+b)^3$ are related to the combinations named in Pascal's triangle. Since there is only one way of obtaining aaa from the factors of $(a+b)(a+b)(a+b)$, the coefficient of a^3 is 1. The coefficient of b^3 is 1 for a similar reason. The product a^2b can be obtained in three ways: as aab, as aba, or as baa. Thus, the coefficient of a^2b in the expansion of $(a+b)^3$ is 3. The coefficient of ab^2 is also 3, since the product ab^2 can be obtained in three ways: as abb, as bab, or as bba.

G In the expansion of $(a+b)^4$, the coefficient of a^2b^2 is 6, or C(4, 2). Explain why a^2b^2 can be obtained in C(4, 2) ways from the factors of $(a+b)(a+b)(a+b)(a+b)$.

Your work with specific expansions, such as $(a+b)^3$ and $(a+b)^4$, can help you develop a general term for the expansion of $(a+b)^n$, where n is any non-negative integer.

Earlier in this lesson, you discovered that you can obtain the terms in the expansion of $(a+b)^4$ by replacing m in $C(4, m)a^{4-m}b^m$ by each member of {0, 1, 2, 3, 4}. This suggests that $C(n, m)a^{n-m}b^m$ is the general term for the expansion of $(a+b)^n$. You can obtain the terms in the expansion by replacing m by each member of {0, 1, 2, . . ., n}.

A If $a+b$ is used as a factor n times, why can $a^{n-m}b^m$ be obtained in $C(n, m)$ ways? In the general term for the expansion of $(a+b)^n$, what is the coefficient of $a^{n-m}b^m$?

B Is $C(n, 0)a^{n-0}b^0$ the first term in the expansion of $(a+b)^n$? What is the second term?

The expansion of $(a+b)^n$ is given in the *binomial theorem*. This theorem, which we will accept without proof, is expressed below.

The universe for n *is the set of non-negative integers. For each* a, b, *and* n, $(a+b)^n = C(n, 0)a^nb^0 + C(n, 1)a^{n-1}b^1 + C(n, 2)a^{n-2}b^2 + \ldots + C(n, m)a^{n-m}b^m + \ldots + C(n, n)a^0b^n$.

The binomial theorem can help you expand any non-negative integral power of a binomial.

C Suppose that you want to find the expansion of $(a+b)^6$. What replacement should you make for n in the binomial theorem? How many terms are contained in the expansion of $(a+b)^6$?

D What are the first seven terms of the expansion of $(a+b)^n$? Use these seven terms to find $(a+b)^6$.

The binomial theorem can also help you expand powers of binomials other than $(a+b)$.

E How many terms are contained in the expansion of $(2x+3y)^4$? What replacements

1 $C(n, 0)a^nb^0 + C(n, 1)a^{n-1}b^1 + C(n, 2)a^{n-2}b^2 + C(n, 3)a^{n-3}b^3 + C(n, 4)a^{n-4}b^4$

2 $C(4, 0)(2x)^4 + C(4, 1)(2x)^3(3y) + C(4, 2)(2x)^2(3y)^2 + C(4, 3)(2x)(3y)^3 + C(4, 4)(3y)^4$

3 $(1)(16x^4) + (4)(8x^3)(3y) + (6)(4x^2)(9y^2) + (4)(2x)(27y^3) + (1)(81y^4)$

4 $16x^4 + 96x^3y + 216x^2y^2 + 216xy^3 + 81y^4$

D6

must you make for a and b in the first five terms of the binomial theorem to help you obtain $(2x + 3y)^4$?

F The steps for obtaining the expansion of $(2x + 3y)^4$ are given in D6. The first five terms of the expansion of $(a + b)^n$ are given in step 1. What replacements were made for a, b, and n to obtain step 2? Justify steps 3 and 4.

Now you will expand $(x - 2y)^5$. To use the binomial theorem, you must consider $(x - 2y)^5$ as $\big(x + (-2y)\big)^5$.

G How many terms are contained in the expansion of $\big(x + (-2y)\big)^5$?

H What replacements must you make for a, b, and n in the first six terms of the expansion of $(a + b)^n$?

I What is the expansion of $(x - 2y)^5$?

J Suppose you want to find the ninth term in the expansion of $(a + b)^{12}$. What replacements must you make for n and m in $C(n, m)$ to determine the coefficient of this term? What is the exponent of a in this term? What is the exponent of b?

By replacing n by 12 and m by 8 in $C(n, m)a^{n-m}b^m$, you obtain $C(12, 8)a^4b^8$ for the ninth term in the expansion of $(a + b)^{12}$. Now you must find $C(12, 8)$.

K By what property do you know that $C(12, 8)$ is equal to $C(12, 4)$?

L What is the coefficient of the ninth term in the expansion of $(a + b)^{12}$? What other term in the expansion of $(a + b)^{12}$ has the same coefficient?

M What is the ninth term in the expansion of $(a + b)^{12}$?

N Suppose you want to find the third term in the expansion of $(3x - 2y)^{10}$. What replacements should you make for n and m in the general term $C(n, m)a^{n-m}b^m$? What replacement should you make for a? For b?

O ? What is the third term in the expansion of $(3x - 2y)^{10}$?

In this lesson you learned to use the binomial theorem to expand any non-negative integral power of a binomial.

On your own

1 Using the members of $\{0, 1, 2, \ldots, 11\}$ as replacements for n and m in $C(n, m)$, make a Pascal's triangle.

For each of exercises 2 through 11, use the binomial theorem and Pascal's triangle to help you expand the given binomial.

2 $(a + b)^8$

3 $(3a + 4b)^3$

4 $(a - b)^5$

5 $(x^3 + 5y)^4$

6 $(x + 3)^{10}$

7 $(6x + 8y)^3$

8 $(2c - d^2)^6$

9 $(ax + by)^7$

10 $(2 - y)^9$

11 $(x^2 - y^3)^5$

12 Find the fifth term in the expansion of $(a - 3b)^9$.

13 Find the seventh term in the expansion of $(2x + y)^{10}$.

14 Is $999^5 = (1000 - 1)^5$? Use the binomial theorem to find a standard name of 999^5.

15 Find a standard name of 101^7 by using the binomial theorem.

SPECIAL CHALLENGE

An important method of mathematical proof depends upon certain properties of the set of positive integers.

A What is the least member of I_p?

B Let S be a subset of I_p. Suppose that $1 \in S$. What is the least member of S? How do you know that $S \neq \emptyset$?

C So far we know that S is not empty, but we do not know whether or not S contains any elements besides 1. Let k represent any positive integer. Suppose that $k \in S \Rightarrow k + 1 \in S$. How do you know that 2 is a member of S?

D Since 2 is an element of S, $2 + 1$, or 3, must be an element of S. How do you know that 4 is an element of S? That 5 is an element of S?

This reasoning could be continued indefinitely and tells us that $S = I_p$. In other words, every positive integer is an element of S. Notice that only two statements are necessary to assure us that a subset of I_p contains every positive integer. This is the *property of induction*, given below. S represents a subset of I_p.

$$\big((1 \in S) \wedge (k \in S \Rightarrow k + 1 \in S)\big) \Rightarrow S = I_p.$$

Study theorem 1 given in D1. This theorem tells you that, for each positive integer n, 5 divides $n^5 - n$. We will prove theorem 1 by using the property of induction.

E What is the value of $n^5 - n$ when $n = 1$? When $n = 2$? When $n = 3$?

F Remember, every positive integer is a factor of, or divides, zero. Thus, theorem 1 is true for $n = 1$. How do you know that theorem 1 is true for $n = 2$? For $n = 3$?

G Let set T consist of every positive integer for which theorem 1 is true. We already know that 1, 2, and 3 are elements of T. Show that $4 \in T$. Show that $7 \in T$. Show that $16 \in T$.

H Let k represent any member of T. How do you know that 5 divides $k^5 - k$?

THEOREM 1:
The universe for n is I_p. For each n, $5 \mid n^5 - n$.

THEOREM 2:
The universe for n is I_p. For each n, $1 + 3 + 5 + \ldots + (2n - 1) = n^2$.

THEOREM 3:
The universe for n is I_p. For each n,
$$1^3 + 2^3 + 3^3 + \ldots + n^3 = \frac{n^2}{4}(n + 1)^2.$$

THEOREM 4:
The universe for n is I_p. For each n, $\frac{1}{3}(n^3 + 2n) \in I_p$.

D1

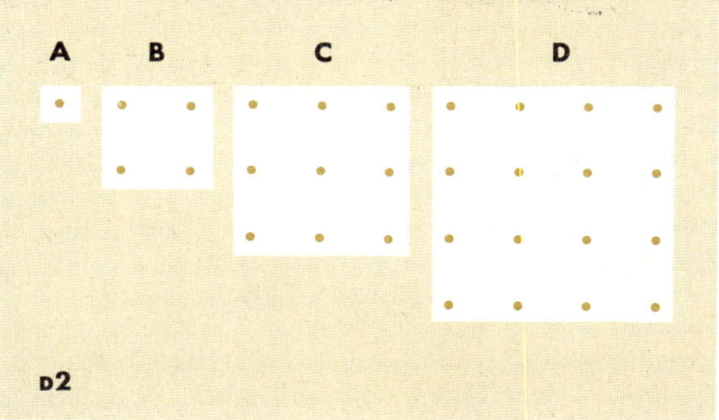

D2

I Now you will decide if $k + 1$ is also an element of T. What expression do you obtain when you replace n in $n^5 - n$ by $k + 1$?

J Use the binomial theorem to expand $(k + 1)^5$. From $(k + 1)^5 - (k + 1)$, show how to derive $(k^5 - k) + 5(k^4 + 2k^3 + 2k^2 + k)$.

K How do you know that 5 divides the expression $(k^5 - k) + 5(k^4 + 2k^3 + 2k^2 + k)$?

L How do you know that $k \in T \Rightarrow k + 1 \in T$? What property tells you that $T = I_p$?

By using the property of induction, we have proved that, for each positive integer n, 5 divides $n^5 - n$.

A $1+3+5+\ldots+(2k+1)=(k+1)^2$.

B $1+3+5+\ldots+(2k-1)+(2k+1)=(k+1)^2$.

C $1^3+2^3+3^3+\ldots+(k+1)^3=\dfrac{(k+1)^2}{4}(k+2)^2$.

D $1^3+2^3+3^3+\ldots+k^3+(k+1)^3=\dfrac{(k+1)^2}{4}(k+2)^2$.

D3

M Look at D2. Notice that the number of dots in each picture is a perfect square. The number of dots in picture A is 1^2; the number of dots in picture B is 2^2; and the number of dots in picture C is 3^2. The number of dots in picture D is what perfect square?

N How many dots were added to go from picture A to picture B? To go from picture B to picture C? To go from picture C to picture D? How many dots must be added to go from picture D to a picture with 5^2 dots?

From exercise N, you can see that $1=1^2$, that $1+3=2^2$, that $1+3+5=3^2$, and that $1+3+5+7=4^2$. This suggests that, if n represents any positive integer, then n^2 is equal to $1+3+5+\ldots+(2n-1)$. This idea is theorem 2, given in D1. The property of induction can be used to prove theorem 2.

O Let set R be the set of positive integers for which theorem 2 is true. Show that $1 \in R$.

P Although it is not necessary to show that any other particular integer is an element of R, you will understand the theorem better if you do so. Show that $2 \in R$. Show that $14 \in R$.

Assume that k is an element of R. That is, assume that $1+3+5+\ldots+(2k-1)=k^2$. Now you will decide if $k+1$ is also an element of R. This means that you must see if you obtain a true statement when you replace n by $k+1$ in theorem 2.

Q Show that, when you replace n by $k+1$ in theorem 2, you obtain statement A, expressed in D3. How do you know that statement B is the same as statement A? That the left side of statement B is equal to $k^2+(2k+1)$?

R Is $k^2+(2k+1)=(k+1)^2$? Do you obtain a true statement from theorem 2 when n is replaced by $k+1$? How do you know that $k \in R \Rightarrow k+1 \in R$?

S How do you know that theorem 2 is true?

T Study theorem 3, given in D1. Let M be the set of positive integers for which theorem 3 is true. Show that $1 \in M$. Show that $5 \in M$.

U Assume that $k \in M$. What true statement do you obtain from theorem 3 when you replace n by k?

Now you will show that $k+1$ is also an element of M. Statement C, given in D3, is the statement that you obtain from theorem 3 when you replace n by $k+1$. To show that $k+1$ is an element of M, you must show that statement C is true.

V How do you know that statement D is the same as statement C? How do you know that the left side of statement D is equal to the expression $\dfrac{k^2}{4}(k+1)^2+(k+1)^3$? Show that this expression is equal to $\dfrac{(k+1)^2}{4}(k+2)^2$. Is statement C true?

W Explain why $k \in M \Rightarrow k+1 \in M$. How do you know that theorem 3 is true?

X Prove theorem 4, given in D1, by using the property of induction.

APPLYING MATHEMATICS

For each problem, first give the basic condition. Next, develop a system of conditions whose solution set is the domain of the function determined by the basic condition. Then make a graph of the domain. Finally, give the answer to the problem.

1 A clothing manufacturer plans to produce shorts and slacks. He can sell a pair of shorts at a profit of \$2, and he can sell a pair of slacks at a profit of \$5. The shorts and the slacks require work by two machines. Each of these machines is available 240 minutes per day at most. Each pair of shorts requires 10 minutes of work by machine A and 6 minutes of work by machine B; each pair of slacks requires 6 minutes of work by machine A and 10 minutes of work by machine B. How many pairs of shorts and how many pairs of slacks should the manufacturer produce per day to maximize his profit? Assume that the manufacturer will be able to sell as many pairs of shorts and slacks as he is able to produce.

2 A toy company wishes to sponsor a weekly puppet show on television. Each minute of commercial time costs \$100, and each minute of the puppet show costs \$125. The toy company wants to sponsor at most 45 minutes per week and they insist on at least 6 minutes of commercial time. The television network insists that the commercial time be less than $\frac{1}{5}$ of the time for the puppet show. To minimize the cost, how many minutes of commercial time and how many minutes of puppet-show time should the toy company sponsor?

3 A manufacturer of bolts has received a rush order for at least 4000 bolts to be picked up at the end of the day. Each of the 2 machines that can make this kind of bolt will be available for at most 60 minutes. Machine A can make 80 bolts per minute at a cost of $\frac{1}{2}$ cent per bolt; machine B can make 66 bolts per minute at a cost of $\frac{1}{3}$ cent per bolt. For how many minutes should the manufacturer use each machine if he wants to make the bolts at the minimum cost?

4 Bill and Andy plan to make and sell two kinds of toys. Toy A requires 1 spool, 1 wheel, 13 eyelets, and 9 inches of doweling. Toy B requires 8 spools, 2 wheels, 16 eyelets, and 5 inches of doweling. The boys have available 128 spools, 38 wheels, 384 eyelets, and 225 inches of doweling. They plan to sell toy A for \$.20 and toy B for \$.80. They know that they will be able to sell every toy that they make. How many toys of each kind should Bill and Andy make to receive a maximum profit? Disregard the cost of materials and assume that there is no waste in cutting the doweling.

KEEPING SKILLFUL

For each of exercises 1 through 8, find the product.

1 $(3x^3)(4x^2)(10xy)$

2 $25x(x^2 - 16x)$

3 $2(x - 4)(3x + 1)$

4 $15y^2(x^2y - xy - 20)$

5 $4(x^2 - 8)(x^2 + 8)$

6 $(5y - 3)(12y + 1)$

7 $\frac{3}{xy} \cdot \frac{5x^2y^2}{21} \cdot \frac{15}{xy}$

8 $\frac{3y^2}{x-5} \cdot \frac{x^2 - 25}{x+1} \cdot \frac{x^2 - 3x - 4}{y}$

For each of exercises 9 through 15, find the quotient.

9 $\frac{20a}{3x^2y} \div \frac{16a^2}{12xy^3}$

10 $\frac{x^3y^3}{a+4} \div xy$

11 $\frac{25a^2}{16y} \div \frac{5a}{4xy}$

12 $\frac{1}{x^2 - y^2} \div \frac{3}{x - y}$

13 $\frac{15x - 5}{2a} \div \frac{3x - 1}{4a^2}$

14 $\frac{18a^2}{35x^3y^3z} \div \frac{9a}{5x^2y^2}$

15 $\frac{x^2 - 10x + 21}{x^2 - 16} \div \frac{x^2 - 6x - 7}{x + 4}$

CHECKING UP

If you have trouble with this test, you can find help in lessons 295 through 298.

Test 272

Tell what words or symbols best complete the following exercises.

1 The symbol ~~~ refers to the number of combinations of 8 elements taken 2 at a time.

2 $a+b \neq 0$. The expansion of $(a+b)^0$ is ~~~.

3 Any proper subset of {Jack, Bill, Dick} contains fewer than ~~~ members.

4 The numerical coefficient in $12ax^3$ is ~~~.

5 A list of subsets of {a, b, c} includes {a}, {b}, {c}, {a, b}, {a, c}, {b, c}, ~~~, and the empty set.

6 The third term in the expansion of $(3x - y)^5$ is ~~~.

7 There are ~~~ permutations of the elements of {pencil, pen, paper, eraser, ruler} taken 2 at a time.

8 The expansion of $(a+b)^n$ contains ~~~ terms.

9 The coefficient in the seventh term of the expansion of $(x+y)^{11}$ is ~~~.

10 A 6-element set has ~~~ subsets.

11 The number of combinations of 9 elements taken 2 at a time is the same as the number of combinations of 9 elements taken ~~~ at a time.

12 There are ~~~ combinations of the elements of {A, B, C, D} taken 2 at a time.

13 There are ~~~ combinations of 9 objects taken 4 at a time.

14 A given set has 16 subsets. The given set has ~~~ members.

15 The number of 2-element subsets of set T is 55. Set T has ~~~ members.

16 In the fifth row of Pascal's triangle, the third entry is the numeral ~~~.

25 | 299 Exploring ideas

Probability

You will recall that in *Book 2* you studied several lessons concerning the "measure of chance," or the probability, of an event. You learned about sample spaces, events, mutually exclusive events, and independent events.

In this lesson you are going to review some ideas related to probability. Then, in the next two lessons, you will see how certain probabilities are related to the expansion of a binomial.

A Read the problem in D1. How many outcomes are possible when only the red die is rolled? Is each outcome equally likely?

B How many outcomes are possible when only the green die is rolled? Is each of these outcomes equally likely?

Notice that the experiment described in D1 concerns rolling *both* dice. Therefore, you can use an ordered pair of numbers to represent each possible outcome of this experiment. One component of each ordered pair can represent an outcome of rolling the red die. The other

> Two dice, a red one and a green one, are rolled. Each die has a different number of spots (from 1 through 6) on each face. If the dice are rolled once, what is the probability that 9 will be the sum of the numbers indicated on the dice?
>
> **D1**

component can represent an outcome of rolling the green die.

C If R is the set of all 6 possible outcomes of rolling the red die and G the set of all 6 possible outcomes of rolling the green die, is $R \times G$ a sample space of the experiment that involves rolling both dice? How many elements are contained in the sample space? Is each element equally likely?

> REMINDER
>
> A sample space of an experiment is a set whose elements are all possible outcomes of the experiment. The elements of the sample space are sample points.
>
> *See lesson 201, page 454, Book 2.*

The ordered pairs that are elements of $R \times G$ are given in the chart in D2. The first component of each ordered pair refers to a number of spots on the red die; the second component refers to a number of spots on the green die.

D Use the letter F to name the set of favorable outcomes of the experiment. A favorable outcome in this case is obtaining a sum of 9. Use r as a variable for the number indicated on the red die; use g as a variable for the number indicated on the green die. The universe for (r, g) is $R \times G$. Give a standard description of F.

E Use the chart in D2 to help you tabulate $\{(r, g) \mid r + g = 9\}$.

You will recall from *Book 2* that a subset of a sample space of an experiment is an event. Therefore, $\{(r, g) \mid r + g = 9\}$ is an event.

F How many sample points are contained in event F?

Now that we know the number of sample points in the event as well as the number of sample points in the sample space, we can find the probability of the event. You will recall that we can use the symbol P(F) to refer to the probability of event F.

In *Book 2* you used the formula $P(M) = \frac{m}{n}$ to determine the probability of an event when all the elements in the sample space are equally

$r \backslash g$	1	2	3	4	5	6
1	(1, 1)	(1, 2)	(1, 3)	(1, 4)	(1, 5)	(1, 6)
2	(2, 1)	(2, 2)	(2, 3)	(2, 4)	(2, 5)	(2, 6)
3	(3, 1)	(3, 2)	(3, 3)	(3, 4)	(3, 5)	(3, 6)
4	(4, 1)	(4, 2)	(4, 3)	(4, 4)	(4, 5)	(4, 6)
5	(5, 1)	(5, 2)	(5, 3)	(5, 4)	(5, 5)	(5, 6)
6	(6, 1)	(6, 2)	(6, 3)	(6, 4)	(6, 5)	(6, 6)

D2

A $X = \{(1, 5), (2, 4), (3, 3), (4, 2), (5, 1)\}$.
B $Y = \{(4, 1), (4, 2), (4, 3), (4, 4), (4, 5), (4, 6)\}$.
C $X \cap Y = \{(4, 2)\}$.
D $X \cup Y = \{(1, 5), (2, 4), (3, 3), (4, 2), (5, 1), (4, 1), (4, 3), (4, 4), (4, 5), (4, 6)\}$.

D3

likely outcomes. In the formula, $P(M)$ is a variable for the probability of the event; m is a variable for the number of sample points in the event; and n is a variable for the number of sample points in the sample space.

G What replacements can you make for the ? variables in $P(M) = \frac{m}{n}$ to determine the probability of event F?

H How do you know that $P(F) = \frac{1}{9}$?

So far, you have considered the probability that a single event will occur. Now you will consider the probability that a first event *and* a second event will occur and also the probability that a first event *or* a second event will occur.

You will again be working with the experiment of rolling a red die and a green die. The events tabulated in D3 are subsets of the sample space given in D2.

A Look at D3. Event X is the event that you get a sum of 6 in one roll of the dice. Give a standard description of X. How do you know that $\frac{5}{36}$ is the probability of X?

B Describe event Y in words. Give a standard ? description of Y. What is the probability of Y?

Since X is $\{(r, g) \mid r + g = 6\}$ and since Y is $\{(r, g) \mid r = 4\}$, the event that X and Y will occur is $\{(r, g) \mid r + g = 6 \wedge r = 4\}$. From your knowledge of conditions involving "and," you know that this set is the intersection of $\{(r, g) \mid r + g = 6\}$ and $\{(r, g) \mid r = 4\}$. Thus, $X \cap Y$ is the event that X and Y will occur, and the probability that X and Y will occur is the probability of $X \cap Y$.

C Look again at D3. How many elements are contained in $X \cap Y$? What is $P(X \cap Y)$?

You can use the idea of union of sets to find the probability that X or Y will occur. The connective "or" here means "one or the other or both." The event that X or Y will occur is $\{(r, g) \mid r + g = 6 \vee r = 4\}$, which is the union of $\{(r, g) \mid r + g = 6\}$ and $\{(r, g) \mid r = 4\}$. Thus, $X \cup Y$ is the event that X or Y will occur, and the probability that X or Y will occur is the probability of $X \cup Y$.

D How many elements are contained in the event $X \cup Y$, tabulated in D3? What is the probability of $X \cup Y$?

E Read the problem in D4. This problem also refers to the sample space given in D2. Event A is the event that the numbers indicated on the dice are the same. Is $A = \{(r, g) \mid r = g\}$? Tabulate this event. What is P(A)?

F Event B is the event that the sum of the numbers indicated on the dice is 5. What is a standard description of B? Tabulate this event. What is P(B)?

Two dice, a red one and a green one, are rolled. What is the probability that the numbers indicated on the two dice are the same or that the sum of the numbers is 5?

D4

G Do A and B have any elements in common? Are they mutually exclusive events?

> REMINDER
>
> Mutually exclusive events are events of a finite sample space that have no elements in common. Mutually exclusive events are disjoint sets.
>
> *See lesson 202, page 460, Book 2.*

H What is $A \cap B$? How do you know that 0 ? is the probability of the intersection of two mutually exclusive events?

I Tabulate $A \cup B$. How is the number of elements ? in $A \cup B$ related to the sum of the number of elements in A and the number of elements in B?

J For two events that are not mutually exclu- ? sive, is the number of elements in their union the same as the sum of the numbers of elements contained in the two events? Explain your answer.

In *Book 2* you learned that, if M and N are events in a finite sample space, then $P(M \cup N)$ is equal to $P(M) + P(N) - P(M \cap N)$. You also learned that, if M and N are mutually exclusive events, then $P(M \cup N) = P(M) + P(N)$.

K Show that $P(A) + P(B) - P(A \cap B)$ is equal ? to $P(A) + P(B)$. To find $P(A \cup B)$, how do you know that you can use either formula expressed in the preceding paragraph? What is $P(A \cup B)$?

L What is the answer to the problem in D4?

M Read the problem in D5. H is the event that ? the absolute value of the difference of the numbers indicated on the dice is 3. How do you know that $H = \{(r, g) \mid |r - g| = 3\}$? Is $H = \{(r, g) \mid |g - r| = 3\}$?

N Tabulate H. How many sample points are contained in H? What is P(H)?

Two dice, a red one and a green one, are rolled. What is the probability that the numbers indicated on the two dice are the same or that the sum of the numbers is 5?

D4

Two dice, a red one and a green one, are rolled. What is the probability that the absolute value of the difference of the numbers indicated on the two dice is 3 and that the number indicated on the green die is greater than 5?

D5

O Event K is the event that the number indicated on the green die is greater than 5. Give a standard description of K. Tabulate K. What is P(K)?

P Tabulate $H \cap K$.

Q What is $P(H \cap K)$? What is $P(H) \cdot P(K)$?

R Are H and K independent events?

> REMINDER
>
> Independent events are related as follows: M and N are subsets of a finite sample space. $P(M \cap N) = P(M) \cdot P(N)$ if and only if M and N are independent events.
>
> *See lesson 203, page 465, Book 2.*

S Are H and K mutually exclusive events?

T Explain why two independent events that ? are non-empty sets cannot be mutually exclusive.

U What is the answer to the problem in D5?

In this lesson you reviewed the ideas of sample space, sample point, event, and probability of an event. You also reviewed your knowledge of mutually exclusive events and independent events.

On your own

Use the experiment described in D6 in connection with exercises 1 through 13. You are to assume that the pointer always stops on one of the numerals, never on the marks between them. You are also to assume that the sections marked off on the spinners are of equal size.

1 Each pair of numbers that can be obtained when a player spins both pointers is an outcome of the experiment. Make a chart that gives a sample space. Use the numbers named on the red spinner for the first components of the ordered pairs in the sample space. Use (r, y) to represent each sample point in the sample space.

2 What is the probability that the red pointer will stop on the numeral 3? That the yellow pointer will stop on the numeral 4? Are these mutually exclusive events? Are they independent events?

3 Event A is $\{(r, y) \mid r + y = 5\}$. Describe A in words. Tabulate A. What is P(A)?

4 Event B is $\{(r, y) \mid r + y = 8\}$. Describe B in words. Tabulate B. What is P(B)?

5 Are A and B mutually exclusive events? Are they independent events?

6 What is the probability that events A and B will occur?

7 What is the probability that A or B will occur?

8 C = {(1, 1), (2, 2), (3, 3), (4, 4), (5, 5)}. D = {(2, 1), (2, 2), (2, 3), (2, 4), (2, 5), (2, 6)}. Describe each event in words. Give a standard description of each event.

9 What is P(C)? What is P(D)?

10 Are C and D mutually exclusive events?

11 What is the probability that C and D will occur?

Two spinners like the ones shown in the sketch below are used in a game. Spinner A has a red pointer. Spinner B has a yellow pointer. At each turn, one of the players spins both pointers.

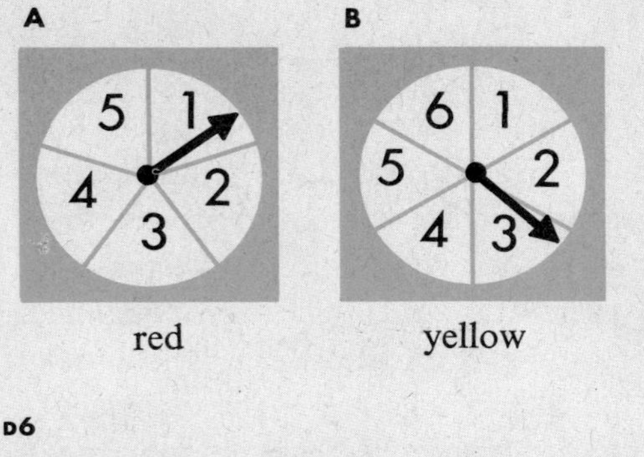

D6

A bag contains 2 yellow marbles, 3 red marbles, 6 green marbles, and 1 white marble. Joe is to take a marble from the bag without looking.

D7

12 What is the probability that C or D will occur?

13 How do you know that C and D are independent events?

Use the experiment described in D7 in connection with exercises 14 through 17.

14 Each marble that Joe can take is an outcome of the experiment. Tabulate the sample space. Call the marbles "y_1," "y_2," "r_1," and so on.

15 What is the probability that Joe will take a red marble? A green marble? A yellow marble? A white marble?

16 What is the probability that Joe will not take a yellow marble?

17 What is the probability that Joe will take a green or a yellow marble?

There are 7 tags in a box. On the tags, the numerals 1 through 7 are written, with one numeral on each tag. Martha draws 2 tags from the box without looking.

D8

Three of the girls on a high-school cheerleading squad are seniors. Three girls must be selected to replace them after they graduate. Five of the eight girls who tried out have qualified. Since each of the five girls is equally good, the judge will write their names on cards and select three names from a hat without looking. The girls who qualified are Jane, Sally, Ann, Mary, and Sandra.

D9

Use the experiment described in D8 in connection with exercises 18, 19, and 20.

18 Each pair of numbers named on the two tags Martha draws is an outcome of the experiment. If Martha does not replace the first tag before she draws the second tag, will the sample space contain such pairs as (2, 2), (3, 3), and (7, 7)? Tabulate the sample space.

19 What is the probability that the numbers named on the two tags are even? Are odd?

20 What is the probability that the sum of the two numbers is even? That the sum is 13? That the sum is divisible by 3? That the sum is a prime number?

Use the experiment described in D9 in connection with exercises 21 through 24.

21 Each outcome is a 3-element subset of {Jane, Sally, Ann, Mary, Sandra}. Tabulate the sample space.

22 What is the probability that Ann will be chosen for the squad?

23 What is the probability that Sandra and Ann will be chosen? That neither Mary nor Ann will be chosen?

24 What is the probability that Mary, Sandra, and Jane will be chosen? What is the probability that one or two, but not all three, of these girls will be chosen?

KEEPING SKILLFUL

Each condition expressed in exercises 1 through 4 determines a function. The domain is $\{(-1, -5), (-1, 5), (1, -5), (1, 5)\}$. Tabulate each function. Then give its maximum and minimum values.

1 $f(x, y) = x + y + 2.$

2 $f(x, y) = x - y - 2.$

3 $f(x, y) = 2x + y - 4.$

4 $f(x, y) = 10x + 3y + 12.$

Each exercise below gives a condition that determines a function and a system of conditions whose solution set is the domain of the function. For each function, make a graph of the convex set that is the locus of the domain. Then give the coördinates of the corner points and find the maximum and minimum values of the function.

5 $f(x, y) = 2x - y + 2.$

$y \leqq x + 3$

$x \leqq 1$

$y \geqq -1.$

6 $f(x, y) = x + 3y - 2.$

$x + y \leqq 3$

$y \geqq 1$

$x \geqq -2.$

7 $f(x, y) = x - y + 10.$

$y \geqq 2x - 4$

$x + y \leqq 2$

$x \geqq 0.$

A binomial experiment

In this lesson you will discover that the probabilities of events in certain sample spaces are related to the terms of the expansion of a binomial.

First consider an experiment in which each outcome is the result of tossing a tack once on a level surface. The two possible outcomes of the experiment are shown in D1. Let U represent the outcome in which the tack lands point up, and let D represent the outcome in which the tack lands point down.

From your work with a similar experiment in *Book 2*, you know that the two outcomes of tossing the tack are not equally likely. Therefore, we obtain an approximation of the probability that the tack will land point up by tossing the tack many times and then making a prediction based on our observations. We will assume that, in this case, we have obtained $\frac{1}{4}$ for the probability that the tack will land point up.

A ? How do you know that the probability that the tack will land point down is $1 - \frac{1}{4}$, or $\frac{3}{4}$?

B ? Suppose that you toss the tack three times in succession. Does the outcome of any one toss affect the outcome of any other toss? Why is $\frac{1}{4} \cdot \frac{3}{4} \cdot \frac{1}{4}$ the probability that the tack will land point up on the first toss, point down on the second toss, and point up on the third toss?

Now consider an experiment in which each outcome is a result of tossing the tack three times. An outcome of this experiment can be represented by an ordered triple. For example,

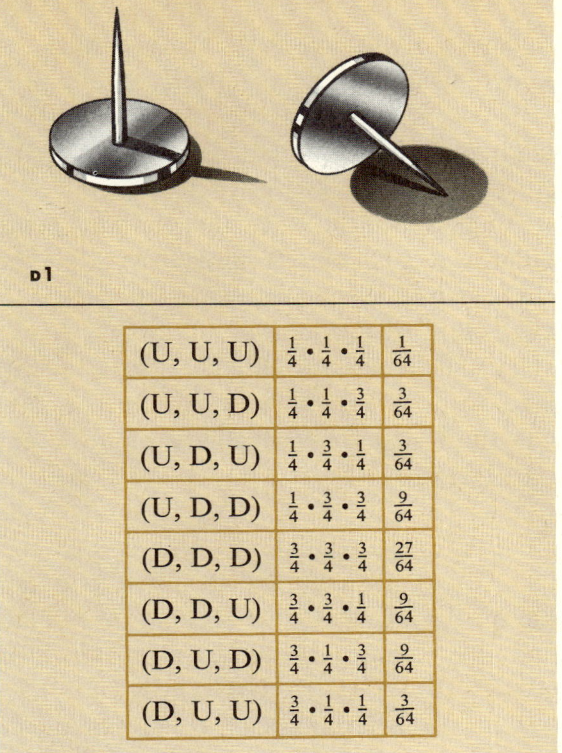

D1

(U, U, U)	$\frac{1}{4} \cdot \frac{1}{4} \cdot \frac{1}{4}$	$\frac{1}{64}$
(U, U, D)	$\frac{1}{4} \cdot \frac{1}{4} \cdot \frac{3}{4}$	$\frac{3}{64}$
(U, D, U)	$\frac{1}{4} \cdot \frac{3}{4} \cdot \frac{1}{4}$	$\frac{3}{64}$
(U, D, D)	$\frac{1}{4} \cdot \frac{3}{4} \cdot \frac{3}{4}$	$\frac{9}{64}$
(D, D, D)	$\frac{3}{4} \cdot \frac{3}{4} \cdot \frac{3}{4}$	$\frac{27}{64}$
(D, D, U)	$\frac{3}{4} \cdot \frac{3}{4} \cdot \frac{1}{4}$	$\frac{9}{64}$
(D, U, D)	$\frac{3}{4} \cdot \frac{1}{4} \cdot \frac{3}{4}$	$\frac{9}{64}$
(D, U, U)	$\frac{3}{4} \cdot \frac{1}{4} \cdot \frac{1}{4}$	$\frac{3}{64}$

D2

(U, D, U) can represent the outcome in which the tack lands point up on the first toss, point down on the second toss, and point up on the third toss.

C Use the fundamental counting property to find the number of possible outcomes of tossing the tack three times.

All the possible outcomes of the experiment are given in the first column of the chart in D2. The second column of the chart shows how you can determine the probability of obtaining each outcome. The third column gives the probability.

D Explain why $\frac{1}{4} \cdot \frac{1}{4} \cdot \frac{1}{4}$, or $\frac{1}{64}$, is the probability of obtaining (U, U, U). Why is $\frac{3}{4} \cdot \frac{3}{4} \cdot \frac{1}{4}$, or $\frac{9}{64}$, the probability of obtaining (D, D, U)?

E Are the eight outcomes of this experiment equally likely? Explain your answer.

Now we will consider some events in the sample space of this experiment.

F Is {(D, D, D)} the event that the tack never lands point up in three tosses? What is the probability of this event?

G Think about the event that the tack lands point up exactly once in three tosses. Use the chart in D2 to help you name the three outcomes that are members of this event.

To find the probability that the tack will land point up exactly once in three tosses, you must find the probability of the event {(U, D, D), (D, D, U), (D, U, D)}, which is {(U, D, D)} ∪ {(D, D, U)} ∪ {(D, U, D)}. Since the events {(U, D, D)}, {(D, D, U)}, and {(D, U, D)} are mutually exclusive, you can use the formula $P(M \cup N) = P(M) + P(N)$ to find the number that is the probability of {(U, D, D)} ∪ {(D, D, U)} ∪ {(D, U, D)}.

H Look again at D2. What is the probability of obtaining (U, D, D)? Of obtaining (D, D, U)? Of obtaining (D, U, D)?

I What is the probability that the tack will land point up once in three tosses?

J Tabulate the event that the tack will land point up twice in three tosses. Why is the probability of this event $\frac{3}{64} + \frac{3}{64} + \frac{3}{64}$?

K Tabulate the event that the tack will land point up three times in three tosses. What is the probability of this event?

In exercises F through K, you have considered the probabilities of four events. The sum of these probabilities is expressed in D3. Notice that the first term in the sum is the probability that the tack will never land point up in three tosses; the second term is the probability that the tack will land point up once; the third term is the probability that the tack will land point up twice; the fourth term is the probability that the tack will land point up three times.

(U, U, U)	$\frac{1}{4} \cdot \frac{1}{4} \cdot \frac{1}{4}$	$\frac{1}{64}$
(U, U, D)	$\frac{1}{4} \cdot \frac{1}{4} \cdot \frac{3}{4}$	$\frac{3}{64}$
(U, D, U)	$\frac{1}{4} \cdot \frac{3}{4} \cdot \frac{1}{4}$	$\frac{3}{64}$
(U, D, D)	$\frac{1}{4} \cdot \frac{3}{4} \cdot \frac{3}{4}$	$\frac{9}{64}$
(D, D, D)	$\frac{3}{4} \cdot \frac{3}{4} \cdot \frac{3}{4}$	$\frac{27}{64}$
(D, D, U)	$\frac{3}{4} \cdot \frac{3}{4} \cdot \frac{1}{4}$	$\frac{9}{64}$
(D, U, D)	$\frac{3}{4} \cdot \frac{1}{4} \cdot \frac{3}{4}$	$\frac{9}{64}$
(D, U, U)	$\frac{3}{4} \cdot \frac{1}{4} \cdot \frac{1}{4}$	$\frac{3}{64}$

D2

$$\frac{27}{64} + \frac{27}{64} + \frac{9}{64} + \frac{1}{64}$$

D3

L ? Is the sum named in D3 equal to 1? Why should the sum of the four probabilities be equal to 1?

Think again about how each term of the sum is determined.

The first term is the probability of obtaining (D, D, D) because this is the only outcome in which the tack never lands point up. From the chart in D2, you can see that the probability of obtaining (D, D, D) is $(\frac{3}{4})^3$, or $\frac{27}{64}$.

Consider the second term. The probability that the tack will land point up once is found by adding the probabilities of obtaining (U, D, D), obtaining (D, D, U), and obtaining (D, U, D). Since each of these outcomes contains two D's and one U, each of the three probabilities is equal to $(\frac{3}{4})^2(\frac{1}{4})$. Thus, we obtain $3(\frac{3}{4})^2(\frac{1}{4})$, or $\frac{27}{64}$, as the probability that the tack will land point up once.

Consider the third term. The probability that the tack will land point up twice is found by adding the probabilities of obtaining (U, U, D), obtaining (U, D, U), and obtaining

(D, U, U). Since each of these outcomes contains one D and two U's, each of the three probabilities is equal to $(\frac{3}{4})(\frac{1}{4})^2$. Thus, we obtain $3(\frac{3}{4})(\frac{1}{4})^2$, or $\frac{9}{64}$, as the probability that the tack will land point up twice.

Consider the fourth term. The only outcome in which the tack lands point up three times is (U, U, U). Thus, the probability of obtaining (U, U, U), which is $(\frac{1}{4})^3$, is the probability that the tack will land point up three times.

The sum expressed in D3 is expressed again in D4. Notice that, in D4, each term is expressed in such a way that you can tell how it was obtained. Suppose that we let p represent the probability that the tack lands point up and q represent the probability that the tack lands point down. Then $q^3 + 3q^2p + 3qp^2 + p^3$ represents the sum expressed in D4. From your work with binomial expansions, you know that this is the expansion of $(q+p)^3$.

M If p represents the probability that a tack lands point up and q represents the probability that it lands point down, what probability does $q+p$ represent? How do you know that $q+p=1$?

N If $q+p=1$, then $(q+p)^3$ is equal to what number?

O Can the expansion of $(q+p)^3$ be expressed as $C(3, 0)q^3 + C(3, 1)q^2p + C(3, 2)qp^2 + C(3, 3)p^3$? How do you know that each term of the sum expressed in D5 is equal to the corresponding term of the sum expressed in D4?

$$(\tfrac{3}{4})^3 + 3(\tfrac{3}{4})^2(\tfrac{1}{4}) + 3(\tfrac{3}{4})(\tfrac{1}{4})^2 + (\tfrac{1}{4})^3$$

D4

$$C(3, 0)(\tfrac{3}{4})^3 + C(3, 1)(\tfrac{3}{4})^2(\tfrac{1}{4}) + C(3, 2)(\tfrac{3}{4})(\tfrac{1}{4})^2 + C(3, 3)(\tfrac{1}{4})^3$$

D5

P Is the sum expressed in D5 the expansion of $(\frac{3}{4}+\frac{1}{4})^3$?

In the expansion of $(q+p)^3$, the coefficients tell you the number of ways in which a certain kind of outcome can occur. For example, in the expansion, q^2p represents the probability of an outcome that contains one U. The coefficient of q^2p, which is C(3, 1), indicates that there are C(3, 1) ways of obtaining one U in three tosses. Also, qp^2 represents the probability of an outcome that contains two U's. The coefficient of qp^2, which is C(3, 2), indicates that there are C(3, 2) ways of obtaining two U's in three tosses.

Because the probabilities of events in the tack experiment can be related to the terms of a binomial expansion, the experiment is called a *binomial experiment*. In the next lesson you will study in detail the features of a binomial experiment.

In this lesson you studied an experiment that is called a binomial experiment. You learned that the probabilities of certain events in such an experiment are the terms of a binomial expansion.

On your own

Exercises 1 through 13 concern rolling a die. Each of the six faces of the die has from 1 through 6 spots on it.

1 Let T represent the outcome in which you roll the die once and obtain a 2. Let N represent the outcome in which you do not obtain a 2. If the die is rolled once, why is $\frac{1}{6}$ the probability of obtaining T? What is the probability of obtaining N?

2 Consider an experiment in which each outcome is a result of rolling the die four times in succession. For example, (T, N, T, T) represents one outcome. How many such outcomes does the experiment have?

3 Make a chart like the one used in this lesson to show each possible outcome of the die experiment. In your chart, show the probability of each outcome.

4 What is the probability of obtaining no T's in four rolls of the die?

5 Tabulate the event that you obtain one T in four rolls of the die. What is the probability of this event?

6 Tabulate the event that you obtain two T's. What is the probability of this event?

7 What is the probability of obtaining three T's?

8 What is the probability of obtaining four T's?

9 Which of the probabilities that you determined in exercises 4 through 8 is equal to $C(4, 0)(\frac{5}{6})^4$? Which probability is equal to $C(4, 3)(\frac{5}{6})(\frac{1}{6})^3$?

10 Express the sum of the five probabilities that you determined for exercises 4 through 8. Express each term of the sum so that one factor is a power of $\frac{5}{6}$, one factor is a power of $\frac{1}{6}$, and one factor is $C(4, x)$, where x is an element of $\{0, 1, 2, 3, 4\}$.

11 The sum that you expressed for exercise 10 is the expansion of what binomial?

12 Consider an experiment in which each outcome is a result of rolling the die five times in succession. For example, (T, T, N, N, T) represents one possible outcome. Explain why there are 2^5 such outcomes.

13 What is the probability of each outcome that contains two T's? Why are there C(5, 2) such outcomes? What is the probability of obtaining two T's in five rolls of the die?

Exploring ideas

Features of a binomial experiment

In the last lesson you studied an experiment that involved tossing a tack three times. In this lesson you will study the special features that make the tack experiment a binomial experiment. Then you will consider other experiments that have the same features.

In the tack experiment, each toss of the tack is an experiment in itself and is called a *trial.* In a binomial experiment, we are always interested in the results of a fixed number of repeated trials. For example, we are interested in the result of three repeated trials in the tack experiment.

A binomial experiment always concerns two possible outcomes of each trial. It is customary to call one outcome a *success* and the other outcome a *failure.* The success and the failure must be mutually exclusive and complementary events. For example, in a trial of the tack experiment, U could be called a success and D could be called a failure. U and D are mutually exclusive, since the tack cannot land point up and point down at the same time. U and D are complementary, since the tack must land in one of the two ways.

The trials in a binomial experiment must be identical so that the probability of success in each trial is the same. For example, in the tack experiment, if each trial consists in tossing the same tack, or an identical tack, under the same conditions, then the probability that the tack lands point up is the same for each trial.

1 The experiment consists of a fixed number of trials.

2 For each trial, there are a success and a failure, which are two mutually exclusive and complementary events.

3 The probability of success is the same for each trial.

4 The outcomes of different trials are independent.

5 The experiment concerns the number of successes, rather than the order in which the successes occur.

D1

Each of four baseball players has a batting average of .250. If each player has one time at bat, facing the same pitcher, what is the probability that exactly two of the players will get hits?

D2

The outcomes of different trials of a binomial experiment must be independent. In the tack experiment, the outcomes of different trials are independent because the outcome of tossing the tack one time has no effect on the outcome of tossing the tack another time.

You will recall that, in the tack experiment, we were interested in the probability that the tack would never land point up in three trials, that the tack would land point up once in three trials, and so on. Notice that the events just described concern the number of successes in three trials, and not the order in which the successes occur. This is another feature of a binomial experiment.

The five features of a binomial experiment, which have just been described, are summarized in D1.

Read the problem in D2.

A How many trials make up the experiment that is described in D2?

B For each trial, if you think of a hit as a success, what outcome is a failure?

C What is the probability of success for each trial?

D Are the outcomes of different trials independent?

E Does it matter which two of the four players get hits?

F Does the problem in D2 involve a binomial experiment?

Now we will develop a general term for finding probabilities in any binomial experiment that is made up of 3 trials. We will use the tack experiment to develop the general term.

Consider U a success and D a failure in the tack experiment. This means that the probability of success in each trial is $\frac{1}{4}$ and the probability of failure is $\frac{3}{4}$. The chart that you used in the previous lesson is given again in D3.

A Which outcome contains 0 successes? How can you determine that $C(3, 0)(\frac{3}{4})^3$ is the probability of 0 successes?

(U, U, U)	$\frac{1}{4} \cdot \frac{1}{4} \cdot \frac{1}{4}$	$\frac{1}{64}$
(U, U, D)	$\frac{1}{4} \cdot \frac{1}{4} \cdot \frac{3}{4}$	$\frac{3}{64}$
(U, D, U)	$\frac{1}{4} \cdot \frac{3}{4} \cdot \frac{1}{4}$	$\frac{3}{64}$
(U, D, D)	$\frac{1}{4} \cdot \frac{3}{4} \cdot \frac{3}{4}$	$\frac{9}{64}$
(D, D, D)	$\frac{3}{4} \cdot \frac{3}{4} \cdot \frac{3}{4}$	$\frac{27}{64}$
(D, D, U)	$\frac{3}{4} \cdot \frac{3}{4} \cdot \frac{1}{4}$	$\frac{9}{64}$
(D, U, D)	$\frac{3}{4} \cdot \frac{1}{4} \cdot \frac{3}{4}$	$\frac{9}{64}$
(D, U, U)	$\frac{3}{4} \cdot \frac{1}{4} \cdot \frac{1}{4}$	$\frac{3}{64}$

D3

Each of four baseball players has a batting average of .250. If each player has one time at bat, facing the same pitcher, what is the probability that exactly two of the players will get hits?

D2

(U, U, U)	$\frac{1}{4} \cdot \frac{1}{4} \cdot \frac{1}{4}$	$\frac{1}{64}$
(U, U, D)	$\frac{1}{4} \cdot \frac{1}{4} \cdot \frac{3}{4}$	$\frac{3}{64}$
(U, D, U)	$\frac{1}{4} \cdot \frac{3}{4} \cdot \frac{1}{4}$	$\frac{3}{64}$
(U, D, D)	$\frac{1}{4} \cdot \frac{3}{4} \cdot \frac{3}{4}$	$\frac{9}{64}$
(D, D, D)	$\frac{3}{4} \cdot \frac{3}{4} \cdot \frac{3}{4}$	$\frac{27}{64}$
(D, D, U)	$\frac{3}{4} \cdot \frac{3}{4} \cdot \frac{1}{4}$	$\frac{9}{64}$
(D, U, D)	$\frac{3}{4} \cdot \frac{1}{4} \cdot \frac{3}{4}$	$\frac{9}{64}$
(D, U, U)	$\frac{3}{4} \cdot \frac{1}{4} \cdot \frac{1}{4}$	$\frac{3}{64}$

D3

B Which outcomes contain 1 success? Why is $C(3, 1)(\frac{3}{4})^2(\frac{1}{4})$ the probability of 1 success?

C Which outcomes contain 2 successes? How can you determine that $C(3, 2)(\frac{3}{4})(\frac{1}{4})^2$ is the probability of 2 successes?

D Which outcome contains 3 successes? How can you determine that $C(3, 3)(\frac{1}{4})^3$ is the probability of 3 successes?

E The probabilities for 0, 1, 2, and 3 successes are given in the chart in D4. For each x, is $C(3, x)(\frac{3}{4})^{3-x}(\frac{1}{4})^x$ the probability of x successes? Explain your answer.

F Let p represent the probability of success in each trial and let q represent the probability of failure in each trial. How can you represent $C(3, x)(\frac{3}{4})^{3-x}(\frac{1}{4})^x$?

You can use $C(3, x)q^{3-x}p^x$ as a general term for finding the probability of x successes in any binomial experiment involving 3 trials.

G Suppose that you want to know the probability of 1 success in a binomial experiment of 3 trials. For this experiment, the probability of success in each trial is $\frac{3}{5}$. How do you know that the probability of failure is $1 - \frac{3}{5}$? What replacements can you make in $C(3, x)q^{3-x}p^x$? What is the probability?

H What is the probability of 2 successes in a binomial experiment of 3 trials if the probability of success in each trial is $\frac{2}{3}$?

In a similar way, we can use the baseball experiment that is described in D2 to develop a general term for finding probabilities in a binomial experiment that is made up of 4 trials.

I In the baseball experiment, we will consider a hit a success. How do you know that $(.75)^4$ is the probability of any outcome that contains no hits? Are there C(4, 0) such outcomes?

J The chart in D5 gives probabilities of successes in the baseball experiment. Explain how the probability of 0 successes was obtained.

K How do you know that $(.75)^3(.25)$ is the probability of any outcome that contains 1 hit? Why are there C(4, 1) such outcomes? The probability of 1 success is given in the chart in D5. How was this probability obtained?

L What is the probability of any outcome that contains 2 hits? How many such outcomes are there? Explain how the probability of 2 successes was obtained.

M How was the probability of 3 successes obtained? How was the probability of 4 successes obtained?

Notice that, for each x, the probability of x successes is $C(4, x)(.75)^{4-x}(.25)^x$. If p represents the probability of success in each trial and q represents the probability of failure, then $C(4, x)q^{4-x}p^x$ represents the probability of x successes in a binomial experiment of 4 trials.

N Read the problem in D2 again. What replacements can you make in $C(4, x)q^{4-x}p^x$ to

x	0	1	2	3
Probability of x successes	$C(3, 0)(\frac{3}{4})^3$	$C(3, 1)(\frac{3}{4})^2(\frac{1}{4})$	$C(3, 2)(\frac{3}{4})(\frac{1}{4})^2$	$C(3, 3)(\frac{1}{4})^3$

D4

x	0	1	2	3	4
Probability of x successes	$C(4, 0)(.75)^4$	$C(4, 1)(.75)^3(.25)$	$C(4, 2)(.75)^2(.25)^2$	$C(4, 3)(.75)(.25)^3$	$C(4, 4)(.25)^4$

D5

If you roll five dice, what is the probability of getting five 3's or two 4's?

D6

obtain the answer to the problem? What is the answer?

We have determined that the probability of x successes in an experiment of 3 trials is $C(3, x)q^{3-x} p^x$. We have also determined that the probability of x successes in an experiment of 4 trials is $C(4, x)q^{4-x} p^x$. These results suggest that a general term for the probability of x successes in a binomial experiment of 5 trials is $C(5, x)q^{5-x} p^x$.

O What is the probability of x successes in a binomial experiment of 6 trials? Of 7 trials?

P Suppose that you wish to know the probability of 2 successes in a binomial experiment of 5 trials. The probability of success in each trial is $\frac{1}{3}$. What replacements should you make in $C(5, x)q^{5-x} p^x$? What is the probability of 2 successes?

Q What is the probability of 0 successes in a binomial experiment of 7 trials? The probability of success in each trial is $\frac{3}{4}$.

Now you will find probabilities in experiments of rolling dice.

Read the problem in D6.

A Let A be the event that you get exactly five 3's and let B be the event that you get exactly two 4's. How do you know that $A \cup B$ is the event that you get five 3's or two 4's?

B Is $P(A) + P(B)$ the probability that you get five 3's or two 4's? Explain your answer.

C You can think of event A as an event in a binomial experiment involving 5 trials. Each roll of a die is a trial of the experiment. If you consider that getting a 3 is a success, what is the probability of success in each trial? What is the probability of failure?

D The probability of event A is the probability of getting 5 successes in 5 trials. How do you know that $C(5, 5)(\frac{1}{6})^5$ is P(A)?

E Now think of event B as an event in a binomial experiment of 5 trials. If you consider that getting a 4 is a success, what is the probability of success in each trial? What is the probability of failure?

F What is P(B)?

G What is the answer to the problem in D6?

Read the problem in D7.

H Is the probability of getting at least two 5's the same as the probability of getting two 5's or three 5's or four 5's?

I Why can you use $C(4, x)q^{4-x} p^x$ to obtain the probability of getting two 5's? What is the probability of getting two 5's? Of getting three 5's? Of getting four 5's?

J What is the sum of the probabilities that you obtained for exercise I? Why is this sum the probability of getting at least two 5's?

K What is the answer to the problem in D7?

In this lesson you studied the five features of a binomial experiment. Then you learned to find probabilities of events in binomial experiments involving x trials.

If you roll four dice, what is the probability of getting at least two 5's?

D7

A Four dice are rolled.

B A bag contains three blue marbles, five red marbles, and two white marbles. Without looking, a boy makes three drawings of one marble, replacing the marble in the bag after each drawing.

C A quiz contains six true-false questions. A student selects the answers without reading the questions.

D8

On your own

For each of problems 1 through 4, tell whether or not the problem involves a binomial experiment. If the experiment involved is not binomial, tell which features of a binomial experiment are missing. Do not answer the problems.

1 Five men gave their coats to a checkroom girl in a restaurant. What is the probability that the girl will return the right coats to two of the men if she does not remember which coat belongs to which man and if the five men are the only ones who have checked their coats?

2 Four coins are tossed. What is the probability that the first and fourth coins will land "heads" and the second and third coins will land "tails"?

3 The 13 hearts are taken from a deck of cards. From the 13 hearts, three different cards are drawn in succession. What is the probability that one of the three cards is an ace?

4 A quiz has 20 multiple-choice questions. There are four choices for the answer to each question. If a student selects one answer for each question, without reading the questions, what is the probability that he will select fewer than four correct answers?

Use experiment A described in D8 in connection with exercises 5 through 8.

5 What is the probability of getting three 2's or two 3's?

6 What is the probability of getting at least three 1's?

7 What is the probability of getting four 5's or two 6's?

8 What is the probability of getting fewer than three 4's?

Use experiment B described in D8 in connection with exercises 9 through 13.

9 What is the probability that three blue marbles will be drawn?

10 What is the probability that three red marbles will be drawn?

11 What is the probability that three white marbles will be drawn?

12 What is the probability that three blue marbles or two white marbles will be drawn?

13 What is the probability that at least one red marble will be drawn?

Use experiment C described in D8 in connection with exercises 14 through 17.

14 What is the probability that the student will select at least two correct answers?

15 What is the probability that the student will select exactly three correct answers?

16 What is the probability that the student will select fewer than three correct answers?

17 What is the probability that the student will select six correct answers?

SPECIAL CHALLENGE

In the following discussion, we will be interested in certain subsets of a given set.

A Let $R = \{2, 4, 7, 9\}$. How many subsets does set R have?

B Consider the subsets $\{7\}$ and $\{2, 4, 9\}$. Tabulate the union of these two subsets. Tabulate their intersection.

The subsets $\{7\}$ and $\{2, 4, 9\}$ form a *partition* of R. Two or more non-empty sets, each two of which are disjoint, form a partition of their union.

C Explain why $\{7, 9\}$, $\{2\}$, and $\{4, 7\}$ do not form a partition of R. Explain why $\{2, 9\}$ and $\{4, 5, 6, 7\}$ do not form a partition of R.

D Set R can be partitioned into 4 subsets in only one way. This is a *4-way* partition. List the 4 subsets in this partition.

E In how many ways can R be partitioned into 3 subsets? List these partitions.

F List all the 2-way partitions of R.

Look at D1. Sets A_1 and A_2 form a 2-way partition of set S. Sets B_1 and B_2 form another 2-way partition of S.

G Do the sets named below form a 4-way partition of S? Tabulate each of these sets.

$A_1 \cap B_1 \quad A_1 \cap B_2 \quad A_2 \cap B_1 \quad A_2 \cap B_2$

$S = \{a, b, c, d, e, f, g, h\}$.
$A_1 = \{a, b, d\}$.
$A_2 = \{c, e, f, g, h\}$.
$B_1 = \{b, d, e, f, g, h\}$.
$B_2 = \{a, c\}$.

D1

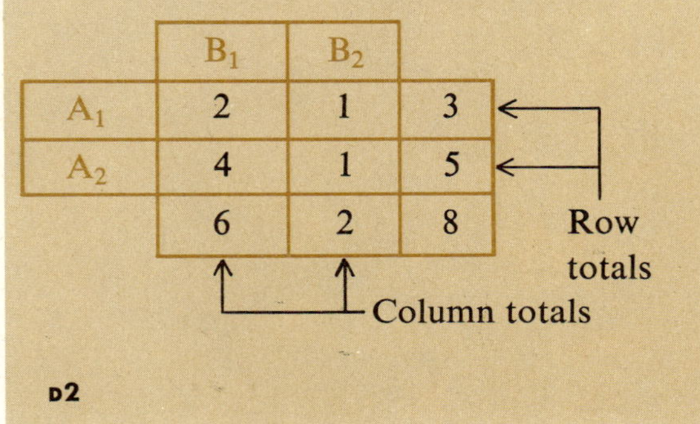

B1
B2
A1
2
1
3
A2
4
1
5
6
2
8
Row totals
Column totals

D2

H The 4 sets named in exercise G form a *cross partition* of S. How many members are in each set in this cross partition?

I Look at the table in D2. This table consists of *cells* that give the number of members in the sets of the cross partition of S. What do the cells for the row totals tell you? What do the cells for the column totals tell you?

J The cell in the lower right corner gives the number of members in S. How does this number compare with the sum of the row totals? With the sum of the column totals?

K Now suppose that S, tabulated in D1, is a sample space consisting of 8 equally likely sample points. Since A_1 is an event containing 3 of these sample points, $P(A_1) = \frac{3}{8}$. Notice that, when you divide the total of row A_1 by 8, you obtain $P(A_1)$. How is $P(A_2)$ related to the total of row A_2?

L How are $P(B_1)$ and the total of column B_1 related? What is $P(B_2)$?

M When you divide the number given in the cell for $A_1 \cap B_1$ by 8, you obtain $P(A_1 \cap B_1)$.

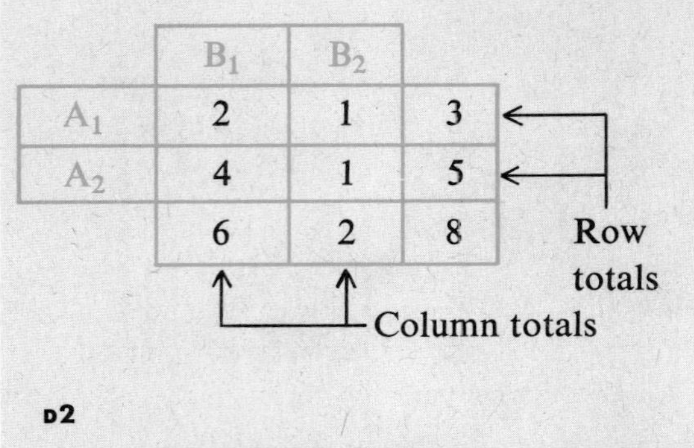

	B_1	B_2	
A_1	2	1	3
A_2	4	1	5
	6	2	8

D2

	M	~M	
S	14	55	69
~S	4	27	31
	18	82	100

D3

What is $P(A_1 \cap B_1)$? What is $P(A_2 \cap B_1)$? How does the sum of these two probabilities compare with $P(B_1)$?

Recall that two events, *M* and *N*, are independent if and only if $P(M \cap N)$ is equal to $P(M) \cdot P(N)$.

N How do you know that A_1 and B_1 are not independent events?

Consider two jars labeled B_1 and B_2. The jar labeled B_1 contains 6 tags with the letters b, d, e, f, g, and h. Jar B_2 contains 2 tags with the letters a and c.

O If you draw a tag from jar B_1, what is the probability that it will name a member of A_2?

The probability that you named for exercise O is the *conditional* probability of event A_2, given B_1. In other words, it is the probability that A_2 will occur, if B_1 has already occurred. This probability can be found from the table in D2 by dividing the number given in the cell for $A_2 \cap B_1$ by the column total for B_1.

P What is the conditional probability of B_2, given A_1? What is the conditional probability of B_2, given A_2? How do these conditional probabilities compare with $P(B_2)$?

The previous discussion should further your understanding of probabilities associated with independent events. Now look at D3. Two 2-way partitions were formed from 100 seniors in Westbrook High School. First, the students were partitioned according to whether or not they were taking a mathematics course (M or ~ M). Second, they were partitioned according to whether or not they were taking a science course (S or ~ S).

Q What is the probability that, if one of the 100 students is chosen at random, he will be taking both a mathematics course and a science course? Show by finding the product of two probabilities that taking a mathematics course and taking a science course do not seem to be independent events.

R Use one instance of conditional probability to show that taking a mathematics course and taking a science course do not seem to be independent events.

Partitions of sets are used in many experimental studies. Drawing valid conclusions from a table like the one in D3, however, requires a further study of mathematics.

KEEPING SKILLFUL

For each of exercises 1 through 9, give a standard name of the number expressed.

1 P(3, 2)	**4** P(8, 5)	**7** C(8, 1)
2 C(7, 6)	**5** C(5, 2)	**8** P(9, 3)
3 C(5, 5)	**6** P(10, 6)	**9** C(12, 10)

For each of exercises 10 through 15, use the binomial theorem to help you expand the given binomial.

10 $(a + b)^5$	**13** $(5a + 3b)^3$
11 $(2a + b)^4$	**14** $(6 - a)^8$
12 $(3a - b)^7$	**15** $(a^2 - b)^6$

APPLYING MATHEMATICS

Give the answer to each of the following problems.

1 A basketball player has a record of successfully making $\frac{2}{3}$ of the free throws that he attempts. What is the probability that he will successfully make 3 of the next 5 free throws that he attempts? Assume that the result of each of the 5 attempts does not change his record significantly.

2 A survey shows that the probability that a housewife uses a certain brand of detergent is $\frac{1}{7}$. If three housewives are selected at random, what is the probability that at least one of them uses the given brand of detergent?

3 A hat contains five green tags and three white tags. Without looking, a person draws two tags, replacing the first tag before he draws the second tag. What is the probability that the first tag will be green and the second tag will be white?

4 What is the probability that two green tags will be drawn?

5 If the first tag is not replaced before the second tag is drawn, what is the probability that one tag of each color will be drawn?

6 Mrs. Holt's granddaughter tore the labels off 8 cans of peaches, 6 cans of peas, 4 cans of apricots, and 2 cans of beans. Without the labels, the cans were identical. Mrs. Holt selected a can at random. What is the probability that it contained a vegetable?

7 At a large company, the probability that an employee will be hospitalized during the next year is .09. Two employees are selected at random. What is the probability that at least one of them will be hospitalized during the next year?

8 Mr. Peters has found that, on his farm, about 20% of the eggs that his hens lay are jumbo size, 50% are large, 25% are medium, and 5% are small. What is the probability that at least 1 of the next 4 eggs that are laid will be jumbo size?

9 What is the probability that the next 4 eggs that are laid will all be jumbo size?

10 What is the probability that, if 2 eggs are laid, they will both be large or both be medium?

11 If a coin is tossed 10 times, what is the probability of obtaining exactly 3 tails? Assume that the probability of obtaining tails in one trial is $\frac{1}{2}$.

12 A die is rolled, a coin is tossed, and a card is drawn from a standard deck of 52 cards that are face down. What is the probability of getting 2 on the die, tails on the coin, and a king from the deck of cards?

13 What is the probability of getting an even number greater than 2 on the die, or heads on the coin, or a heart less than the 5 of hearts from the deck of cards?

14 The probability that Clark will hit the bull's-eye in a game of darts is .02. If he throws 3 darts, what is the probability that exactly 2 darts will hit the bull's-eye?

15 If Clark throws 6 darts, what is the probability that half of them will hit the bull's-eye?

16 A die is rolled two times. What is the probability that the sum of the numbers indicated on the two rolls of the die will be 5?

17 What is the probability that a 5 will be obtained on at least one of the two rolls of the die?

18 Mrs. Lancaster invited 10 guests to a party. What is the probability that at least half of them will attend? Assume that the probability that a guest will attend the party is $\frac{1}{2}$ and that one guest's decision will not affect another guest's decision.

CHECKING UP

The small numerals within parentheses tell what pages to turn to for help if you need it.

Test 273

1 Tabulate a subset of {Chicago, New York} that is not a proper subset. (452)

2 Four identical coins are tossed. Each outcome of the experiment is an ordered 4-tuple, such as (H, T, H, H). How many outcomes are possible? (479)

3 Tabulate all the sets that are subsets of {apple, pear, orange}. (453)

4 How many terms are in the expansion of $(2x + y)^6$? (468)

5 What is a standard name of C(7, 2)? (457)

6 Tabulate each of the 3-element subsets of {A, B, C, D}. (457)

7 A sample space S contains 17 equally likely outcomes. What is the probability of event A if A is a subset of S that contains 12 members? (474)

8 What are the numerical coefficients in the terms of the expansion of $(x + y)^4$? (468)

9 How many 2-element combinations can be formed from {red, yellow, blue, green}? (457)

10 Use the binomial theorem to obtain the expansion of $(2x + y^2)^5$. (468)

11 Sample space S consists of equally likely outcomes. Event B is a subset of S that contains 5 elements. The probability of event B is $\frac{1}{4}$. How many outcomes are in S? (474)

12 What are the first five terms in the expansion of $(a + b)^n$? (468)

Test 274

From the list below each exercise, choose the correct answer for the exercise.

13 The symbol ø represents ~~~. (452)

a the empty set
b a closed interval
c an irrational number
d an operation in the set of real numbers

14 A and B are non-empty subsets of a sample space. If $P(A \cap B) = P(A) \cdot P(B)$, then A and B are ~~~. (476)

a disjoint sets
b independent events
c complementary events
d mutually exclusive events

15 The expression ~~~ is not a term in the expansion of $(3x + 4y)^4$. (468)

a $144x^3y$ b $864x^2y^2$ c $768xy^3$ d $256y^4$

16 The set ~~~ has the same number of 3-element combinations as 5-element combinations. (462)

a {1, 2, 3, 4, 5}
b {A, B, C, D, E, F, G, H}
c {a, b, c, d, e, f}
d {z, y, x, w, v, u, t, s, r, q, p}

17 Suppose that each trial in a binomial experiment consists in rolling a die. Obtaining a number greater than 2 is a success. The probability of failure in each trial is ~~~. (485)

a $\frac{1}{3}$ b $\frac{5}{6}$ c $\frac{1}{2}$ d $\frac{2}{3}$

18 $C(n, m - 1) +$ ~~~ $= C(n + 1, m)$. (463)

a $C(n + 1, n)$ c $C(m, n - 1)$
b $C(n - 1, m)$ d $C(n, m)$

19 If A and B are two non-empty sets that are mutually exclusive events, then ~~~. (476)

a $P(A \cap B) = P(A) + P(B)$
b $P(A) - P(B) = P(A \cup B)$
c $P(A \cup B) = P(A) + P(B)$
d $P(A) \cdot P(B) = P(A) + P(B)$

20 $C(n, m) =$ ~~~. (460)

a $\dfrac{m!}{n!}$

b $\dfrac{n!}{(n - m)!\, m!}$

c $n(n - 1)(n - 2) \ldots (n - m + 1)$

d $\dfrac{m!\,(m - n)!}{1 \cdot 2 \cdot \ldots \cdot m}$

21 In a binomial experiment, it is not necessarily true that ——. (483)

a there is a fixed number of trials

b the probability of success is the same in each trial

c the trials are independent

d the probability of success in each trial is the same as the probability of failure

22 In each trial of a binomial experiment, the probability of success is $\frac{1}{4}$. The probability of exactly 3 successes in 4 trials is ——. (484)

a $\frac{1}{256}$ **b** $\frac{3}{64}$ **c** $\frac{27}{64}$ **d** $\frac{27}{128}$

23 In a binomial experiment, .2 is the probability of success in each trial. The probability of at least 5 successes in 6 trials is ——. (485)

a .000064 **b** .9984 **c** .0016 **d** .001536

Test 275

Exercises 24, 25, and 26 refer to an experiment in which three dice are rolled.

24 What is the probability that all three dice will indicate the same number? (473)

25 What is the probability that one die will indicate 5, another will indicate 3, and the third will indicate 2? (473)

26 What is the probability that the number indicated by each die will be less than 3? (473)

Exercises 27, 28, and 29 refer to the following situation.

Miss Jarvis gives her mathematics class a test that consists of five multiple-choice questions. For the answer to each question, there are three choices, only one of which is correct.

27 What is the probability that, without reading the questions, a student will guess five correct answers? (485)

28 What is the probability that a student will guess five incorrect answers? (485)

29 Lucy has answered three of the questions correctly. If she guesses the answers to the remaining questions, what is the probability of getting at least four correct answers? (485)

CHECKING UP

The small numerals within parentheses tell what pages to turn to for help if you need it.

Test 276

1 What is the vector sum of $(-5, 7)$ and $(4, -2)$? (49)

2 What is the repeating decimal for $\frac{5}{13}$? (69)

3 Make a truth table for $p \vee \sim q$ showing all possible pairs of truth values for p and q. (121)

4 What number do you obtain when you raise -4 to the zero power? (171)

5 What polynomial is the sum of $3x^2 - 2x + 5$ and $2x^2 + 7x - 8$? (185)

6 Tabulate the set of positive integers that are factors of 18. (205)

7 Reduce $\dfrac{10xy - 20y}{15x^2y - 30xy}$ to lowest terms. (221)

8 Find the expression that is the product of $\dfrac{8x(x+3)}{3y(x^2-4)}$ and $\dfrac{15y^2(x+2)}{2x^2(x-y)}$. Give your answer in lowest terms. (225)

9 What number satisfies $4(6 - x) = x - 1$? (260)

10 Give a quadratic condition whose solution set is $\{5, -3\}$. (357)

11 What term completes the square whose first two terms are x^2 and $-5x$? (360)

12 What is the quotient of $\frac{3}{5}$ and $1\frac{1}{9}$? (42)

Test 277

What words or symbols best complete exercises 13 through 25?

13 In a certain scale drawing, $\frac{1}{6}$ in. represents 1 ft. In this drawing, $3\frac{1}{2}$ in. represents —— ft. (12)

14 The reciprocal of $1\frac{3}{5}$ is ——. (177)

15 Suppose that p represents a true statement and q represents a false statement. Then $p \Rightarrow q$ represents a —— statement. (123)

16 The muldiv of 4 and 6, modulus 7, is ——. (75)

17 The polynomial $3x^5 + x^3 - 7x^2 + 2x - 32$ has ______ terms. (175)

18 You obtain ______ when you simplify the expression $-5.2x - 8.7 - (1.3x - 5.4)$. (189)

19 The quotient of $\frac{3x^3y}{10}$ and $\frac{6xy^2}{5}$, in lowest terms, is ______. (226)

20 Relation S contains both (5, 8) and (5, −2). Therefore, S is not a ______. (300)

21 A ______ function is a function determined by a condition of the form $f(x) = k$. (326)

22 Every quadratic condition for equality in one variable can be put in the form ______. (356)

23 The locus of $2x - 3y = 5$ is a line whose slope is ______. (344)

24 The fourth term in the expansion of $(\frac{3}{4}x - \frac{1}{3}y)^7$ is ______. (468)

25 You obtain ______ from $x^3 - 2x^2 + 5x - 8$ when x is replaced by 5. (182)

Test 278

From the list below each exercise, choose the correct answer for the exercise.

26 In the expression $3x$, you can refer to 3 and x as ______. (175)

a constants **c** terms
b factors **d** components

27 In the condition $a = -\frac{1}{5}b^2$, a varies ______ b varies. (312)

a directly as
b inversely as
c directly as the square of
d inversely as the square of

28 The ______ of a given conditional is a conditional that is obtained by interchanging the antecedent and the consequent of the given conditional. (126)

a converse **c** disjunction
b negation **d** contrapositive

29 If the value of $b^2 - 4ac$ for a given quadratic condition is ______, then there are no real numbers that satisfy the condition. (365)

a 25 **b** 0 **c** 5 **d** −5

30 The condition ______ is equivalent to the condition $6 - 3x < 18$. (253)

a $-3x < 12$ **c** $4 < x$
b $2 - x > 6$ **d** $3x - 6 > 18$

31 The solution set of $x^2 - x - 12 = 0$ is ______. (369)

a $\{4, -3\}$ **c** $\{-2, 6\}$
b $\{12, 1\}$ **d** $\{3, -4\}$

32 The condition $|3x - 8| = 7$ is equivalent to ______. (275)

a $3x - 8 = -7 \wedge 3x + 8 = 7$
b $3x = 1 \vee -3x + 8 = 7$
c $3x - 8 = 7 \wedge 8 - 3x = 7$
d $3x = 15 \vee 3x - 8 = -7$

33 Point (2, 0) is *not* an x-intercept of the locus of ______. (334)

a $y = x^2 - 2x$ **c** $y = x^2 + x - 6$
b $2y = 3x - 6$ **d** $y = 2x$

34 The system $3x - 4y = 10 \wedge 5x + 7y = 18$ and the system $5x + 7y = 18 \wedge$ ______ are equivalent. (407)

a $41y = 4$ **c** $8x + 3y = 8$
b $4x = 9$ **d** $2x + 3y = 8$

35 The (x, y, z) that satisfies $(2x + y = 2) \wedge (x - 2y - 3z = 3) \wedge (x + 2y + 2 = 0)$ is ______. (414)

a (1, 2, 3) **c** (−2, 3, 3)
b (2, −2, 1) **d** (−1, 1, 3)

36 The locus of ______ is the empty set. (425)

a $(x \geqq 0) \wedge (2y + x \leqq -5) \wedge (y \geqq 0)$
b $(3x + 4y \leqq 2) \wedge (y \geqq 0) \wedge (x \geqq 0)$
c $(y \geqq 0) \wedge (x \geqq 0) \wedge (3x + y \geqq 4)$
d $(x \geqq 0) \wedge (y \geqq 0) \wedge (x + 3y \leqq 8)$

37 The intersection of two or more closed half-planes is ______. (431)

a the interior of an angle
b a set consisting of two parallel lines
c a polygonal convex set
d an angle

1 2 3 4 5 6 7 8 9 10 11 12 13 14 15 16 17 18 19 20 21 22 23 24 25 R 70 69 68 67 66 65 64

Symbols and how to read them

These displays show you how to read the mathematical symbols used in this book. They are arranged in the order in which they were introduced. Whenever, in your work, you come to a symbol that you have forgotten how to read, look for one like it among those on the pages in this section. If you need more information about the symbol, turn to the page of the book whose numeral is given above the symbol. There you will find a complete explanation of the meaning of the symbol.

book 1 page 11

$\{$ Michigan, Huron, Superior, Erie, Ontario $\}$

"The set whose members are Michigan, Huron, Superior, Erie, Ontario"

book 1 page 16

$x + 6 = 9.$

"x plus six equals nine."

book 1 page 19

$K = \{5, 6, 7, 8, 9, 10\}.$

"K equals the set whose members are five, six, seven, eight, nine, ten."

book 1 page 20

$x + 2 > 6.$

"x plus two is greater than six."

book 1 page 20

$2n < 9.$

"Two times n is less than nine."

book 1 page 22

$\{0, 1, 2, \ldots, 1000\}$

"The set whose members are the natural numbers from 0 through 1000"

book 1 page 23

$\{0, 1, 2, \ldots\}$

"The set whose members are the natural numbers"

book 1 page 27

$\{x \mid x < 6\}$

"The set whose members are all x that satisfy the condition that x is less than six"

book 1 page 33

$\overleftrightarrow{RS}$

"Line RS"

book 1 page 38

$\overline{XZ}$

"Segment XZ"

book 1 page 39

$\overline{AB} \cong \overline{CD}.$

"Segment AB is congruent to segment CD."

book 1 page 83

$\{1, 2, 3, 4\} \cap \{2, 4, 6\}$

"The intersection of the set whose members are one, two, three, four and the set whose members are two, four, six"

book 1 page 83

$C \cap D = \{2, 4\}.$

"The intersection of C and D equals the set whose members are two, four."

book 1 page 87

$\{5, 10\} \cup \{6, 8, 10\}$

"The union of the set whose members are five, ten and the set whose members are six, eight, ten"

book 1 page 87

$C \cup D = \{5, 6, 8, 10\}.$

"The union of C and D equals the set whose members are five, six, eight, ten."

book 1 page 91

$x + 3 > 7 \wedge 6 + x < 14.$

"x plus three is greater than seven and six plus x is less than fourteen."

book 1 page 91

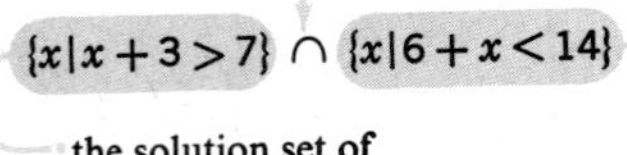

"The intersection of the solution set of $x+3>7$ and the solution set of $6+x<14$"

book 1 page 104

$\overleftrightarrow{AB}$ — "Ray AB"

book 1 page 105

∠ABC — "Angle ABC"

book 1 page 109

△ABC — "Triangle ABC"

book 1 page 123

(Paris, Spain) — "The ordered pair whose first component is Paris and whose second component is Spain"

book 1 page 124

(1, 2) — "The ordered pair one, two"

book 1 page 127

A × B — "A cross B"

book 1 page 128

(a, b) — "The ordered pair a, b"

book 1 page 138

{ (x, y) | $x>y$ } — "The set whose members are all ordered pairs x, y that satisfy the condition that x is greater than y"

book 1 page 139

point (1, 4) — "Point 1, 4"

book 1 page 169

(2, 7) ~ (4, 14). — "The ordered pair two, seven is equivalent to the ordered pair four, fourteen."

book 1 page 174

1/15 ~ 2/30. — "One to fifteen is equivalent to two to thirty."

book 1 page 174

{ 4/7, . . . } — "The set whose members are the rate pair 4/7 and all rate pairs equivalent to 4/7"

book 1 page 175

{ (x, y) | x/y ~ 4/7 } — "The set whose members are the ordered pairs x, y that satisfy the condition that x to y is equivalent to four to seven"

book 1 page 187

88 % — "Eighty-eight per cent"

book 1 page 216

1033_{four} — "one zero three three, base four"

book 1 page 227

10^2 — "The second power of ten"

book 1 page 238

256, 193, 462, 109 — "256 billion 193 million 462 thousand 109"

book 1 page 249

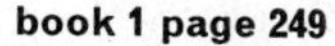

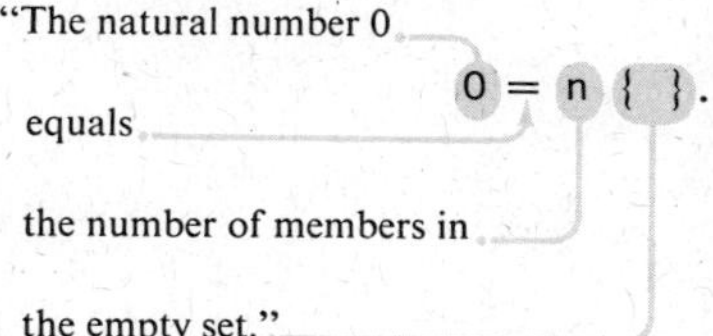

"The natural number 0
equals
the number of members in
the empty set."
0 = n { }.

book 1 page 257

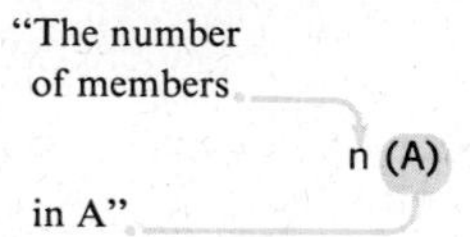

"The number
of members
in A"
n (A)

book 1 page 257

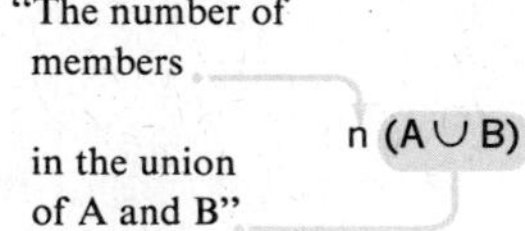

"The number of
members
in the union
of A and B"
n (A ∪ B)

book 1 page 262

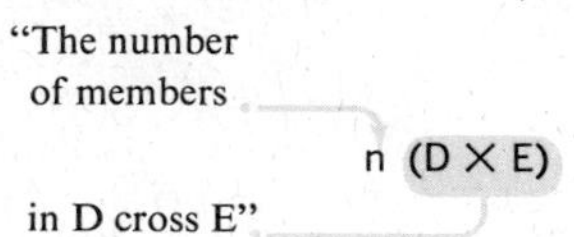

"The number
of members
in D cross E"
n (D × E)

book 1 page 311

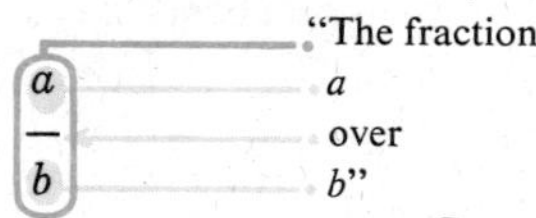

"The fraction
a
over
b"
a/b

book 1 page 311

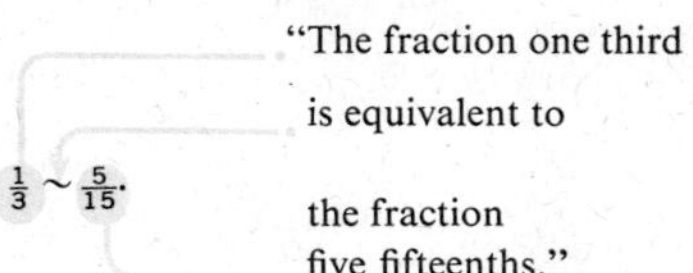

"The fraction one third
is equivalent to
the fraction
five fifteenths."
$\frac{1}{3} \sim \frac{5}{15}$.

book 1 page 314

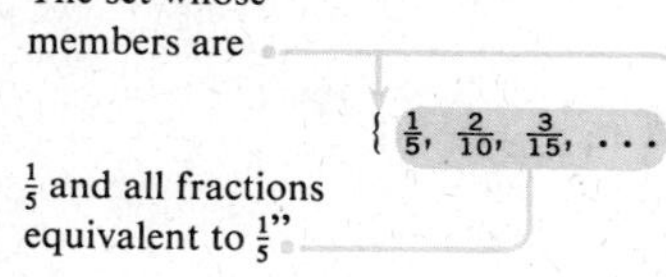

"The set whose
members are
$\frac{1}{5}$ and all fractions
equivalent to $\frac{1}{5}$"
$\{\frac{1}{5}, \frac{2}{10}, \frac{3}{15}, \ldots\}$

book 1 page 371

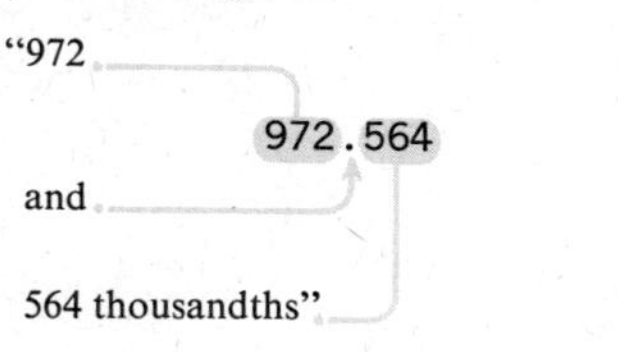

"972
and
564 thousandths"
972.564

book 1 page 372

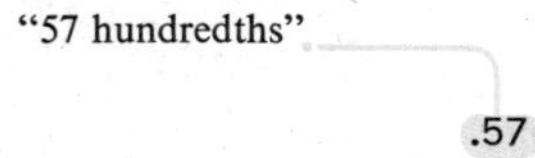

"57 hundredths"
.57

book 1 page 385

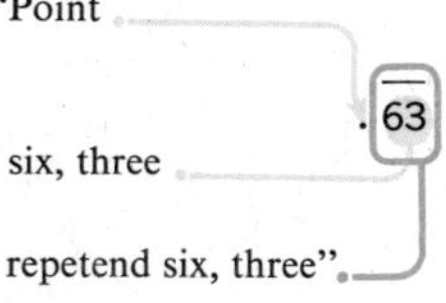

"Point
six, three
repetend six, three"
$.\overline{63}$

book 1 page 385

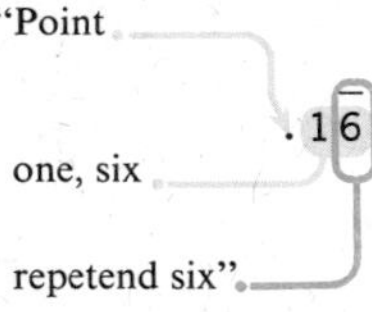

"Point
one, six
repetend six"
$.1\overline{6}$

book 1 page 427

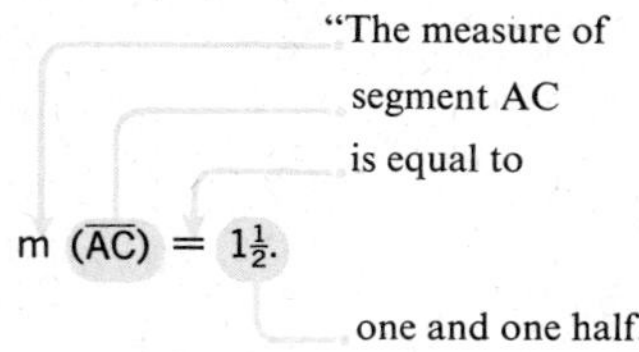

"The measure of
segment AC
is equal to
one and one half."
$m(\overline{AC}) = 1\frac{1}{2}$.

book 1 page 443

"The measure in
degrees of
angle ABC
is equal to
40."
$\angle ABC° = 40$.

book 2 page 9

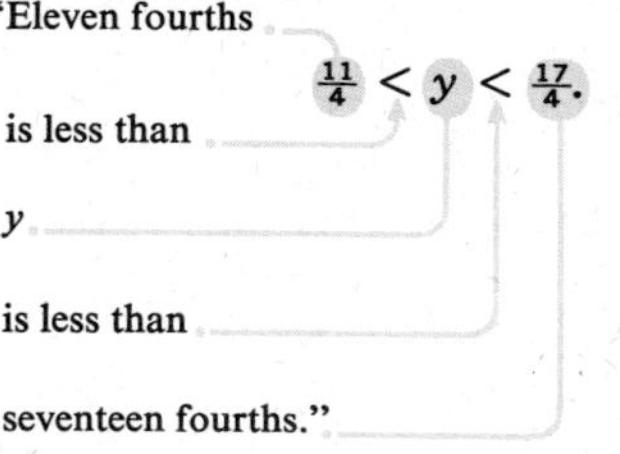

"Eleven fourths
is less than
y
is less than
seventeen fourths."
$\frac{11}{4} < y < \frac{17}{4}$.

book 2 page 11

"s plus two is

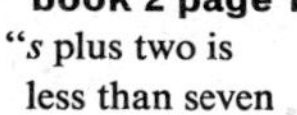

less than seven

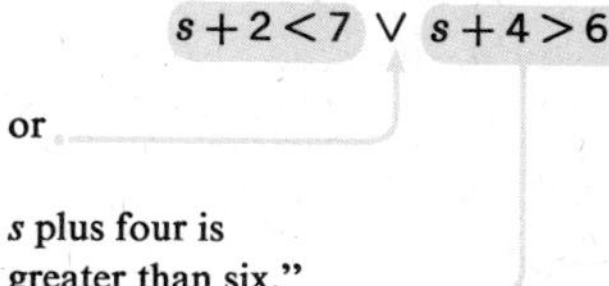

or
s plus four is
greater than six."
$s + 2 < 7 \vee s + 4 > 6$.

book 2 page 12

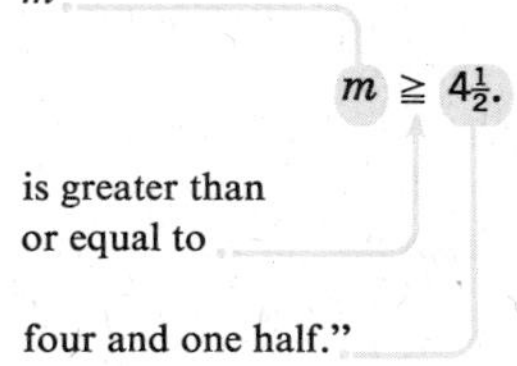

"m
is greater than
or equal to
four and one half."
$m \geqq 4\frac{1}{2}$.

book 2 page 13

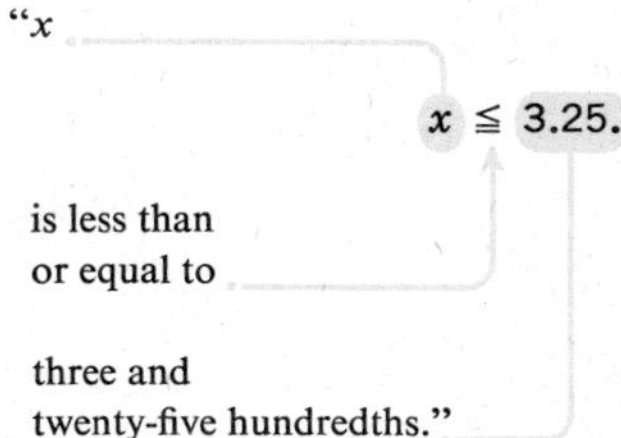

"x
is less than
or equal to
three and
twenty-five hundredths."
$x \leqq 3.25$.

book 2 page 20

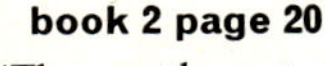

"The complement of

$\overline{\{1, 4, 5\}} = \{2, 3\}.$

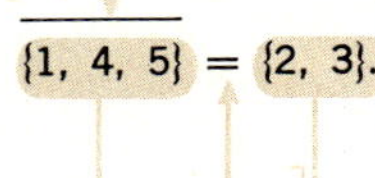

the set whose members are one, four, five

is equal to

the set whose members are two, three."

book 2 page 21

"The complement of M

$\overline{M} = \{2, 3\}.$

is equal to

the set whose members are two, three."

book 2 page 22

"It is not the case that

$\sim (x > 6).$

x is greater than six."

book 2 page 29

"Seventeen

is a member of

$17 \in \{a | a > 8\frac{3}{5}\}.$

the solution set of $a > 8\frac{3}{5}$."

book 2 page 30

"x

is approximately equal to

$x \approx 7.$

seven."

book 2 page 32

"x

is approximately equal to

$x \approx_1 7.$

seven

with a tolerance of one."

book 2 page 32

U = Z.

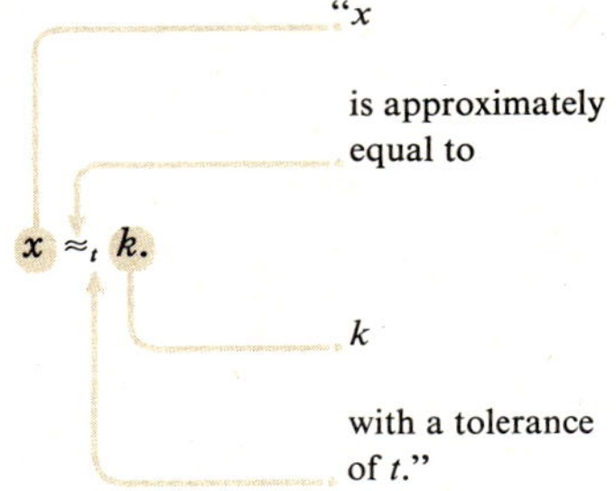

"x

is approximately equal to

$x \approx_t k.$

k

with a tolerance of t."

book 2 page 34

"The ordered triple

$(4, 2, 6)$

four, two, six "

book 2 page 35

"The set whose members are

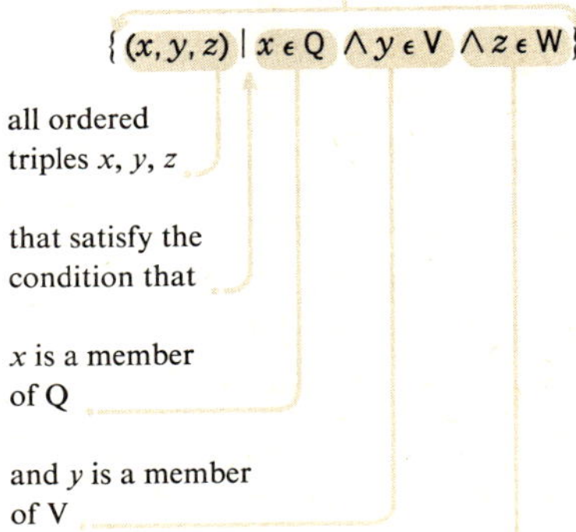

$\{(x, y, z) \mid x \in Q \wedge y \in V \wedge z \in W\}$

all ordered triples x, y, z

that satisfy the condition that

x is a member of Q

and y is a member of V

and z is a member of W"

book 2 page 56

"Circle

$\odot S$

S"

book 2 page 60

"Arc

$\overset{\frown}{EHF}$

EHF"

book 2 page 61

"The measure in degrees of

minor $\overset{\frown}{PR}\,° = 70.$

minor arc PR

is equal to

70."

book 2 page 64

"Segment XY

$\overline{XY} \parallel \overline{WZ}.$

is parallel to

segment WZ."

book 2 page 65

"Segment EF

$\overline{EF} \perp \overline{FG}.$

is perpendicular to

segment FG."

book 2 page 96

"The directed segment

$\overrightarrow{RS}$

RS"

book 2 page 110

"The set whose members are

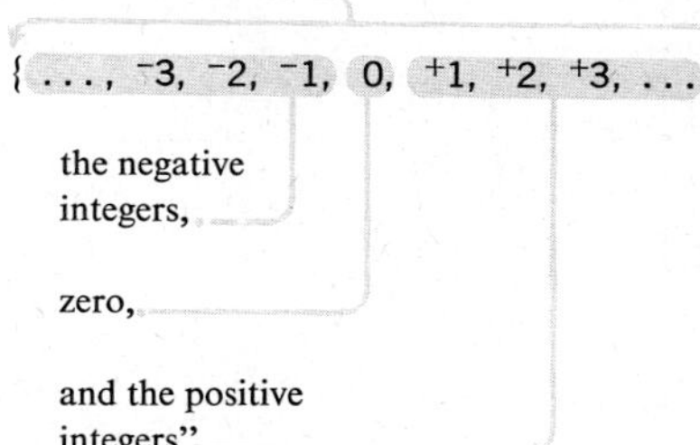

the negative integers,

zero,

and the positive integers"

book 2 page 147

"The additive inverse of

$^{-}(^{+}3)$

positive three"

book 2 page 198

"The principal square root of

$\sqrt{a}$

a"

book 2 page 255

"A length of 150 ft.

150 ft. ± 5

with a greatest possible error of 5 ft."

book 2 page 268

"Triangle ABC

$\triangle ABC \sim \triangle DEF.$

is similar to

triangle DEF."

book 2 page 276

"The tangent of 30

$\tan 30 \approx .5774.$

is approximately equal to

.5774."

book 2 page 420

"The ordered quadruple

(Mike, Tom, Eric, John)

Mike, Tom, Eric, John"

book 2 page 422

"Four factorial

$4! = 4 \times 3 \times 2 \times 1.$

is equal to

the product of four, three, two, and one."

book 2 page 423

"The number of permutations

P(4, 4)

of four different objects

taken four at a time"

book 2 page 424

"The number of permutations

P(6, 3)

of six different objects

taken three at a time"

book 2 page 429

"The number of combinations

C(8, 4)

of eight elements

taken four at a time"

book 2 page 434

"The number of divisors

$\tau\ (18) = 6.$

of eighteen

is equal to six."

book 2 page 437

"The sum of the divisors

$\sigma\ (10) = 18.$

of ten

is equal to eighteen."

book 2 page 451

"The probability

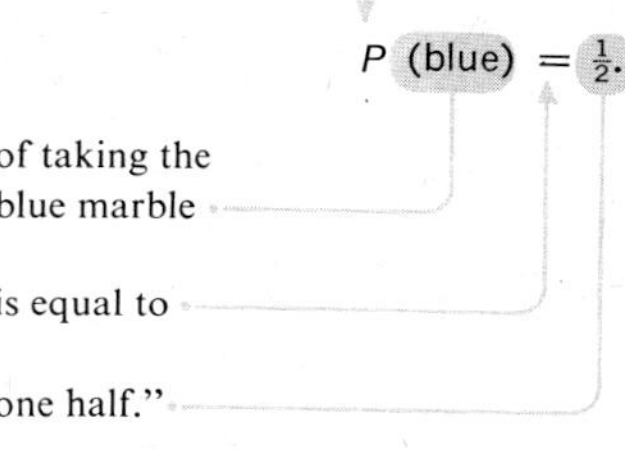

of taking the blue marble

is equal to

one half."

book 3 page 6

"The vector

$\overrightarrow{AB}$

AB"

book 3 page 7

"The sum of

$\overrightarrow{AB} \oplus \overrightarrow{BC} = \overrightarrow{AC}.$

vector AB and vector BC

is equal to vector AC."

book 3 page 27

"50 degrees

west of

N 50° W

north"

book 3 page 44

"Vector

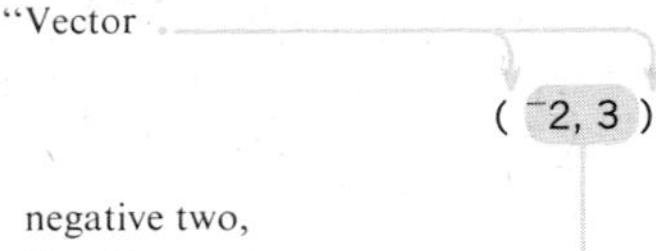

negative two,
three"

book 3 page 56

"The product of

the scalar 3

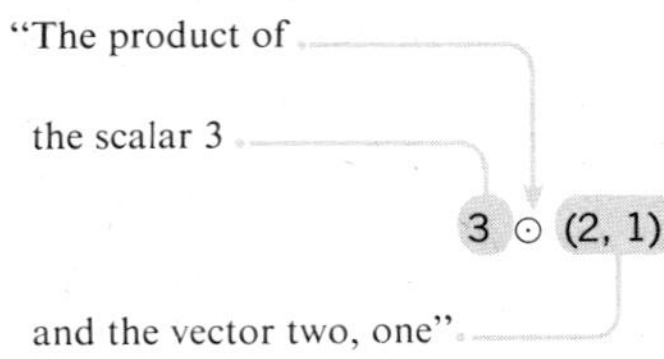

and the vector two, one"

book 3 page 74

"The addiv of
3 and 4

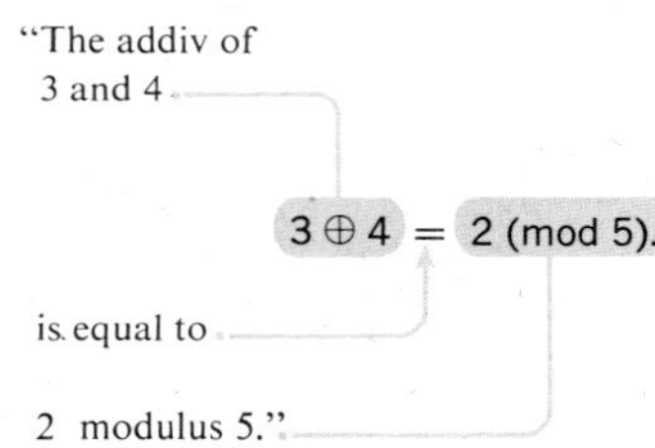

is equal to

2 modulus 5."

book 3 page 125

"If
p

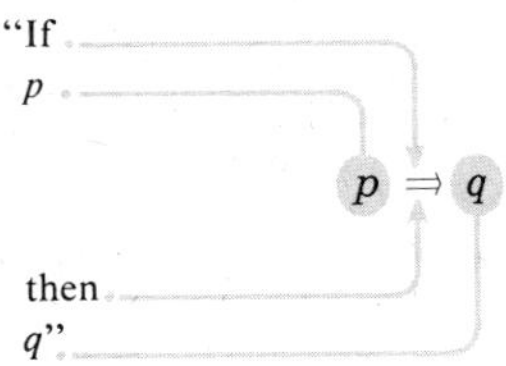

then
q"

book 3 page 131

"*p*

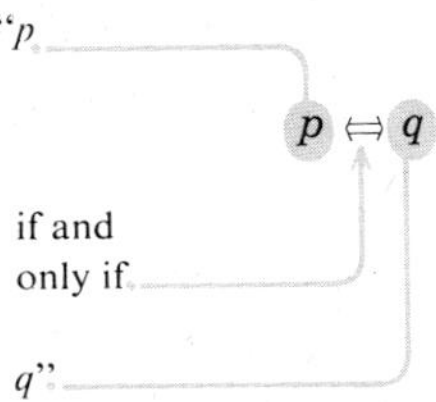

if and
only if

q"

book 3 page 255

"The solution set
of $r^2 = 4$

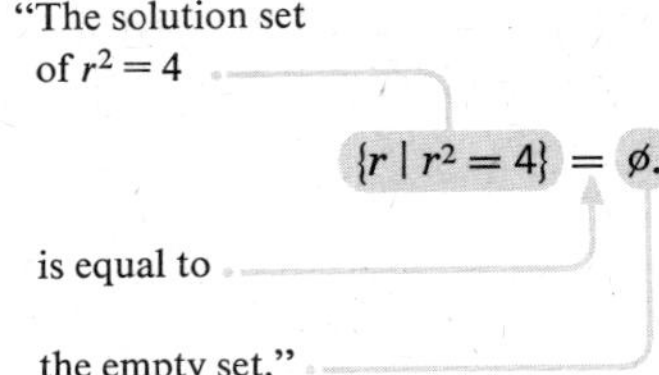

is equal to

the empty set."

book 3 page 273

"The absolute value of

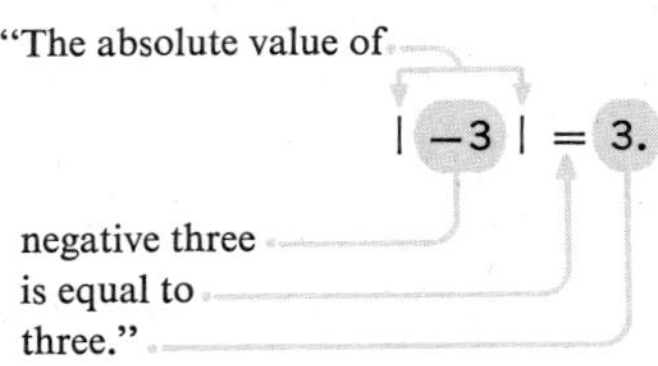

negative three
is equal to
three."

book 3 page 305

"f
of

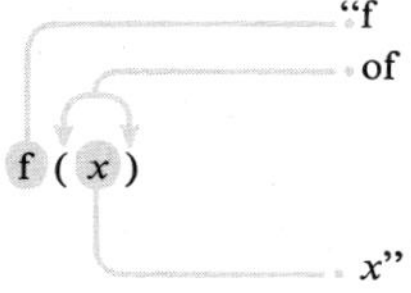

x"

book 3 page 306

"*b*
is equal to

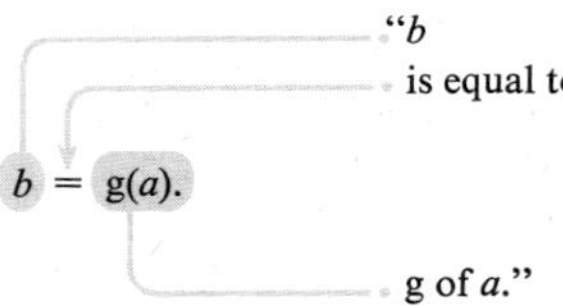

g of *a*."

book 3 page 326

"Negative one
is equal to

the greatest of the
integers that is
less than or equal to

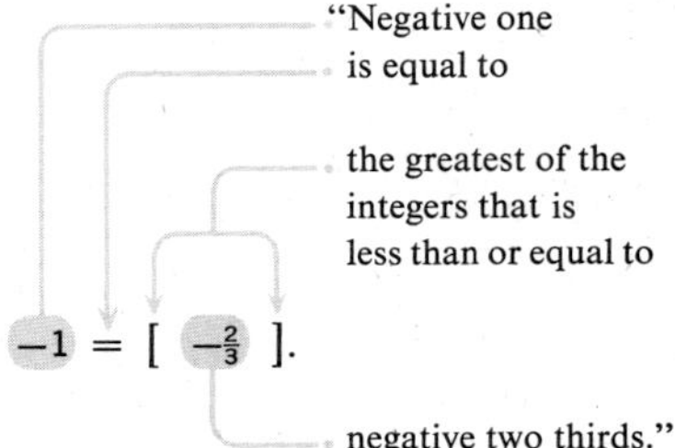

negative two thirds."

These displays explain the symbols used in this book for the various sets of numbers and their subsets.

N This symbol names the set of natural numbers. The symbol is read "the set of natural numbers." You learned about this set in lesson 6, *Book 1*, pages 22, 23, and 24.

C This symbol names the set of counting numbers. The symbol is read "the set of counting numbers." You learned about this set in lesson 20, *Book 1*, page 73.

R_a This symbol names the set of rational numbers of arithmetic. The symbol is read "the set of rational numbers of arithmetic." You learned about this set in lesson 73, *Book 1*, page 318.

Z This symbol names the set of non-zero rational numbers of arithmetic. The symbol is read "the set of non-zero rational numbers of arithmetic." You learned about this set in lesson 85, *Book 1*, page 367.

R This symbol names the set of rational numbers. The symbol is read "the set of rational numbers." You learned about this set in lesson 128, *Book 2*, page 105.

R_p This symbol names the set of positive rational numbers. The symbol is read "the set of positive rational numbers." You learned about this set in lesson 127, *Book 2*, pages 99 and 100.

R_n This symbol names the set of negative rational numbers. The symbol is read "the set of negative rational numbers." You learned about this set in lesson 128, *Book 2*, pages 103 to 105.

$\bar{R}_n$ This symbol names the set of non-negative rational numbers. The symbol is read "the set of non-negative rational numbers." You learned about this set in lesson 134, *Book 2*, page 129.

Z_r This symbol names the set of non-zero rational numbers. The symbol is read "the set of non-zero rational numbers." You learned about this set in lesson 140, *Book 2*, page 153.

I This symbol names the set of integers. The symbol is read "the set of integers." You learned about this set in lesson 129, *Book 2*, page 110.

I_p This symbol names the set of positive integers. The symbol is read "the set of positive integers." You learned about this set in lesson 129, *Book 2*, page 110.

I_n This symbol names the set of negative integers. The symbol is read "the set of negative integers." You learned about this set in lesson 129, *Book 2*, page 110.

D This symbol names the set of real numbers. The symbol is read "the set of real numbers." You learned about this set in lesson 151, *Book 2*, page 205.

$\bar{R}$ This symbol names the set of irrational numbers. The symbol is read "the set of irrational numbers." You learned about this set in lesson 151, *Book 2*, page 204.

Formulas

Numerals in parentheses refer to *Book 2* unless otherwise indicated.

BUSINESS

Cost (315)

$c = np.$

- c — total cost
- n — number of items
- p — price

Interest (323)

$i = prt.$

- i — interest
- p — principal
- r — rate
- t — time

Amount (323)

$a = p + i.$

- a — amount
- p — principal
- i — interest

$A = p(1 + r)^n$. (Book 3, 165)

- A — amount
- p — original principal
- r — rate of interest for 1 period
- n — number of periods

Selling price (323)

$s = c + o + p.$

- s — selling price
- c — cost
- o — overhead
- p — profit

SCIENCE

Temperature (326)

$C = \frac{5}{9}(F - 32).$

$F = \frac{9}{5}C + 32.$

- C — number of degrees centigrade
- F — number of degrees Fahrenheit

Work (324)

$w = fd.$

- w — work
- f — force
- d — distance

Power (324)

$p = \frac{w}{t}.$

- p — power
- w — work
- t — time

Electricity (325)

$I = \frac{E}{R}.$

$W = EI.$

- I — number of amperes of current
- E — number of volts of pressure
- R — number of ohms of resistance
- W — number of watts of power

GEOMETRY

Regular polygon

Perimeter (356)

$p = ns.$

- p — perimeter
- n — number of sides
- s — measure of a side

Area (363)

$A = \frac{1}{2}ans.$

$A = \frac{1}{2}ap.$

- A — area
- a — measure of an apothem
- n — number of sides
- s — measure of a side
- p — perimeter

Number of diagonals of a polygon (Book 3, 387)

$d = \frac{n^2 - 3n}{2}.$

- d — number of diagonals
- n — number of sides

Trapezoid

Area (331)

$A = \frac{1}{2}a(b_1 + b_2).$

- A — area
- a — measure of an altitude
- b_1, b_2 — measures of the bases

Parallelogram

Area (329)

$A = ab.$

- A — area
- a — measure of an altitude
- b — measure of the base

Rectangle

Perimeter (327)

$p = 2l + 2w.$

- p — perimeter
- l — length
- w — width

Area (329)

$A = lw.$

- A — area
- l — length
- w — width

Triangle

Perimeter (328)

$p = a + b + c.$

- p — perimeter
- a, b, c — measures of the sides

Area (329)

$A = \frac{1}{2}ab.$

- A — area
- a — measure of an altitude
- b — measure of the base

Equilateral triangle

Perimeter (328)

$p = 3s.$

- p — perimeter
- s — measure of a side

Circle

Circumference (360)

$c = 2\pi r.$

$c = \pi d.$

- c — circumference
- r — measure of a radius
- d — measure of a diameter

Area (365)

$A = \pi r^2.$

$A = \pi(\frac{d}{2})^2.$

- A — area
- r — measure of a radius
- d — measure of a diameter

Right prism

Volume (384)

$V = Bh.$

$V = \frac{1}{2}aph.$

- V — volume
- B — area of a base
- a — measure of an apothem of a base
- p — perimeter of a base
- h — height

Rectangular right prism

Surface area (380)

$S = 2(lw + hw + lh).$

- S — surface area
- l — length
- w — width
- h — height

Volume (384)

$V = lwh.$

- V — volume
- l — length
- w — width
- h — height

Cube

Surface area (380)

$S = 6e^2.$

- S — surface area
- e — measure of an edge

Volume (385)

$V = e^3.$

- V — volume
- e — measure of an edge

Triangular right prism

Surface area (381)

$S = ab + hp.$

- S — surface area
- a — measure of an altitude of a triangle that determines a base
- b — measure of the base of the triangle
- h — height
- p — perimeter of a base

Volume (385)

$V = \frac{1}{2}abh.$

- V — volume
- a — measure of an altitude of a triangle that determines a base
- b — measure of the base of the triangle
- h — height

Right circular cylinder

Surface area (381)

$S = 2\pi r(r + h).$

- S — surface area
- r — measure of a radius of a base
- h — height

Volume (385)

$V = \pi r^2 h.$

V — volume

r — measure of a radius of a base

h — height

Regular pyramid

Volume (392)

$V = \frac{1}{3}Bh.$

$V = \frac{1}{6}aph.$

V — volume

B — area of the base

h — height

a — measure of an apothem of the base

p — perimeter of the base

Square regular pyramid

Volume (392)

$V = \frac{1}{3}e^2 h.$

V — volume

e — measure of an edge

h — height

Triangular regular pyramid

Volume (392)

$V = \frac{1}{6}abh.$

V — volume

a — measure of an altitude of the triangle that determines the base

b — measure of the base of the triangle

h — height

Right circular cone

Surface area (Book 3, 165)

$S = \pi r(r + s).$

S — surface area

r — measure of a radius of the base

s — slant height

Volume (393)

$V = \frac{1}{3}Bh.$

$V = \frac{1}{3}\pi r^2 h.$

V — volume

B — area of the base

r — measure of a radius of the base

h — height

Sphere

Surface area (403)

$S = 4\pi r^2.$

S — surface area

r — measure of a radius

Volume (405)

$V = \frac{4}{3}\pi r^3.$

V — volume

r — measure of a radius

Pythagorean property (350)

$c^2 = a^2 + b^2.$

c — measure of the hypotenuse

$\left.\begin{matrix} a \\ b \end{matrix}\right\}$ — measures of the sides opposite the acute angles of a right triangle

Trigonometry

$\tan t = \frac{y}{x}.$ (317)

$\sin t = \frac{y}{r}.$ (317)

$\cos t = \frac{x}{r}.$ (317)

t — measure of an acute angle of a right triangle

x — measure of side adjacent to acute angle

y — measure of side opposite acute angle

r — measure of hypotenuse of right triangle

MISCELLANEOUS

Distance (314)

$d = rt.$

d — distance

r — rate

t — time

$d = v_0 t - 16t^2.$ (Book 3, 387)

d — distance

v_0 — initial velocity

t — number of seconds

Percentage (315)

$p = br.$

p — percentage

b — base

r — rate

Average (316)

$a = \frac{t}{n}.$

a — average

t — total

n — number of items

Conversion (316)

$l = kg.$

l — lesser unit of measure

k — constant

g — greater unit of measure

Arithmetic progression

Given term (413)

$l = a + (n - 1)d.$

l — given term

a — first term

n — number for position of given term

d — common difference

Sum of terms (414)

$s = \frac{n(a + l)}{2}.$

s — sum of the terms

n — number of terms

a — first term

l — last term

Permutations and combinations

$P(n, n) = n!.$ (424)

$P(n, m) = n(n - 1)(n - 2) \ldots$ (m factors). (424)

$C(n, m) = \frac{P(n, m)}{P(m, m)}.$ (430)

$P(n, n)$ — number of permutations of n different objects taken n at a time

$P(n, m)$ — number of permutations of n different objects taken m at a time

$C(n, m)$ — number of m-element combinations of the n elements of a given set

$P(m, m)$ — number of permutations of m different objects taken m at a time

Probability of an event (457)

$P(M) = \frac{m}{n}.$

$P(M)$ — probability of the event

m — number of elements in the event

n — number of elements in the sample space

Probability of the union of two events (460)

$P(M \cup N) = P(M) + P(N) - P(M \cap N).$

$P(M \cup N)$ — probability of the union of events M and N

$P(M)$ — probability of event M

$P(N)$ — probability of event N

$P(M \cap N)$ — probability of the intersection of events M and N

Probability of the union of two mutually exclusive events (461)

$P(M \cup N) = P(M) + P(N).$

$P(M \cup N)$ — probability of the union of events M and N

$P(M)$ — probability of event M

$P(N)$ — probability of event N

Probability of the complement of an event (462)

$P(\overline{M}) = 1 - P(M).$

$P(\overline{M})$ — probability of the complement of event M

$P(M)$ — probability of event M

Probability of the intersection of two independent events (465)

$P(M \cap N) = P(M) \cdot P(N).$

$P(M \cap N)$ — probability of the intersection of events M and N

$P(M)$ — probability of event M

$P(N)$ — probability of event N

Arithmetic mean (479)

$\overline{x} = \frac{x_1 + x_2 + x_3 + \ldots + x_n}{n}$

$\overline{x}$ — arithmetic mean

$x_1 + x_2 + x_3 + \ldots + x_n$ — sum of n measures

n — number of measures

Responses to ? exercises

Responses to ? exercises are keyed to your book by page number and exercise letter. For example, the response for exercise D on page 254 is labeled 254 D. When an exercise includes two or more questions, the responses to these questions are separated by an asterisk (*).

254 D Because every polynomial expression is also a rational expression

254 G Because every polynomial expression is also an algebraic expression * Because every rational expression is also an algebraic expression, every rational condition is also an algebraic condition.

254 J Division by zero is undefined, and if y is replaced by 0 in condition F, two of the divisors become 0. Therefore, $\frac{1}{6}y^2 - \frac{5}{2y}$ and $\frac{2}{y}$ do not yield real numbers when y is replaced by 0.

255 F {3} * Yes. Conditions I and K have the same solution set; hence, they are equivalent.

255 I Yes * When you subtract 5 from both sides of condition I, you obtain condition K. The solution set of both conditions is {3}; therefore, they are equivalent.

256 J The well-defined property of multiplication

256 K Yes. $\frac{3}{10} + \frac{2}{10} = \frac{5}{10}$.

256 M When you multiply both sides of condition I by x, you obtain $x^2 + 2x = 5x$. * The well-defined property of multiplication

256 O No * Condition N has a different solution set from condition I.

257 R $x^2 + 2x = 5x \Rightarrow x + 2 = 5$. * 0 * No. If x is replaced by 0 in $x^2 + 2x = 5x \Rightarrow x + 2 = 5$, then the antecedent is true, the consequent is false, and the conditional is false.

257 C 95 * No. $p \Rightarrow q$ is true when p is false and q is true. This means that it would still be true that $\frac{2}{5}x - 30 = 8 \Rightarrow x = 95$ even if 95 did not satisfy $\frac{2}{5}x - 30 = 8$.

257 E $x = 95 \Rightarrow \frac{2}{5}x - 30 = 8$. * You know that 95 satisfies $x = 95$. Therefore, 95 must satisfy $\frac{2}{5}x - 30 = 8$ because a true conditional cannot have a true antecedent and a false consequent.

257 H From the proofs given in D10 and D12, you know that conjunction D is true for each x. Biconditional E is equivalent to conjunction D; therefore, biconditional E must be true for each x.

257 I Since $\frac{2}{5}x - 30 = 8$ has the same truth value as $x = 95$ for each x, $\frac{2}{5}x - 30 = 8$ and $x = 95$ must have the same solution set. Conditions that have the same solution set are equivalent. * {95}

257 J We first proved the conditional $\frac{2}{5}x - 30 = 8 \Rightarrow x = 95$ to obtain the condition $x = 95$, whose solution set is immediately obvious. However, the fact that 95 satisfies $x = 95$ does not necessarily mean that 95 satisfies $\frac{2}{5}x - 30 = 8$ because the conditional $\frac{2}{5}x - 30 = 8 \Rightarrow x = 95$ would be true when x is replaced by 95 even if its antecedent were false. Thus, we also had to prove the converse, $x = 95 \Rightarrow \frac{2}{5}x - 30 = 8$. A proof of this converse shows that, since 95 satisfies $x = 95$, it must also satisfy $\frac{2}{5}x - 30 = 8$ because a true conditional cannot have a true antecedent and a false consequent. * 95 is the only solution of $x = 95$, which is equivalent to $\frac{2}{5}x - 30 = 8$ and therefore has the same solution set.

258 K Condition G: Well-defined property of multiplication.
Condition H: Definition of reciprocal.
Condition I: Well-defined property of addition and difference theorem of real numbers.
Condition J: Definition of additive inverse (or subtraction).
Condition K: Well-defined property of multiplication.
Condition L: Division and identity-element property of multiplication
*0

258 N $0 = x \Rightarrow \frac{1}{x} = 2 + \frac{1}{x}$ is not true for each x. * When x is replaced by 0, the statement obtained from $0 = x$ is true, but the statement obtained from $\frac{1}{x} = 2 + \frac{1}{x}$ is meaningless since division by 0 is not defined.

260 J $ax + b = 0 \Rightarrow x = \frac{-b}{a}$. * $\frac{-b}{a}$

260 K No. The conditional $p \Rightarrow q$ is true for the case in which p is false and q is true. This means that, even if $\frac{-b}{a}$ is not a solution of $ax + b = 0$, it is still true that $ax + b = 0 \Rightarrow x = \frac{-b}{a}$.

262 D $\frac{4}{5}(10 + 15x) - 5x = (8 + 12x) - 5x$. $(8 + 12x) - 5x = 8 + 7x$. * Since $\frac{4}{5}(10 + 15x) - 5x = 8 + 7x$ and $8 + 7x = 7x + 8$, condition E can be put in the form $ax + b < 0$, where $a = 7$ and $b = 8$.

263 G "If $b > a$, then $b + c > a + c$" has the same meaning as "If $a < b$, then $a + c < b + c$." Therefore, by the sum property of "less than" for real numbers, you obtain an equivalent condition if you add the same real number to both sides of J. If you add $-1x$ to both sides of condition J, you obtain condition K.

264 D No. The conditional $ax + b > 0 \Rightarrow x > \frac{-b}{a}$ is true even if $x > \frac{-b}{a}$ is true and $ax + b > 0$ is false.

265 G For each $a > 0$ and for each b and x, $(ax + b > 0) \Leftrightarrow \left(x > \frac{-b}{a}\right)$. * The biconditional $p \Leftrightarrow q$ is true only if both p and

q are true or both p and q are false. Therefore, $ax+b>0$ is true only if $x>\frac{-b}{a}$ is true, which means that these two conditions must have the same solutions. * Yes

265 L $ax+b<0 \Leftrightarrow x<\frac{-b}{a}$. * A biconditional is true only when both components have the same truth value; therefore, $ax+b<0$ is true only when $x<\frac{-b}{a}$ is true. * Yes * Yes. The set of real numbers less than any given number is infinite.

265 P $ax+b>0$.
$ax>0-b$.
Sum property of "less than."
$ax>-b$.
Identity-element property of addition.
$\frac{1}{a}(ax)<\frac{1}{a}(-b)$.
Negative-multiplier property of "less than."
$x<\frac{-b}{a}$.
Definition of reciprocal and product property of quotients.

$x<\frac{-b}{a}$.
$ax>a\left(\frac{-b}{a}\right)$.
Negative-multiplier property of "less than."
$ax>-b$.
Definition of reciprocal and product property of quotients.
$ax+b>-b+b$.
Sum property of "less than."
$ax+b>0$.
Definition of additive inverse

265 S $ax+b<0$.
$ax<0-b$.
Sum property of "less than."
$ax<-b$.
Identity-element property of addition.
$\frac{1}{a}(ax)>\frac{1}{a}(-b)$.
Negative-multiplier property of "less than."
$x>\frac{-b}{a}$.
Definition of reciprocal and product property of quotients.

$x>\frac{-b}{a}$.
$ax<a\left(\frac{-b}{a}\right)$.
Negative-multiplier property of "less than."
$ax<-b$.
Definition of reciprocal and product property of quotients.
$ax+b<-b+b$.
Sum property of "less than."
$ax+b-0$.
Definition of additive inverse

272 C Yes * For example, suppose that the coördinate of point x is -5.8. The measure of the segment determined by point -5.8 and the origin is $5.8-0$, or 5.8. Since $x=-5.8$, $-x=-(-5.8)$ and $-(-5.8)=5.8$. Thus, the measure of the segment that is determined by point -5.8 and the origin is equal to $-x$.

275 C $|x|=3$ has the same solution set as $x=3 \vee x=-3$, which is $\{3, -3\}$.

277 D Yes. Both of these sets contain 2, -2, and every real number between 2 and -2. * The solution set of $|x| \leqq 2$ is a closed interval. * The limits of this interval are 2 and -2.

277 G Yes. Both of these sets contain every real number between 2 and -2. * The solution set of $|x|<2$ is an open interval. * The limits of this interval are 2 and -2.

278 A Every point to the right of point 2 and every point to the left of point -2 have coördinates that satisfy both $|x| \geqq 2$ and $|x|>2$ because the solution sets of both conditions contain every real number greater than 2 and every real number less than -2. * The coördinates of the points between point 2 and point -2 do not satisfy either $|x| \geqq 2$ or $|x|>2$.

279 N The condition $|x|=-3$ requires that the absolute value of the replacement for x be negative. Thus, the solution set of this condition is the empty set because the absolute value of every real number is non-negative.

279 O { } or $\emptyset$ * Yes. The absolute value of every real number is non-negative, and every non-negative real number is greater than -3.

282 F No. The only numbers that provide sensible answers to the problem in D4 are numbers like 2, 3, or 15, which are positive integers. * Yes. $x \in I_p$ requires that the replacement for x be a positive integer.

282 J $2(1\frac{1}{2}x+3)+2(x+3)>10(1\frac{1}{2}x)$.
$3x+6+2x+6>15x$.
$5x+12>15x$.
$12>10x$.
$\frac{6}{5}>x$. *
The measure of length is always positive.
* $x>0$.

283 N Yes. Since each bushel of the mixture will sell for at least \$1.50, the selling price for 200 bushels will be at least 1.50(200) dollars. * The condition $1.14x+1.74(200-x) \geqq 1.50(200)$ requires that the total value of the mixture, $1.14x+1.74(200-x)$, be at least 1.50(200). If this requirement is met, then each bushel of the mixture will be worth at least \$1.50. * The condition $x>0$ requires that the number of bushels of corn in the mixture be greater than 0. This is necessary because, otherwise, the "mixture" would not be a mixture.

283 S The number of pennies must be a positive integer. Answers like -5 pennies, $\frac{1}{2}$ penny, or 0 pennies are meaningless in this situation.

291 F The fundamental counting property may be expressed as follows: The universe for r and s

Responses to ? page 292

is I_p. If a first event can occur in r ways, and, if after the first event has occurred, a second event can occur in s ways, then the two successive events can occur in rs ways. Now there are 7 ways of choosing the first component of an ordered pair that is to be a member of A × B. After the first component is chosen, there are 29 ways of choosing the second component. Thus, there are 7 × 29, or 203, members in A × B.

292 J No * Each member of B × A has an integer from 1 through 29 for its first component and a day of the week for its second component. Therefore, no member of B × A is like the members of M, each of which has a day of the week as its first component and an integer from 1 through 29 as its second component.

293 D No. When the universe for (x, y) is D × D, $\{(x, y) \mid y = x\}$ is not a subset of S × S because it contains ordered pairs like $(\frac{1}{2}, \frac{1}{2})$ and $(-\sqrt{13}, -\sqrt{13})$, which are not elements of S × S. * No. The set described in exercise C is not a subset of I × I because it contains ordered pairs whose components are not integers. * Yes. The set described in exercise C is a subset of D × D.

294 H $y > x$.

294 I Yes. For example, (3, 4), (3, 8), and $(3, \sqrt{10})$ are all members of relation J; also, $(-5\frac{1}{2}, 0)$, $(-5\frac{1}{2}, \sqrt{2})$, and $(-5\frac{1}{2}, .03)$ are all members of J.

296 B R = {(North America, Chicago), (South America, Buenos Aires), (Africa, Nairobi), (Europe, Paris), (North America, New York)}.

296 G A relation in a Cartesian set is a subset of the Cartesian set. If the Cartesian set is finite, then the set of first components is finite and the set of second components is also finite. This is so because, if either of these two sets were infinite, then the Cartesian set would be infinite. A subset of a finite set is finite. Therefore, the domain of a relation in a finite Cartesian set must be finite because the domain is a subset of the finite set of first components. The range must also be finite because it is a subset of the finite set of second components.

297 F The relation determined by $y = 2x$, when the universe is E × F, contains exactly four members. Relation P is an infinite set because there are infinitely many elements of D × D whose second components are twice as great as their first components.

297 H Yes. For each x, there is a y that satisfies $y = 2x$ because multiplication is closed in D. * The domain of P is D.

297 I If you could replace y in $y = 2x$ by each real number in turn, you would obtain a corresponding real number x because the quotient of any real number and 2 is an element of D. Hence, the range of P is D.

297 K You cannot divide by 0. However, the quotient of 4 and any non-zero real number is a real number; therefore, every non-zero real number is a first component of one of the elements of the relation determined by $y = \frac{4}{x}$. * You cannot divide 4 by a real number to obtain 0. However, for any given non-zero real number, there is a real number by which you can divide 4 to obtain the given real number. Therefore, every non-zero real number is a second component of a member of the relation.

298 L If x is less than -3, then $\sqrt{x+3}$ is negative. There is no real number that is the square root of a negative number. Hence, none of the first components of the elements of the relation is less than -3. * The symbol $\sqrt{}$ refers to the positive square root or 0. This means that none of the second components of the elements of the relation is negative.

301 M First, R_2 is a relation because it is a set of ordered pairs. Second, R_2 is not a function because some members of R_2 have the same first component. For example, three members of R_2 have a first component of 0.

301 C One * $y = x + 1$ determines a set of ordered pairs, no two of which have the same first component.

301 J ℓ_1 is not a vertical line because a vertical line is the locus of a condition whose solutions all have the same first component. Since ℓ_1 is not vertical, it is not parallel to any coplanar vertical line. Two coplanar lines that are not parallel are intersecting lines, and their intersection contains exactly one point.

302 P Yes * If a relation is not a function, then there are at least two members of the relation that have the same first component. The points associated with these ordered pairs determine a vertical line.

302 Q If a vertical line is to intersect the locus of a relation in more than one point, it is necessary for the relation to contain at least two elements with the same first component. But if a relation is a function, then no two members of the relation have the same first component.

302 E Yes * Each real number is a meaningful replacement for x in $y = x^2$.

302 F Because, for each real number that is used as a replacement for x, the replacement for x^2 is a non-negative real number * The range of the relation is the set of non-negative real numbers.

303 I One

303 **M** Each non-negative real number is the square of a real number, and the square of any real number is a non-negative real number. * D

303 **O** Each element, except zero, in the domain of $\{(x, y) \mid x = y^2\}$ is paired with two elements in the range.

306 **I** Because both b and g(a) represent the second component of a member of function g that corresponds to a

306 **A** Since the universe for the function determined by $f(x) = 4x + 3$ is not specified, you should assume that the universe is $D \times D$. Because multiplication and addition are closed in D, every real number is a meaningful replacement for x in $4x + 3$. Therefore, the domain of the function determined by $f(x) = 4x + 3$ is D.

310 **D** If you replace k by 0 in $y = kx$, you obtain $y = 0x$, or $y = 0$. Each real number is the first component of a member of $\{(x, y) \mid y = 0\}$, and 0 is the second component of each member of the set. Hence, each element of the domain of $\{(x, y) \mid y = 0\}$ is paired with exactly one element of the range. * The domain of this function is D, and the range is $\{0\}$.

310 **E** For each non-zero k, $y = kx$ determines a set of (x, y) in which each real number occurs as a first component and each first component is paired with exactly one second component. * The domain is D and the range is D.

312 **G** If $k > 0$ in $f(x) = kx$, then the components of each ordered pair that satisfies $f(x) = kx$ are either both positive or both negative. Every ordered pair whose components are either both positive or both negative is associated with a point in the first or third quadrant.

312 **P** If $k < 0$, then the only ordered pairs that satisfy $y = kx$ are those that have one negative component and one positive component. These ordered pairs are associated with points in the second and fourth quadrants.

312 **T** The locus of this condition will be a line that slants downward more "steeply" than ℓ_4, but less "steeply" than ℓ_3.

312 **A** The domain is D and the range is the set of non-zero real numbers. * For each value of x, you obtain only one value of y from condition G.

313 **F** Because $g(x) = 2x^2$ is not of the form $g(x) = kx$

313 **G** The second component of each ordered pair is equal to the product of k and the square of the first component.

313 **I** The domain is D and the range is the set of non-negative real numbers. * The domain is D and the range is the set that consists of 0 and every negative real number; that is, the set of non-positive real numbers.

313 **A** Point (0, 0) * Point (0, 0) is in the locus of every condition of the form $g(x) = kx^2$.

314 **E** From exercise D, you know that when $k > 0$, the ordered pairs that satisfy $g(x) = kx^2$ have a second component that is either 0 or positive. The first and second quadrants are the only quadrants that contain points associated with ordered pairs whose second components are positive.

314 **L** For any given x, the absolute value of the g(x) that satisfies $g(x) = -2x^2$ is the same as the g(x) that satisfies $g(x) = 2x^2$. This means that each point in the locus of $g(x) = -2x^2$ is the same distance from the x-axis as its corresponding point in the locus of $g(x) = 2x^2$. Each point in the locus of $g(x) = -2x^2$ is either below the x-axis or in the x-axis. Each point in the locus of $g(x) = 2x^2$ is either above the x-axis or in the x-axis.

316 **J** The domain and the range are the set of non-zero real numbers. Since both k and x are non-zero, f(x) cannot be zero.

317 **N** Because, when $k > 0$, the components of each $(x, f(x))$ that satisfies $f(x) = \frac{k}{x}$ are either both positive or both negative

318 **Q** Because, when $k < 0$, the components of each $(x, f(x))$ that satisfies $f(x) = \frac{k}{x}$ have opposite signs. That is, one component is negative and one is positive.

318 **R** No * The locus of $f(x) = \frac{k}{x}$ does not contain the origin and does not intersect either axis because 0 is not an element of either the domain or the range of the function determined by $f(x) = \frac{k}{x}$.

318 **K** The range is the set of positive real numbers. * The range is the set of negative real numbers.

318 **L** Because 0 is not in either the domain or the range of $h(x) = \frac{64}{x^2}$

319 **R** No. Because 0 is not the first component of any ordered pair that satisfies condition F, the locus of condition F does not intersect the h(x)-axis. * No. Because 0 is not the second component of any ordered pair that satisfies condition F, the locus of condition F does not intersect the x-axis.

323 **A** $\frac{1}{2}$ as much time would be required for the return trip. * 3 times as much time would be required for the return trip.

325 **C** $f(x) = 0$.

325 **E** Yes * No * For each member of D, there is a corresponding member of function f. Since D is an infinite set, function f is also infinite.

327 **K** The set of $(x, g(x))$ tabulated for exercise D is a subset of function g.

327 M The set of integers
327 O The first coördinates of these points are the members of the interval that is the solution set of $-2 \leqq x < -1$. * Yes * No
327 P -1 is the greatest integer that is less than or equal to each member of the interval that is the solution set of $-1 \leqq x < 0$.
327 S Yes * Yes
328 F The range of the absolute-value function is the set of non-negative real numbers.
328 H Yes * If $x < 0$, then $|x| = -x$.
328 N Because the absolute value of every number is non-negative, there is no point in the locus of the absolute-value function that has a negative number as its second coördinate.
335 K The solution set of $-4 \leqq x \leqq 4$. No point in the locus of function h is to the left of point $(-4, 0)$, and no point in the locus is to the right of point $(4, 0)$. * The solution set of $0 \leqq h(x) \leqq 4$. No point in the locus is below the x-axis, and no point in the locus is above point $(0, 4)$.
335 S $h(x) = \sqrt{16 - x^2}$.
Given.
$h(-x) = \sqrt{16 - (-x)^2}$.
Replacing x by $-x$.
$h(-x) = \sqrt{16 - x^2}$.
Definition of the square of $-x$.
$h(x) = h(-x)$.
Transitive property of equality
335 T You could first represent the points in the locus of function f that are associated with positive values of x. Then you could locate by inspection the corresponding points that are associated with the negative values of x.
336 A $\{x \mid x \in D \wedge x \neq 0\}$
336 E Because the image of each element in the range of function f is a positive number, each point in the locus of function f has a second coördinate that is positive. * The locus does not have an x-intercept because $f(x)$ can never be 0. * No
337 Q Because the range of function h contains each real number that is greater than or equal to 1 * 0 is not in the range of function h.
339 M The second coördinate of an x-intercept of a locus is 0. The first component of a member of a function whose second component is 0 is a zero of the function.
340 D Yes. Since b is added to mx to determine every value of the function and b is a constant, b cannot affect the rate of change of the function. * Yes. The locus of a function always slants upward to the right if the value of the function (the second component) increases as x (the first component) increases.
340 L Yes. Since b is added to mx to determine every value of the function and b is a constant, b cannot affect the rate of change of the function. * Yes. The locus of a function always slants downward to the right if the value of the function (the second component) decreases as x (the first component) increases.
341 R When $m > 0$, the locus of the function slants upward to the right. This locus intersects the x-axis at point $\left(\frac{-b}{m}, 0\right)$. To the right of this point, the line is above the x-axis and $f(x) > 0$. * $x < \frac{-b}{m}$.
341 U When $m < 0$, the locus of the function slants downward to the right. This line intersects the x-axis at point $\left(\frac{-b}{m}, 0\right)$. To the right of this point, the line is below the x-axis and $f(x) < 0$. * $x < \frac{-b}{m}$.
343 M For each point in the coördinate plane, the y-coördinate tells how many units the point is from the x-axis. All points in a line that is the x-axis or that is parallel to the x-axis are the same distance from the x-axis. Therefore, any two points in a line that is the x-axis or that is parallel to the x-axis have the same y-coördinate. * Yes
343 N 0
344 P 0 * 0
344 Q No * No * Consider a segment that is parallel to the x-axis or that is included in the x-axis. Suppose that points (x_1, y_1) and (x_2, y_2) are the endpoints of this segment. Then $x_1 = x_2$ and $x_2 - x_1 = 0$. Therefore, $\frac{y_2 - y_1}{x_2 - x_1}$ is undefined because division by 0 is impossible.
344 E Yes * If point $(0, 0)$ and point (x, mx) are the endpoints of a segment, then the slope of the segment is $\frac{mx - 0}{x - 0}$, which is equal to m. * m
344 F m * m
345 K Point $(0, b)$. If $m = 0$ and $x = 0$, then $f(x) = b$. * Only if $b = 0$. If $m = 0$ and $b \neq 0$, then the locus of $f(x) = mx + b$ is a line that is parallel to the x-axis. * Yes. The locus of a condition of the form $f(x) = b$ contains point $(0, b)$, where either $b = 0$ or $b \neq 0$.
348 D D. Because each real number is a meaningful replacement for x in $f(x) = ax^2$ * The set of non-negative real numbers. If $a > 0$, then for each replacement of x in ax^2, $f(x)$ is a non-negative real number.
348 I Yes. To show that $f(x)$ decreases as x increases, suppose that $a = 1$. Then $f(x) = x^2$. In this case, $f(-5) = 25$, $f(-4) = 16$, and $f(-3) = 9$. * $f(x)$ increases as x is replaced by successively greater positive numbers. Again suppose that $a = 1$. Then $f(x) = x^2$. In this case, $f(1) = 1$, $f(2) = 4$, and $f(3) = 9$.
348 J The $f(x)$-axis * The locus of any function determined by a condition

of the form $f(x) = ax^2$ is symmetric with respect to the f(x)-axis because the value of f(x) is the same as the value of f($-x$).
348 K Point (0, 0) * Point (0, 0) * Point (0, 0) is both the x-intercept and the f(x)-intercept of the locus of any function whose condition is of the form $f(x) = ax^2$.
348 M The domain of the function is D because every real number is a meaningful replacement for x in $f(x) = ax^2$. The range of the function is the set of non-positive real numbers because, if $a < 0$, then ax^2 is negative for each x.
349 O For any function determined by $f(x) = ax^2$, if $a < 0$, f(x) increases as x is replaced by successively greater negative numbers. * For any function determined by $f(x) = ax^2$, if $a < 0$, f(x) decreases as x is replaced by successively greater positive numbers.
349 B Each point in the locus of $f(x) = ax^2 + c$, where $c > 0$, is c units above each corresponding point in the locus of $f(x) = ax^2$. * Each point in the locus of $f(x) = ax^2 + c$, where $c < 0$, is $-c$ units below a corresponding point in the locus of $f(x) = ax^2$.
350 G Yes. If the locus of $f(x) = ax^2 + c$ intersects the x-axis, then there is at least one point in the locus that has 0 as a second component. This means that there is at least one x such that $f(x) = 0$ or such that $ax^2 + c = 0$. * Yes. $ax^2 + c = 0$ is equivalent to $ax^2 = -c$. $ax^2 = -c$ is equivalent to $x^2 = \frac{-c}{a}$. $x^2 = \frac{-c}{a}$ is equivalent to $x = \sqrt{\frac{-c}{a}} \vee x = -\sqrt{\frac{-c}{a}}$. * Yes. Points $\left(\sqrt{\frac{-c}{a}}, 0\right)$ and $\left(-\sqrt{\frac{-c}{a}}, 0\right)$ are in the x-axis and both points have coördinates that satisfy $f(x) = ax^2 + c$.
350 I There are no x-intercepts in the locus of function g because there is no real number that satisfies $0 = 4x^2 + 1$.
350 K In $f(x) = ax^2 + c$, the value of f(x) is the same as the value of f($-x$).
351 L If $a > 0$ in $f(x) = ax^2 + c$, then f(x) decreases as x is replaced by successively greater negative numbers. * f(x) increases as x is replaced by successively greater positive numbers. * If $a < 0$ in $f(x) = ax^2 + c$, then, as x is replaced by successively greater negative numbers, f(x) increases. As x is replaced by successively greater positive numbers, f(x) decreases.
351 F The domain of the function is D and the range is the set of real numbers that are less than or equal to $2\frac{1}{4}$. * $-\frac{1}{2}$ * $-\frac{1}{2}$
351 G No. If you could fold the coördinate plane along the f(x)-axis, the parts of the locus of $f(x) = -x^2 - x + 2$ on each side of the f(x)-axis would not coincide. * Yes. If you could fold the coördinate plane along the locus of $x = -\frac{1}{2}$, then the parts of the locus of $f(x) = -x^2 - x + 2$ on each side of the locus of $x = -\frac{1}{2}$ would coincide.
356 I Because both $\sqrt{\frac{-c}{a}}$ and $-\sqrt{\frac{-c}{a}}$ satisfy $f(x) = ax^2 + c$. Remember, if $c = 0$, then $f(x) = ax^2 + c$ has only one zero, namely 0. * If function f has at least one zero, then the values of a and c in $f(x) = ax^2 + c$ are such that $\frac{-c}{a} \geqq 0$.
357 N Yes. If $f(x) = 0$, then $ax^2 + bx + c = 0$. This is actually the definition of the zero, or zeros, of a function.
360 H $f(4 + \sqrt{2}) = (4 + \sqrt{2})^2 - 8(4 + \sqrt{2}) + 14$. $(4 + \sqrt{2})^2 - 8(4 + \sqrt{2}) + 14 = (16 + 8\sqrt{2} + 2) - (32 + 8\sqrt{2}) + 14$. $(16 + 8\sqrt{2} + 2) - (32 + 8\sqrt{2}) + 14 = 18 + 8\sqrt{2} - 32 - 8\sqrt{2} + 14$. $18 + 8\sqrt{2} - 32 - 8\sqrt{2} + 14 = 0$. Therefore, $f(4 + \sqrt{2}) = 0$.

$f(4 - \sqrt{2}) = (4 - \sqrt{2})^2 - 8(4 - \sqrt{2}) + 14$. $(4 - \sqrt{2})^2 - 8(4 - \sqrt{2}) + 14 = (16 - 8\sqrt{2} + 2) - (32 - 8\sqrt{2}) + 14$. $(16 - 8\sqrt{2} + 2) - (32 - 8\sqrt{2}) + 14 = 18 - 8\sqrt{2} - 32 + 8\sqrt{2} + 14$. $18 - 8\sqrt{2} - 32 + 8\sqrt{2} + 14 = 0$. Therefore, $f(4 - \sqrt{2}) = 0$.
361 B The coefficient of the second term of $x^2 - 3x$ is -3. To complete the square, you must first find one half of this coefficient and then square the result. The square of one half the coefficient of $-3x$ is $\frac{9}{4}$, which is the last term of the square of the binomial.
361 H The coefficient of the second term of $x^2 + \frac{3}{2}x$ is $\frac{3}{2}$. The square of one half of this coefficient is the square of $\frac{1}{2} \times \frac{3}{2}$, which is $\frac{9}{16}$.
361 N $5x^2 + 3 = -16x$. $5x^2 + 16x + 3 = 0$. $(5x + 1)(x + 3) = 0$. $5x + 1 = 0 \vee x + 3 = 0$. $x = -\frac{1}{5} \vee x = -3$.
362 S $\frac{1}{4}$ is the term that completes the square of the binomial because you can think of 1 as the coefficient of the second term of $x^2 + x$ and the square of $\frac{1}{2} \times 1$ is $\frac{1}{4}$. * $x^2 + x = -2$. $x^2 + x + \frac{1}{4} = \frac{1}{4} + (-2)$. $x^2 + x + \frac{1}{4} = -\frac{7}{4}$. $(x + \frac{1}{2})^2 = -\frac{7}{4}$.
362 T If x is a real number, then $x + \frac{1}{2}$ is a real number. The square of a real number cannot be negative. Therefore, $(x + \frac{1}{2})^2$ cannot equal $-\frac{7}{4}$ when x is a real number.
362 U { } * If the locus of the function determined by $f(x) = x^2 + x + 2$ were

to intersect the x-axis, $x^2+x+2=0$ would have to have a real solution. However, you know that this is not the case because the solution set of $x^2+x+2=0$ is $\emptyset$.

364 H Yes * In this case, statement 5 is false for each x because there is no real number whose square is negative.

364 J $\pm\frac{\sqrt{b^2-4ac}}{\sqrt{4a^2}}$ was obtained from $\pm\sqrt{\frac{b^2-4ac}{4a^2}}$ by using the property $\sqrt{\frac{a}{b}}=\frac{\sqrt{a}}{\sqrt{b}}$. Then the divisor of $\pm\frac{\sqrt{b^2-4ac}}{\sqrt{4a^2}}$ was rationalized by finding the square root of $4a^2$.

365 B $\{-2\frac{1}{2}\}$ * One

365 F One * Since $\{-1\}$ is the solution set of $0=x^2+2x+1$, there is only one zero of the function determined by $f(x)=x^2+2x+1$.

365 J Two * Since $0=2x^2-9x-18$ has two solutions, there are two zeros of function f.

365 L The discriminant of $x^2-4x+7=0$ is less than 0. * Because the discriminant of $x^2-4x+7=0$ is a negative number and there is no real number that is the square root of a negative number, there are no real numbers that satisfy $x^2-4x+7=0$.

365 M The locus of the function determined by $f(x)=x^2-4x+7$ does not intersect the x-axis.

366 U 2 * 0 and $\sqrt{2}$ * No. The discriminant is positive and it is not the square of a rational number; however, one solution of the condition is rational and one solution is irrational.

371 N $(7x+3)(x-1)=2x(x-6)$.
$7x^2-4x-3=2x^2-12x$.
$5x^2+8x-3=0$.
$a=5$, $b=8$, and $c=-3$.

$x=\frac{-8\pm\sqrt{64-4(5)(-3)}}{2(5)}$.

$x=\frac{-8\pm\sqrt{64+60}}{10}$.

$x=\frac{-8\pm2\sqrt{31}}{10}$.

$x=\frac{-4\pm\sqrt{31}}{5}$. The solutions of the condition are $\frac{-4+\sqrt{31}}{5}$ and $\frac{-4-\sqrt{31}}{5}$. *

$x=\frac{-4\pm5.568}{5}$.

$x=\frac{-4+5.568}{5}$ $\vee$

$x=\frac{-4-5.568}{5}$. The rational approximations of the solutions of the condition are .314 and -1.914.

373 D The only way that you can obtain a quotient of 0 is to have a dividend of 0. You cannot divide by 0. * The quotient of 0 and any real number is 0.

377 G For each a and b, if $a=b$, then $a^2=b^2$. In this case, $a=\sqrt{x+3}$ and $b=7$.

377 I Yes * 46 is the only solution of $x+3=49$.

380 B 3 * $-5x$

381 K $\{x \mid x>-4\}$ * $\{x \mid x>-2\}$ * You know that $x+4$ is positive if $x>-4$ and $x+2$ is positive if $x>-2$. Both $x+4$ and $x+2$ are positive if $x>-2$ because, if x is greater than -2, then x is also greater than -4. * You know that both $x+4$ and $x+2$ are positive if $x>-2$. Therefore, if $x>-2$, the product of $x+4$ and $x+2$ is positive because the product of two positive numbers is positive.

381 L $\{x \mid x<-4\}$ * $\{x \mid x<-2\}$ * Both $x+4$ and $x+2$ are negative if $x<-4$ because, if $x<-4$, then x is also less than -2. * If $x<-4$, then the product of $x+4$ and $x+2$ is positive because the product of two negative numbers is positive.

381 N The solution set of $(x+4)(x+2)\leqq 0$ contains those members of the universe, and only those members, that do not satisfy $(x+4)(x+2)>0$. Hence, every point that is not in the locus of $(x+4)(x+2)>0$ is in the locus of $(x+4)(x+2)\leqq 0$.

381 O $\{x \mid x>-2 \vee x<-4\}$

381 S 7 * -1 * By replacing $(x>7 \wedge x>-1)$ in condition J by the equivalent condition $x>7$ and by replacing $(x<7 \wedge x<-1)$ by the equivalent condition $x<-1$

382 U $\{x \mid -1\leqq x\leqq 7\}$ * This solution set is a closed interval.

383 A -3 and -1 * $(-3)^2+4(-3)+3=9-12+3$ and $9-12+3=0$. $(-1)^2+4(-1)+3=1-4+3$ and $1-4+3=0$. * Points $(-3, 0)$ and $(-1, 0)$

383 C From the graph, you can see that each point that is in the locus of $f(x)=x^2+4x+3$ and that is located above the x-axis has a first coördinate that is less than -3 or greater than -1. Therefore, $f(x)>0$ when $x<-3 \vee x>-1$. * $f(x)>0$ is the same as $x^2+4x+3>0$, and $x^2+4x+3>0$ is a standard form of $x^2+4x>-3$. Hence, $\{x \mid x<-3 \vee x>-1\}$ is the solution set of $x^2+4x>-3$.

386 N The problem tells you that, after a square was cut from each corner of the cardboard, the base of the box was in the shape of a square. * x also represents the width of the cardboard in inches.

386 O Because George cut a 3-inch square from each corner of the piece of cardboard, he cut 6 inches from the length of each side of the cardboard. Therefore, $x-6$ represents the length of each side of the base of the box.

388 E Yes. $\{x \mid -6<x<\frac{14}{3}\}$ is the

solution set of $-6 < x < \frac{14}{3}$, and $(2x+1)^2 - x^2 < 85$ and $-6 < x < \frac{14}{3}$ are equivalent conditions. * Yes * $\{x \mid 0 < x < \frac{14}{3}\}$

389 M In the formula $d = rt$, d represents distance, r represents rate, and t represents time. Therefore, $\frac{20}{4-r}$ represents the time that it took Harris to make the trip upstream, and $\frac{20}{4+r}$ represents the time that it took him to make the return trip downstream.

398 O First replace a by 0 in $ax + by + c = 0$ to obtain $by + c = 0$. Then subtract c from each side of $by + c = 0$ to obtain $by = -c$. Finally, divide each side of $by = -c$ by b to obtain $y = \frac{-c}{b}$. * The locus of $y = \frac{-c}{b}$ is the x-axis or a line that is parallel to the x-axis at a distance of $|\frac{-c}{b}|$ units.

399 B Point (0, 5) * −1

399 E Point (2, 3) * (2, 3) satisfies both $x + y - 5 = 0$ and $3x - 2y = 0$.
$2 + 3 - 5 = 0$.
$3(2) - 2(3) = 0$.

399 G The intersection of ℓ_9 and ℓ_{10} is the empty set. * { }

400 L The conditions in system N have the same solution set. Therefore, the intersection of their solution sets is an infinite set that is the same as the solution set of either condition in the system.

400 M $3x - 3y + 6 = 0$ can be obtained from $x - y + 2 = 0$ by multiplying each side of $x - y + 2 = 0$ by 3.

402 N The locus of $x = 0$ is the y-axis. The locus of $y = 0$ is the x-axis. * Yes. The solution set of both system C and system E is $\{(0, 0)\}$.

402 O No * The solution set of $2x - y = 0 \wedge y - 5 = 0$ is $\{(2\frac{1}{2}, 5)\}$. Since the system that is made up of $2x - y = 0$ and $y - 5 = 0$ does not have the same solution set as system C, the two systems are not equivalent.

402 T Systems of conditions that have the same solution set are equivalent. The solution set of a system of conditions whose loci are ℓ_{11} and ℓ_{12} is $\{(-3, -2)\}$; this set is the same as the solution set of system F.

402 U $y + 2 = 0$ has ℓ_{11} as its locus. * $x + 3 = 0$ has ℓ_{12} as its locus.

402 V Point $(-3, -2)$ is the point of intersection of the loci of $x + 3 = 0$ and $y + 2 = 0$. $(-3, -2)$ satisfies both $x + 3 = 0$ and $y + 2 = 0$.

403 A Yes. Any solution of system H satisfies $x + y - 2 = 0$. Therefore, any solution of system H also satisfies $4(x + y - 2) = 4(0)$. * Yes. Any solution of system H satisfies $5x + y - 6 = 0$. Therefore, any solution of system H satisfies $-2(5x + y - 6) = -2(0)$.

403 G Any solution of system H satisfies $x + y - 2 = 0$ and, therefore, satisfies $m(x + y - 2) = m \cdot 0$ for each m. * Any solution of system H satisfies $5x + y - 6 = 0$ and, therefore, satisfies $n(5x + y - 6) = n \cdot 0$ for each n.

404 I $-3(x + y - 2) + 1(5x + y - 6) = 0$.
$-3x - 3y + 6 + 5x + y - 6 = 0$.
$2x - 2y = 0$.
$x - y = 0$. * Any solution of system H is also a solution of $m(x + y - 2) + n(5x + y - 6) = 0$ for each m and n.

406 E For each m and n, each solution of the system $ax + by + c = 0 \wedge dx + ey + f = 0$ is a solution of $m(ax + by + c) + n(dx + ey + f) = 0$. In this case, $a = 3$, $b = -1$, $c = 0$, $d = 4$, $e = 1$, and $f = -7$.

407 J (1, 3) * (1, 3) is, obviously, the only solution of $x = 1 \wedge y = 3$. Since $x = 1 \wedge y = 3$ is equivalent to system A, (1, 3) must be the only ordered pair that satisfies system A.

407 L Yes. $4x - y - 2 = 0$ is the standard form of $4x - y = 2$ because $4x - y - 2 = 0$ is of the form $ax + by + c = 0$ where $a = 4$, $b = -1$, and $c = -2$. Likewise, $x + y - 3 = 0$ is the standard form of $x + y = 3$ because $x + y - 3 = 0$ is of the form $ax + by + c = 0$ where $a = 1$, $b = 1$, and $c = -3$. *

Responses to ? page 409

Yes * For each m and n, each solution of the system $ax + by + c = 0 \wedge dx + ey + f = 0$ is a solution of $m(ax + by + c) + n(dx + ey + f) = 0$. In this case, $a = 4$, $b = -1$, $c = -2$, $d = 1$, $e = 1$, and $f = -3$.

407 S (1, 2) * Every solution of system G is a solution of condition H. Since (1, 2) is the only solution of H, system G must have only one solution, namely, (1, 2). * Systems F and G are equivalent; therefore, they have the same solution set.

408 E One possible choice is to replace m by 1 and n by −1. * $1(x - 4y + 4) - 1(x + y - 6) = 0$.
$1x - 4y + 4 - 1x - y + 6 = 0$.
$-5y + 10 = 0$.
$-5y = -10$.
$y = 2$. *
For each m and n, each solution of the system $ax + by + c = 0 \wedge dx + ey + f = 0$ is a solution of $m(ax + by + c) + n(dx + ey + f) = 0$. In this case, $a = 1$, $b = -4$, $c = 4$, $d = 1$, $e = 1$, and $f = -6$.

408 I Replace m by 5 and n by 4. $5(3x - 4y - 12) + 4(3x + 5y + 15) = 0$.
$15x - 20y - 60 + 12x + 20y + 60 = 0$.
$27x = 0$.
$x = 0$.

409 J (0, −3) * System M is equivalent to system O. * System L is equivalent to system M.

411 R In a decimal numeral, the tens' digit is associated with 10^1, or 10. The units' digit is associated with 10^0, or 1. Therefore, if t represents the tens' digit and u represents the units' digit, $10t + u$ represents a number whose numeral has two digits.
412 K $\frac{1}{2}$ hour * Dave rode his bicycle $\frac{1}{4}$ hour longer than Jerry. $\frac{1}{2} + \frac{1}{4} = \frac{3}{4}$.
414 G $\{(3, 2, 4)\}$ * System B and system A are equivalent because they have the same solution set.
415 H The left side of condition C is formed from the product of m and the left side of
$x + y + z - 9 = 0$
plus the product of n and the left side of
$2x - y + z - 8 = 0$
plus the product of p and the left side of
$x + 3y - 2z - 1 = 0$.
415 I Any solution of system A makes the left side of condition C equal to $m \cdot 0 + n \cdot 0 + p \cdot 0$, which is equal to 0. This means that any (x, y, z) that satisfies system A also satisfies any condition that you obtain from condition C by making replacements for m, n, and p.
415 M Yes * Because any solution of system A satisfies both F and G
415 O The first condition in system B is the same as the first condition in system A, and any solution of system A satisfies each condition in the system.
415 P The second condition in system B is formed from the first two conditions in system A.
415 Q The third condition in system B is formed from the second condition in system B and the second and third conditions in system A.
416 A Yes * The conditions that make up system K are the same, except in form, as the conditions that make up system J.
416 B The left side of condition L was formed from the product of m and the left side of
$2x + y - 2z - 2 = 0$
plus the product of n and the left side of
$-3x - 2y + 4z + 5 = 0$
plus the product of p and the left side of
$x + y - 8z = 0$.
416 D Because, if $n(-2y) + p(y)$ does not equal 0, you will still have a y term in the condition that you obtain. * $-2y + 2y = 0$.
417 Q $2(-1) + 5 - 2(\frac{1}{2}) - 2 = -2 + 5 - 1 - 2$ and $-2 + 5 - 1 - 2 = 0$. $-3(-1) - 2(5) + 4(\frac{1}{2}) + 5 = 3 - 10 + 2 + 5$ and $3 - 10 + 2 + 5 = 0$. $-1 + 5 - 8(\frac{1}{2}) = -1 + 5 - 4$ and $-1 + 5 - 4 = 0$. * Yes
419 G A numeral for the given number has three digits, a hundreds' digit, a tens' digit, and a units' digit. If h is the hundreds' digit, then h represents a value of $100h$. If t is the tens' digit, then t represents a value of $10t$. If u is the units' digit, then u represents a value of $1u$. Thus, the three digits represent a value of $100h + 10t + u$.
419 H $100u + 10t + h$ * Yes
421 K $4x + 3y$ * $10z - (4x + 3y) = 17$.
421 P No * The problem involves three variables. You must have three conditions to solve such a problem.
421 Q The sum of the measures of the angles of a triangle is 180.
421 R $c = 2a$
$b + c - 3a = 24$
$a + b + c = 180$.
428 H The locus of $x + y > 2 \vee x + y < 2$ is the same as the locus of $x + y \neq 2$ because the condition $x + y > 2 \vee x + y < 2$ is the same as the condition $x + y \neq 2$. * The locus of $x + y \neq 2$ is the union of the set of points whose coördinates have a sum less than 2 and the set of points whose coördinates have a sum greater than 2.
431 S Yes * The polygonal convex set represented in D4 contains every point that is in a boundary of the set because this convex set is the intersection of the two closed half-planes determined by $y = x$ and $y = 2$. A closed half-plane includes its boundary and, hence, the intersection of two closed half-planes is a polygonal convex set that contains every point in its boundary.
433 N The locus of $(x \geqq -2) \wedge (y \leqq 1) \wedge (y \geqq 2x)$ * Point $(-2, 1)$, point $(\frac{1}{2}, 1)$, and point $(-2, -4)$
441 G No. A machine is not used for a negative number of minutes. In this case, a cost of -48 cents is meaningless. * No. The reason for this is explained above.
442 Q $f(x, y) = 4x + 12y$ is the basic condition for the problem because the problem asks you to minimize the cost, and $f(x, y)$, as well as $4x + 12y$, represents the total cost. * $(x \geqq 0) \wedge (y \geqq 0) \wedge (x + y \leqq 100) \wedge (2x + 3y \geqq 240)$. * Because $f(60, 40)$, or 720, is the minimum value of the function determined by $f(x, y) = 4x + 12y$
443 E No. It does not make sense to talk about -1 shirt and $-\frac{1}{3}$ pair of slacks, nor does it make sense to talk about a profit of -3 dollars. * The number of shirts that Mr. Flynn makes per day must be greater than or equal to 0. * The number of pairs of slacks that Mr. Flynn makes per day must be greater than or equal to 0.
452 C Every set except ∅ contains at least one member. Any set that contains at least one member cannot be a subset of ∅.
452 E Yes * A proper subset of a given set is

one that does not contain all the members of the given set. Therefore, $\emptyset$ is the proper subset of set A.

454 F {Arkansas}

456 E Yes. In a combination, order is not considered. * No. In a permutation, order is considered.

457 G By reversing the order of the elements, you can obtain a second permutation. The first element can be chosen in 2 ways, and the second element can be chosen in 1 way. Thus, the two elements can be chosen in 2×1 different ways, or orders.

457 H There are 3 ways of choosing an element of {A, B, C} to be the first component of the permutation. After the first element is chosen, there are 2 remaining ways of choosing the second component. * Yes

458 I $\dfrac{6 \times 5 \times 4 \times 3}{4 \times 3 \times 2 \times 1} = 15$. * 15

459 D The right side of condition I was multiplied by $\dfrac{(n-m)!}{(n-m)!}$. This is permissible since $\dfrac{(n-m)!}{(n-m)!} = 1$. * The reduction property of quotients

459 E Since the dividend of the right side of condition K is the product of n and every positive integer less than n, the dividend is equal to $n!$. To obtain condition L, this dividend was replaced by $n!$.

459 I If $m = n$, then $(n - m)!$ is $0!$, or 1. You know that $\dfrac{n!}{1} = n!$.

460 N If $m = n$, you can replace n in condition P by m without changing the values. * Yes. $\dfrac{m!}{(m-m)!\,m!} = \dfrac{1}{0!}$; $\dfrac{1}{0!} = \dfrac{1}{1}$; and $\dfrac{1}{1} = 1$.

460 O Replace n by 5 and replace m by 0. * $C(5, 0) = \dfrac{5!}{(5-0)!\,0!}$; $\dfrac{5!}{(5-0)!\,0!} = \dfrac{5!}{5!}$; and $\dfrac{5!}{5!} = 1$. So, $C(5, 0) = 1$. * 1

460 P Replace both n and m by 0. * $C(0, 0) = \dfrac{0!}{(0-0)!\,0!}$ and $\dfrac{0!}{(0-0)!\,0!} = \dfrac{1}{1}$, or 1. Therefore, $C(0, 0) = 1$. * 1

461 E When you select a 2-element subset of S, the remaining 3 elements form one of the 3-element subsets of S. For example, if you select {A, D}, the remaining elements of S form {B, C, F}. If you select {C, D}, the remaining elements form {A, B, F}.

466 J Yes * From exercises H and I, you can see that the numerical coefficients in $a^4 + 4a^3b + 6a^2b^2 + 4ab^3 + b^4$ can be expressed as C(4, 0), C(4, 1), C(4, 2), C(4, 3), and C(4, 4).

467 L 2 * In the third term of the expansion of $(a + b)^4$, the replacement for m is 1 less than the number of the term, which is $3 - 1$, or 2.

467 N 3

467 O $C(3, m)a^{3-m}\,b^m$

468 D 3 * There are three binomial factors in $(a + b)^3$. Each of these binomials is, of course, $a + b$. To find how many ways you can get two a's and one b in the expansion of $(a + b)^3$, you can determine the number of ways in which one b can be chosen from the three binomials. This can be done, obviously, in C(3, 1) different ways. * Because a^2b can be obtained in 3 different ways

468 E 3 * To find how many ways you can get one a and two b's, you can determine the number of ways in which two b's can be chosen from the three factors of $(a + b)(a + b)$ $(a + b)$. This can be done in C(3, 2) ways.

468 G a^2b^2 contains two a's and two b's. You can find the number of ways in which a^2b^2 can be obtained by determining the number of ways in which you can choose two b's from the four factors of $(a + b)(a + b)(a + b)(a + b)$. This can be done in C(4, 2) ways.

468 A $a^{n-m}\,b^m$ contains $(n - m)$ a's and (m) b's. You can find the number of ways in which $a^{n-m}\,b^m$ can be obtained by determining the number of ways in which you can choose (m) b's from the n binomial factors of $(a + b)^n$. This can be done in $C(n, m)$ ways. * $C(n, m)$

469 O $1{,}180{,}980x^8y^2$

475 G Replace $P(M)$ by P(F), m by 4, and n by 36.

475 B Event Y is the event that the red die will turn up a 4. * Y = $\{(r, g) \mid r = 4\}$. * $P(Y) = \frac{1}{6}$.

476 H { } * The intersection of two mutually exclusive events is the empty set.

476 I {(1, 1), (2, 2), (3, 3), (4, 4), (5, 5), (6, 6), (1, 4), (2, 3), (3, 2), (4, 1)} * The number of members in $A \cup B$ is the sum of the number of members in A and the number of members in B.

476 J No * Any element that occurs in each of two given sets, occurs exactly once in the union of the given sets.

476 K $P(A) + P(B) - P(A \cap B) = \frac{1}{6} + \frac{1}{9} - 0$. $P(A) + P(B) = \frac{1}{6} + \frac{1}{9}$. $\frac{1}{6} + \frac{1}{9} - 0 = \frac{1}{6} + \frac{1}{9}$. * Since $P(A \cap B) = 0$, both formulas give the same result. * $P(A \cup B) = \frac{5}{18}$.

476 M If r represents the numbers indicated on the red die and g represents the numbers indicated on the green die, either $|r - g|$ or $|g - r|$ represents the absolute value of the numbers indicated on the two dice. The symbol $\{(r, g) \mid |r - g| = 3\}$ is a standard description of the event that $|r - g|$ is equal to 3. * Yes

476 T Consider two non-empty sets, A and B,

that are mutually exclusive. Obviously, $P(A) > 0$, $P(B) > 0$, and $P(A) \cdot P(B) > 0$. However, since $A \cap B = \{\ \}$, $P(A \cap B) = 0$. Therefore, $P(A \cap B) \neq P(A) \cdot P(B)$.

479 **A** Since the tack must land either point up or point down, landing point up and landing point down are complementary events. Thus, the probability that one or the other will occur, which is the sum of their probabilities, is 1. Since the probability that the tack will land point up is $\frac{1}{4}$, the probability that it will land point down is $1 - \frac{1}{4}$.

479 **B** No * Since the outcome of one toss has no effect on the outcome of any other toss, the outcomes of the three tosses can be thought of as independent events. Therefore, the probability of the first tack's landing point up and the second tack's landing point down and the third tack's landing point up is the product of the three individual probabilities.

480 **L** Yes * One of the four events is certain to occur.

484 **G** The probability of success or failure is 1, and the probability of success is $\frac{3}{5}$. Therefore, the probability of failure is $1 - \frac{3}{5}$. * Replace x by 1, q by $\frac{2}{5}$, and p by $\frac{3}{5}$. * $\frac{36}{125}$

485 **P** Replace x by 3, q by $\frac{1}{3}$, and p by $\frac{2}{3}$. * $\frac{80}{243}$

485 **A** The union of two events is the event that contains each sample point that belongs to one or the other or both events. Therefore, the union of A and B is the event that A or B will occur.

485 **B** Yes * If five dice are rolled, it is not possible to get five 3's and also two 4's. Therefore, event A excludes event B and vice versa. Since A and B are mutually exclusive, $P(A \cup B) = P(A) + P(B)$.

liquid measures

2 tablespoonfuls (tbs.)	1 fluid ounce (fl. oz.)
8 fluid ounces (fl. oz.)	1 cup (c.)
2 cups (c.)	1 pint (pt.)
2 pints (pt.)	1 quart (qt.)
4 quarts (qt.)	1 gallon (gal.)
8 pints	1 gallon

dry measures

2 dry pints	1 dry quart
8 dry quarts	1 peck (pk.)
4 pecks (pk.)	1 bushel (bu.)
32 dry quarts	1 bushel

calendar measures

7 days (da.)	1 week (wk.)
52 weeks (wk.)	1 year (yr.)
12 months (mo.)	1 year
365 days (da.)	1 year
366 days	1 leap year

clock measures

60 seconds (sec.)	1 minute (min.)
60 minutes (min.)	1 hour (hr.)
24 hours (hr.)	1 day (da.)

length

12 inches (in.)	1 foot (ft.)
36 inches	1 yard (yd.)
3 feet (ft.)	1 yard
$16\frac{1}{2}$ feet	1 rod (rd.)
5280 feet	1 mile (mi.)
1760 yards (yd.)	1 mile
320 rods (rd.)	1 mile

weight

16 ounces (oz.)	1 pound (lb.)
100 pounds (lb.)	1 hundredweight (cwt.)
2000 pounds	1 ton (T.)

square measures

144 square inches (sq. in.)	1 square foot (sq. ft.)
9 square feet (sq. ft.)	1 square yard (sq. yd.)
160 square rods (sq. rd.)	1 acre (A.)
43560 square feet	1 acre
640 acres (A.)	1 square mile

cubic measures

1728 cubic inches (cu. in.)	1 cubic foot
27 cubic feet	1 cubic yard
231 cubic inches	1 gallon
2150 cubic inches	1 bushel

metric measures

1000 millimeters (mm.)	1 meter (m.)
100 centimeters (cm.)	1 meter
10 decimeters (dm.)	1 meter
10 meters (m.)	1 decameter (dkm.)
100 meters	1 hectometer (hm.)
1000 meters	1 kilometer (km.)
1000 milligrams (mg.)	1 gram (g.)
1000 grams (g.)	1 kilogram (kg.)
1000 milliliters (ml.)	1 liter (l.)
1000 liters (l.)	1 kiloliter (kl.)
1000 cubic centimeters	1 liter

English—metric

.039 inch	1 millimeter
.394 inch	1 centimeter
1.094 yards	1 meter
.621 mile	1 kilometer
.035 ounce	1 gram
2.2 pounds	1 kilogram
1.06 quarts	1 liter

25.4 millimeters	1 inch
2.54 centimeters	1 inch
.914 meter	1 yard
1.6 kilometers	1 mile
28.35 grams	1 ounce
.45 kilogram	1 pound
.94 liter	1 quart

n	n^2	$\sqrt{n}$	n	n^2	$\sqrt{n}$	n	n^2	$\sqrt{n}$	n	n^2	$\sqrt{n}$
1	1	1.000	56	3136	7.483	111	12,321	10.536	166	27,556	12.884
2	4	1.414	57	3249	7.550	112	12,544	10.583	167	27,889	12.923
3	9	1.732	58	3364	7.616	113	12,769	10.630	168	28,224	12.961
4	16	2.000	59	3481	7.681	114	12,996	10.677	169	28,561	13.000
5	25	2.236	60	3600	7.746	115	13,225	10.724	170	28,900	13.038
6	36	2.449	61	3721	7.810	116	13,456	10.770	171	29,241	13.077
7	49	2.646	62	3844	7.874	117	13,689	10.817	172	29,584	13.115
8	64	2.828	63	3969	7.937	118	13,924	10.863	173	29,929	13.153
9	81	3.000	64	4096	8.000	119	14,161	10.909	174	30,276	13.191
10	100	3.162	65	4225	8.062	120	14,400	10.954	175	30,625	13.229
11	121	3.317	66	4356	8.124	121	14,641	11.000	176	30,976	13.266
12	144	3.464	67	4489	8.185	122	14,884	11.045	177	31,329	13.304
13	169	3.606	68	4624	8.246	123	15,129	11.091	178	31,684	13.342
14	196	3.742	69	4761	8.307	124	15,376	11.136	179	32,041	13.379
15	225	3.873	70	4900	8.367	125	15,625	11.180	180	32,400	13.416
16	256	4.000	71	5041	8.426	126	15,876	11.225	181	32,761	13.454
17	289	4.123	72	5184	8.485	127	16,129	11.269	182	33,124	13.491
18	324	4.243	73	5329	8.544	128	16,384	11.314	183	33,489	13.528
19	361	4.359	74	5476	8.602	129	16,641	11.358	184	33,856	13.565
20	400	4.472	75	5625	8.660	130	16,900	11.402	185	34,225	13.601
21	441	4.583	76	5776	8.718	131	17,161	11.446	186	34,596	13.638
22	484	4.690	77	5929	8.775	132	17,424	11.489	187	34,969	13.675
23	529	4.796	78	6084	8.832	133	17,689	11.533	188	35,344	13.711
24	576	4.899	79	6241	8.888	134	17,956	11.576	189	35,721	13.748
25	625	5.000	80	6400	8.944	135	18,225	11.619	190	36,100	13.784
26	676	5.099	81	6561	9.000	136	18,496	11.662	191	36,481	13.820
27	729	5.196	82	6724	9.055	137	18,769	11.705	192	36,864	13.856
28	784	5.292	83	6889	9.110	138	19,044	11.747	193	37,249	13.892
29	841	5.385	84	7056	9.165	139	19,321	11.790	194	37,636	13.928
30	900	5.477	85	7225	9.220	140	19,600	11.832	195	38,025	13.964
31	961	5.568	86	7396	9.274	141	19,881	11.874	196	38,416	14.000
32	1024	5.657	87	7569	9.327	142	20,164	11.916	197	38,809	14.036
33	1089	5.745	88	7744	9.381	143	20,449	11.958	198	39,204	14.071
34	1156	5.831	89	7921	9.434	144	20,736	12.000	199	39,601	14.107
35	1225	5.916	90	8100	9.487	145	21,025	12.042	200	40,000	14.142
36	1296	6.000	91	8281	9.539	146	21,316	12.083	201	40,401	14.177
37	1369	6.083	92	8464	9.592	147	21,609	12.124	202	40,804	14.213
38	1444	6.164	93	8649	9.644	148	21,904	12.166	203	41,209	14.248
39	1521	6.245	94	8836	9.695	149	22,201	12.207	204	41,616	14.283
40	1600	6.325	95	9025	9.747	150	22,500	12.247	205	42,025	14.318
41	1681	6.403	96	9216	9.798	151	22,801	12.288	206	42,436	14.353
42	1764	6.481	97	9409	9.849	152	23,104	12.329	207	42,849	14.387
43	1849	6.557	98	9604	9.899	153	23,409	12.369	208	43,264	14.422
44	1936	6.633	99	9801	9.950	154	23,716	12.410	209	43,681	14.457
45	2025	6.708	100	10,000	10.000	155	24,025	12.450	210	44,100	14.491
46	2116	6.782	101	10,201	10.050	156	24,336	12.490	211	44,521	14.526
47	2209	6.856	102	10,404	10.100	157	24,649	12.530	212	44,944	14.560
48	2304	6.928	103	10,609	10.149	158	24,964	12.570	213	45,369	14.595
49	2401	7.000	104	10,816	10.198	159	25,281	12.610	214	45,796	14.629
50	2500	7.071	105	11,025	10.247	160	25,600	12.649	215	46,225	14.663
51	2601	7.141	106	11,236	10.296	161	25,921	12.689	216	46,656	14.697
52	2704	7.211	107	11,449	10.344	162	26,244	12.728	217	47,089	14.731
53	2809	7.280	108	11,664	10.392	163	26,569	12.767	218	47,524	14.765
54	2916	7.348	109	11,881	10.440	164	26,896	12.806	219	47,961	14.799
55	3025	7.416	110	12,100	10.488	165	27,225	12.845	220	48,400	14.832

Tangents, sines, and cosines

∠A° = x.	tan x	sin x	cos x	∠A° = x.	tan x	sin x	cos x
1	.0175	.0175	.9998	46	1.0355	.7193	.6947
2	.0349	.0349	.9994	47	1.0724	.7314	.6820
3	.0524	.0523	.9986	48	1.1106	.7431	.6691
4	.0699	.0698	.9976	49	1.1504	.7547	.6561
5	.0875	.0872	.9962	50	1.1918	.7660	.6428
6	.1051	.1045	.9945	51	1.2349	.7771	.6293
7	.1228	.1219	.9925	52	1.2799	.7880	.6157
8	.1405	.1392	.9903	53	1.3270	.7986	.6018
9	.1584	.1564	.9877	54	1.3764	.8090	.5878
10	.1763	.1736	.9848	55	1.4281	.8192	.5736
11	.1944	.1908	.9816	56	1.4826	.8290	.5592
12	.2126	.2079	.9781	57	1.5399	.8387	.5446
13	.2309	.2250	.9744	58	1.6003	.8480	.5299
14	.2493	.2419	.9703	59	1.6643	.8572	.5150
15	.2679	.2588	.9659	60	1.7321	.8660	.5000
16	.2867	.2756	.9613	61	1.8040	.8746	.4848
17	.3057	.2924	.9563	62	1.8807	.8829	.4695
18	.3249	.3090	.9511	63	1.9626	.8910	.4540
19	.3443	.3256	.9455	64	2.0503	.8988	.4384
20	.3640	.3420	.9397	65	2.1445	.9063	.4226
21	.3839	.3584	.9336	66	2.2460	.9135	.4067
22	.4040	.3746	.9272	67	2.3559	.9205	.3907
23	.4245	.3907	.9205	68	2.4751	.9272	.3746
24	.4452	.4067	.9135	69	2.6051	.9336	.3584
25	.4663	.4226	.9063	70	2.7475	.9397	.3420
26	.4877	.4384	.8988	71	2.9042	.9455	.3256
27	.5095	.4540	.8910	72	3.0777	.9511	.3090
28	.5317	.4695	.8829	73	3.2709	.9563	.2924
29	.5543	.4848	.8746	74	3.4874	.9613	.2756
30	.5774	.5000	.8660	75	3.7321	.9659	.2588
31	.6009	.5150	.8572	76	4.0108	.9703	.2419
32	.6249	.5299	.8480	77	4.3315	.9744	.2250
33	.6494	.5446	.8387	78	4.7046	.9781	.2079
34	.6745	.5592	.8290	79	5.1446	.9816	.1908
35	.7002	.5736	.8192	80	5.6713	.9848	.1736
36	.7265	.5878	.8090	81	6.3138	.9877	.1564
37	.7536	.6018	.7986	82	7.1154	.9903	.1392
38	.7813	.6157	.7880	83	8.1443	.9925	.1219
39	.8098	.6293	.7771	84	9.5144	.9945	.1045
40	.8391	.6428	.7660	85	11.4301	.9962	.0872
41	.8693	.6561	.7547	86	14.3007	.9976	.0698
42	.9004	.6691	.7431	87	19.0811	.9986	.0523
43	.9325	.6820	.7314	88	28.6363	.9994	.0349
44	.9657	.6947	.7193	89	57.2900	.9998	.0175
45	1.0000	.7071	.7071				

Index

In this index, the numerals in heavy type refer to the dictionary-type definitions expressed in colored boxes throughout the text.

1 2 3 4 5 6 7 8 9 10 11 12 13 14 15 16 17 18 19 20 21 22 23 24 25 R 70 69 68 67 66 65 64